The Clinical Interview

VOLUME TWO

The Clinical Interview

VOLUME ONE: Diagnosis

A Method of Teaching Associative Exploration

VOLUME TWO: Therapy

A Method of Teaching Sector Psychotherapy

The Clinical Interview

VOLUME TWO: THERAPY

A Method of Teaching Sector Psychotherapy

BY

FELIX DEUTSCH, M.D. *and* WILLIAM F. MURPHY, M.D.

INTERNATIONAL UNIVERSITIES PRESS, INC.
New York *New York*

Library of Congress Catalog Card Number: 54-12140

Second Printing, 1960

Printed in the United States of America

CONTENTS

The Clinical Interview

VOLUME TWO: THERAPY

Preface

This treatise represents a logical continuation of Volume I of *The Clinical Interview,* in which a method of teaching associative exploration leading to a structural diagnosis of a neurotic symptom complex has been outlined. It was indicated in the previous volume that the second part of this book would deal with a goal-limited psychotherapy as developed from the associative anamnesis. This therapeutic procedure is called sector therapy,[1] since it acts directly and systematically upon a limited, chosen sector of the patient's symptoms, thereby indirectly influencing the entire personality.

Only after some hesitation, the decision was made to include this topic in a separate volume of *The Clinical Interview.* The reason for this disinclination was the assumption that the not sufficiently oriented reader might mistake this therapeutic procedure for psychoanalysis proper. In order to prevent such a misunderstanding, the differences are repeatedly pointed out and clarified in the contents of the book.

Two other considerations were, on the other hand, in favor of a separate volume on sector therapy. First, as teachers of psychiatric residents, we knew only too well how the theoretically interested student continually clamors for a guide as to what therapeutic tools may be considered to be applicable from a scientific viewpoint, as well as acceptable from a methodologic viewpoint. Our experience as supervisors taught us how far the deterioration of a psychotherapeutic approach can go when the inexperienced psychiatrist, left to his own devices and enticed by accidental successes, considers a systematic approach as dispensable. Secondly, we also realize how much more difficult it is to teach and to restrain a student who has already tasted the narcissistic gratification of those successes which he prefers to the effort of a consciously controlled therapeutic procedure.

As stated repeatedly in this Volume, its purpose is not so much to introduce sector therapy as a new concept of psychotherapy than to recommend an approach which controls the active but unconscious emotional interplay between physician and patient—a relationship which tends to discredit psychotherapy in the eyes of scientifically minded physicians in other fields of medicine. This method puts emphasis on the

[1] Felix Deutsch: Goal-Limited Adjustment, Sector Therapy; in *Applied Psychoanalysis.* New York: Grune & Stratton, 1949.

rule that the therapist should be on his guard lest he loses conscious control of the therapeutic situation and is drawn into the pseudo reality of his patient. Following this technique, the therapist will remain on a level of benevolent impartiality throughout the treatment, as is the case in the analytic procedure. However, the dividing line between analysis and psychotherapy is still kept as sharp as ever.

A method must first be learned thoroughly and then be applied rigidly before deviations from the rules are permissible. That might sound as if the therapist was less interested in the therapeutic result than in the therapeutic process. However, that is not the case. The goal will always be the interpersonal adjustment and social adaptation of the patient on the most stable intrapsychic equilibrium.

Stated in a nutshell: The purpose of this Volume is to supply the student with a guide for therapeutic interviews. This presupposes the knowledge of some psychoanalytic principles as well as of the technique of associative anamnestic interviewing, as described in Volume I. In essence the method consists of a series of such interviews in a chosen sector. Hence, it is a goal-limited psychotherapy. But, by the same token, it is a methodologic depth therapy in contrast to a surface therapy.

We hope that the cases selected for the exemplification of some of the therapeutic problems which may be encountered, are sufficiently illustrative. However, it should be borne in mind that the main reason for their choice has been to demonstrate how the therapeutic process is developing rather than to impress with therapeutic successes.

FELIX DEUTSCH, M.D.
WILLIAM F. MURPHY, M.D.

Boston, March, 1955

CHAPTER I

Introduction to Clinical Sector Psychotherapy

Every scientific therapeutic method aims at eliminating or at rendering harmless the seat of a disease. Psychotherapy is the method which tries to achieve this goal by psychologic means. Here the therapeutic process is observed and evaluated by the therapist directly from the content of the patient's verbal and motor expressions. The cure cannot always be explained on a *post hoc ergo propter hoc* basis. Beyond doubt, gaps in the observation of the therapeutic process constitute one of the most essential sources of error, which are often in part responsible for wrong interpretations. Inexact evaluation of details within the total framework of the interview or failure to take notice of them are the main reasons that the total picture of the therapeutic process frequently remains obscure. In order to clarify it, it is necessary to record and to evaluate all details of the complex processes methodologically, as far as this is possible. Psychoanalysis is the only method which can do full justice to this far-reaching goal. Therefore, any other scientific psychotherapy, short of psychoanalysis, can achieve a similar task only in a limited sector.

Sector psychotherapy is a goal-limited therapy based directly upon psychoanalytic principles. Above all, it is a planned therapy and conducted so as to work on the unconscious factors that influence the reality situation rather than the reality situation itself. The approach to the patient is based on an understanding of his unconscious motives. A patient does not know why he has his symptoms and complaints or what they mean to him in terms of his relationships with himself and others. He believes he is in conscious control of the reality situation, but there are unconscious motivations to his illness of which he must become aware in order to control them. Behind the reality figures of the present with which the patient deals, there are reality figures of a past which is still alive within him and projected onto his present surroundings. For psychotherapy to have any depth and duration, it is necessary that the patient be able to understand his relationship to those in the present in terms of the past; i.e., the reality figures of the past must be separated from those of the present in a manner that the patient can tolerate and will accept. To make unconscious memories and isolated historical events from the past conscious to a patient is of little or no therapeutic value unless the significance of these events in terms of the present is understood. When this is done, a patient's critical faculties and judgment can work unhampered, and he becomes truly able to profit by experience.

This cannot be accomplished by rational discussion. In sector psychotherapy, it is done with the help of an induced positive transference relationship between the patient and the therapist. The associative anamnesis is used in lieu of free association, and the patient's thoughts are continually guided back into the past, and then reintegrated with the present. In this manner, complaints which revolve about relationships with figures in the present are connected with similar complaints about similar figures in the past. By splitting the patient's ego into an adult portion, which is allied with and strengthened by the ego of the therapist through a transient identification and a positive transference relationship, and an infantile portion, which is tolerated but not encouraged, the patient is induced to adopt a broader perspective and made able to tolerate frustration better and solve problems more constructively. He develops an understanding of why he behaves and feels the way he does in a manner that he can accept and utilize. In other words, he becomes able to see that he, the adult, tends to perpetuate in the present, problems which were not mastered by him as a child, and he becomes able to see and exercise a measure of control over the childlike part of him that at times threatens to overwhelm the adult part of his ego.

With this technique, an awareness of the latent meaning of the words the patient uses is of vital importance, and the therapist must be ever alert to utilize the knowledge revealed unwittingly by the patient. Words are symbols which have many meanings for the patient on many different time tracks. All of these cannot be determined, but many are readily apparent. There is no sharp line of demarcation separating waking from dreaming states, and there are various degrees of being awake and in touch with reality. Psychoneurotic and psychotic patients, who are much more concerned with mastering the inner reality associated with memories of the past, can be conceived of as less awake to the present reality situation than those whom we call normal, and this is reflected in their speech, especially when we induce them to talk in response to the stimulation of their own associations. If one listens carefully, one becomes aware that their speech and conversation is replete with many elements ordinarily associated with dream mechanisms. Evidence of symbolization, projection, introjection, denial, condensation, displacement, and reversal into the opposite are to various degrees always present in everyday speech, and the better we are acquainted with the patient's history, the more this becomes apparent. As far as our patients are concerned, we can consider their speech as one long secondary elaboration of many dreamlike elements. The key words chosen for incorporation into our speech and for repetition by us are those which we feel are connected with deeper and, therefore, unconscious material. Repetition of these words has another effect due to their linkage with the past; i.e., it tends to stimulate and revive older patterns of thought in the same manner that introduction of a part of a Gestalt tends to revive the whole.

We speak of sector psychotherapy as being goal-limited and planned because, as a rule, due to exigencies of time, one symptom or set of symptoms is taken and its relationship to figures in the past explored and linked up to figures in the present. In such an interview, the therapist listens but does not play the role of a passive listener; not only does he guide the associations of the patient along lines related to the symptom complex, but he takes advantage of the transference role into which he is cast by the patient, usually that of a father or a mother figure. These figures may induce positive or negative reactions on the part of the patient; but in either case these relationships can be utilized. His attitude is, under all circumstances, one of benevolent detachment. At times it is necessary to encourage positive transference relationships by deliberately playing a certain role, sometimes that of a kindly or strong parent figure. Whether or not one succeeds in this role is determined not only by the reaction of the patient to the therapist but by the countertransference reaction of the therapist to the patient. Here, it is necessary to remember that reactions of the therapist, like those of the patient, are determined largely by unconscious factors. The well-adjusted person who is aware of his unconscious tendencies and in control of himself will naturally be more flexible and free from blind spots than those without these accomplishments; i.e., if a therapist is not familiar with his own unconscious, he does not realize at times what he is doing and how he is behaving, but the patient notices it and his behavior may be unconsciously influenced. Patients sometimes tend to talk and act the way they think the doctor wishes them to, and if a therapist is not aware of his own unconscious needs and wishes, he may be unable to play a proper role in his relationship to the patient. In sector psychotherapy, we try to get the patient away from the present reality situation into the past and then, when this has been accomplished, we bring him back to the present, continually weaving together mnemonic and emotional loose ends. In this manner, we abolish lacunae in the patient's integration of his thoughts, feelings and memories. Sector psychotherapy is, above all, clinically oriented. It can be utilized effectively by residents and beginners in psychiatry with an understanding of dynamic and genetic psychiatric principles.

To the uninitiated, each interview in sector therapy often appears monotonously repetitive. Those repetitions serve to alleviate tensions and accomplish "a working through" by continual confrontation. In this respect, sector therapy makes use of psychoanalytic theory applied to clinical psychotherapy. However, it is a truism that in aiding the patient in one sector, repercussions occur in all other segments of his personality and sectors of his emotional life. In sector therapy the transference is, as a rule, encouraged and maintained. With any goal-limited, abbreviated therapy and unresolved transference, relapses and recrudescences can and usually do occur, and the patient will reappear for additional treatment. This is to be expected. The neurotic person's symptoms and difficulties are his way of life. He suffers in his relation toward other people because of the inconsistency of his thoughts; i.e., the past is too much with him. Symptom removal and abolishment of defenses are always accomplished with much difficulty, and against much resistance.

When the patient reappears, it is usually because of some crisis in his life which seems to have undone all the good work previously accomplished. This is only apparently so, however, and recurring symptoms or anxieties of this type can in most cases be handled in one or two interviews. The follow-up interview is conducted the same as previous interviews, with the exception that the therapist utilizes his knowledge of words, phrases, and contents from the previous interviews, and actively and consistently confronts the patient with the similarity of his present problem or crisis to earlier experiences, based on his knowledge of the patient's past. As in previous interviews, he starts with the symptom or complaint, makes its meaning clear in terms of interpersonal and intrapersonal relationships in both the past and the present, and, in some cases, actively supports constructive ego tendencies.

In each interview, there is an introduction which expands and develops the meaning of the symptoms, a middle section where development continues and the defenses of the patient are brought to light, and the isolated symptoms are related to his life as a whole, and then there is a final, summarizing section, which ties together previously discussed material. These sections are not sharply delineated, and will be considered in detail.

Ordinarily, we begin a therapeutic interview with a new patient by getting a statement of the problem or difficulty that brings him either into the hospital or to the doctor. This will usually appear in the form of a symptom or complaint which as a rule is associated with a disagreeable bodily feeling. By inducing the patient to explain and expand the words related to this feeling state, we can eventually translate the feeling into other disagreeable feelings in connection with interpersonal relationships which occurred in the family setting of the past and are being reduplicated in the present. We become aware that the plot and the characterizations remain the same, even though the setting and the cast vary throughout the years. Getting the patient to become aware of this with all its implications is the main task of our therapy. Once done, the patient himself will solve his own problems on a reality basis. At times a patient will appear to have no symptoms but complain only of interpersonal difficulties and an inability to get along with people. While there may be no difficulty in obtaining historical repetitive material with these cases, there is always the danger of a patient intellectualizing and isolating this verbal material from his day-to-day life. With these cases, one must be on guard for hidden symptoms which usually are in the background. These symptoms act as emotionally charged links between the present and past and serve as key points for integration of the past with the present and, therefore, must be encouraged throughout treatment.

It is a mistake to believe that a patient must show a gradual improvement. Often he must get worse before getting better.

After the symptoms or problems have been elicited, the next goal is to expand the key words relating to the symptoms. This is done in a number of ways, the most common being by repetitious re-echoing, i.e., repeating the word with a questioning tone, or asking the patient what he means by such a word. Another way is to use the patient's words in a different sense, which forces him to explain. As a variation of this method, we can purposefully misunderstand him or act naively. In any case, when a set of symptoms has been taken and one has decided to explore its ramifications in the past, one should ignore side issues as much as possible. When a sector of a patient's life is explored, we usually find that the symptom is related to a key figure, probably a parent or sibling in the past, and a marital partner or employer in the present.

It is imperative to work in a positive transference situation. The best way to do this is by inducing the patient to identify narcissistically with the therapist. This is done by speaking the patient's language and even adopting his postures to some extent. It goes without saying that imitative reflection should be performed without the therapist appearing ingratiating, seductive or sarcastic. Patients with pain as their chief symptom—and especially headache patients—will often develop and maintain negative transference reactions with either overt or ill-concealed hostility. Such patients are handled best by deflecting their rage onto other figures. This may be done by not responding emotionally to their baiting, and by enduring the long silences that usually occur during the interviews with them.

The associations of a patient eventually lead into areas heavily protected from prying therapists as well as himself by shame, guilt, grief, disgust and self-hate. Only a masochistic character can be expected continually to beat his breast in a *mea culpa* fashion, and produce material of this kind freely. The ordinary patient will balk and become silent, evasive, or discuss himself in the abstract or talk about alter-ego figures. While such information is of value to the therapist, it is difficult to utilize it in confrontations. For these reasons, it is necessary to alternate ego-deflating material and confrontations with supportive acceptance and praise. This is accomplished by encouraging the patient to talk about constructive periods of his life.

Any role taking is artificial and inadvisable, because it cannot be predicted which image of the therapist provides for the best-suited identification at the given time. Forced transference never pays. Not only is such role taking difficult, but the entire therapeutic situation may become confused and chaotic.

The main part of any interview consists of gathering material in the past and present, related to the sector we are exploring. We get into the past as quickly as possible through the use of key words, suggesting long-existing patterns, i.e., "always," "never," "used to," "habitually," "frequently," etc. If these are not forthcoming, we may ask the patient how he had been in the past by using words of an opposite connotation to the symptom words used in the present. When friends, relatives or hypothetical characters out of books, plays or fantasies are mentioned, we encourage exhaustive details. The patient in such cases is always talking about alter-ego figures or part images of himself.

We tend to explore the past as much as possible to obtain a knowledge of behavior patterns in their simplest and most meaningful form. However, if a patient tends to remain in the remote past, we must be on the lookout to show him how his past patterns are still with him in the present. The opposite is much more frequently the case; i.e., the patient is so bogged down in his present difficulties that he cannot be induced to talk of anything else.

Before historical or behavioral material can be integrated by a patient, it must, of course, be readily available in the mind of the therapist. The ability to do so is to a large degree dependent upon experience, and also on an awareness of one's own unconscious such as is gained by a personal analysis. However, the latter, no matter how desirable, is not a *sine qua non* for effective use of this method. Frequent reviews of case material and attempts at integration of a number of interviews often pay handsome dividends in an increased awareness of over-all patterns and perceptual acuity.

A knowledge of patterns in the past that are recurrent in the present naturally leads to a splitting of the patient's ego. We endeavor to isolate—let us say—a willful, envious, ignorant, spoiled, frightened, depressed, selfish, childlike part of the past, from an intelligent, yearning, brave, hopeful and friendly adult part which is allied with and strengthened by the ego of the therapist in the present reality situation.

The moral implications of such a statement are obvious. The therapist should by all means avoid impressing his own philosophy on a patient, and such effect obtained by transference will be transient and, in any case, subject to inevitable distortion. The therapist should rather endeavor to aid the patient in formulating and developing his own philosophy which ultimately may or may not involve such matters as divorce or a return to or departure from the religious beliefs of his childhood. In such matters, the patient must be made aware that he alone can make such decisions, as he alone has knowledge of all the facts. As in psychoanalysis, our efforts must be confined to encouraging postponement of vital decisions regarding work, marriage, religion, etc., until the patient himself has reached a state of fairly unambivalent decision. When such a state is reached will vary with each case and the goal in mind. All of this is in keeping with one of the fundamental roles of the associative anamnesis; i.e., the patient's questions are not answered directly, and he is encouraged to consider why he seeks such a short-cut method of making decisions. By far, the majority of questions posed by patients are traps and when answered lead only to further questioning. In this respect, the patient behaves like the small child who, curious about childbirth, asks "Where do oranges come from?" The safest answer to such questions is, "Why do you ask?" or "Could you tell me first of all what you mean by such and such?" (For detailed examples see interviews).

After material of the past and present has been obtained, it must be presented to the patient in a symptom-meaningful relation. This is done throughout the latter part of the interview by weaving the past and present into a continuum. Integration is accomplished by means of the induced split in the ego, and the adult part is encouraged to master the more infantile portion. It is important to realize that the infantile part should not be condemned outright on any grounds other than for its inefficiency. It is unreal, a ghost belonging to the past, and must be discarded with sympathetic understanding; otherwise, it will never emerge long enough into consciousness to be discarded, and insight will be exceedingly temporary. The adult or rational strivings are encouraged warmly as the only practical solution to life's problems over a long run. Of course, what appears practical, rational and adult to some, will be just the opposite to others. Only experience and much soul searching can solve this problem. All in all, each patient must be left with the impression of "There are many battles, but only one campaign."

With each case, there is a gradual shift in emphasis as interviews continue. Introductory material may be emphasized in the first half-dozen interviews, and the greater part of therapy will undoubtedly consist of integrating new present and past material with the problem that brought the patient to therapy. Toward the end of therapy, a shift will be noticed in the direction of transference material. In most cases, this is handled best by decreasing the frequency of interviews, thus allowing the patient to "act out" on other figures in his own reality setting. This can be interpreted to him in conjunction with transference interpretation when necessary, but as a rule such interpretations are kept at a minimum, the positive transference being preserved for as long as possible. One need not fear a parasitic-like attachment because of unresolved transference. It is far wiser for him to return *ad lib* for "booster shots" when he feels the need. In this way, patients can be maintained over the years until life provides other suitable vehicles for satisfaction of their instinctual needs.

A technique is good only when it is handled in such a manner that no one is aware that it is a technique. The uniqueness of each individual case will defeat any attempt to succeed with a stereotyped approach. While there are general principles to follow, their blending is dependent essentially upon the common sense, versatility and experience of the therapist. With reticent and uncommunicative patients, it may be necessary to talk and be fairly active during the initial interviews, i.e., until the case develops. As the patient becomes more communicative, the therapist is able to play a less active role.

The aim of sector therapy is the adjustment of a patient within and to a given life situation to which he was not adjusted previously. Adjustment means having stronger and more flexible defenses at one's disposal through utilizing energies which had formerly been indispensable for other purposes. Sector therapy makes the defenses superfluous in a specific sector, the area to which the free associations were directed. A sector is one of several parts of a total situation to which a neurotic or psychosomatic symptom belongs. Since the symptoms are expressions of conflict, they must appear in a cross-section of different layers in relation to different objects, and their various meanings can be followed up within the chosen sector. The goal-directed free associations lift the debris which has covered the repressed thoughts and feelings connected with the symptoms.

To couple "goal-directed" with "free associations" sounds contradictory, but it means "guiding" the associations within a certain area. The sector may be cut around a symptom, like pain in general, or headache in particular; it may be pursued almost exclusively along the relationship to the mother, or it may be delineated from the feeling of guilt. The content of a sector always overlaps with neighboring ones, but the central core should be kept clean—so to speak. This prevents the approach from extending the field too far, and from making it economically difficult. Working in one area and having one aspect always in mind keeps the dynamic process of the treatment based on transference, identification, confrontation and insight, and the release of tension under control, making it possible to recognize when and why the ego becomes prepared for abandoning defenses.

This event becomes most apparent in a subjective feeling of improvement, which is, of course, only one indication for the termination of sector therapy. However, an area of the associative content can often be thoroughly and repeatedly worked through without the subjective awareness of an improvement, although that should not be the case objectively and theoretically. In that event, the therapeutic result can be evaluated just as successfully as if it were accompanied by subjective feelings of relief. Therefore, the termination of therapy is justified when the ramifications of the symptom into the unconscious have been brought to the surface repeatedly, and frequent confrontations with the verbalizations have become possible. The attempt to carry the approach simultaneously into different sectors with the method of associative anamnesis very often brings the treatment dangerously close to the brink of wild therapy and should be avoided as economically unfeasible.

Therapy can be considered as an intellectual process on the part of the therapist, and as an emotional process in the patient. Therapy which becomes an emotional process in the therapist is conditioned by the emotional identification with and the countertransference to the patient. This feeling has to be kept under control, or else therapy cannot remain within the framework of science.

The tendency to overvalue a technique as being distinguished from the purpose and goal of a therapy must also be controlled. The use of technical tools is not identical with activity. Passivity in the therapeutic procedure does not delay the therapeutic process, but activity without any specific goal, and aimless, impatient, narcissistic prodding can spoil the progress of therapy.

The response to treatment should not be evaluated too soon. Evaluation is necessary at a turning point, or when a shift in the therapeutic goal or a revision of the chosen sector becomes necessary. New terms for the evaluation of psychotherapy have to be found. Statements like cured, improved, unimproved, will eventually have to be abandoned. If behavior has changed, or readjustment to life situations has occurred, it should be noted how they came about, whether the patient had been exposed to confrontations and interpretations, whether the therapist has intervened in life situations and approved of acting out, and to what extent and in what role he has been active in the therapeutic setting.

In a scientific approach, the change in the inner psychic dynamics should be the chief determinant for the evaluation of the results. The judgment on this ground will be more reliable than behavior and performance. The subjective feelings and attitudes should not be disregarded but seen only in the light of repercussions of an intrapsychic process which was set in motion by the therapeutic procedure. The continual guidance of the intrapsychic process permits an evaluation of the therapeutic result which is far more reliable than a change in the behavior pattern. It can estimate the growth of the ego by the disappearance of defenses, by the use of new identification, and by the abandonment of dependencies.

A very pertinent question arises: When should we stop or terminate the treatment? The answer is: When the therapeutic aim is achieved. Since the aim in abbreviated psychotherapy is strictly set at the beginning, the therapist must not become impatient, and should not become too fascinated by his success, or go beyond his goal. We have to be satisfied with the disappearance of the symptom for which the patient sought help, with the return of the patient to social activities from which he had abstained, or with a dynamic change of his attitudes which had brought him into conflict with the environment.

The conflict solution of the patient's problem should always be seen in the light of the past. The interviewing technique should aim to keep the material centered around a certain problem. This is necessary, because otherwise the whole therapeutic procedure can easily become chaotic, i.e., if the psychiatrist does not guide the free-floating thoughts and free associations of the patient. These free associations have to be guided so that they can be kept in a certain realm to which the therapeutic approach may be anchored.

This kind of approach provides a situation in which only a sector of the personality or one problem will be treated, whereas other parts of the patient's personality, and other problems remain untouched. This method of sector treatment always helps the psychotherapist to keep the situation in hand. Much of the material, which in an analysis has to be verbalized and kept away from acting out, has to be handled differently in abbreviated psychotherapy. The acting out, or acting with the patient, has some similarity to that occurring in child analysis. Acting out cannot be avoided, but it has to be limited as far as possible. During the treatment, the patient should be guided continually to see himself as the observer of his own information and verbalizations, like the observing psychotherapist. He should be the observer as well as the observed part at the same time.

To be the observer favors the development of the identification of the patient with the therapist. That can be facilitated further by using only those words or vocabulary which the patient himself used in imparting his information. We have emphasized that by using the same words, the identification of the patient with the therapist is intensified. It is, of course, not an aimless repetition of his words which gives this identification the necessary foundation. The patient can be tested to see whether or not this identification is increasing, by noting his acceptance or repetition of the new words which the psychotherapist has introduced. By keeping the situation constantly centered around a certain point, the result is that every interviewing hour appears like an analytic hour. Leading the patient in a certain direction, the interviewing hour can always be made an entity. It is, therefore, necessary not to allow the patient to run away from the material which has been chosen as the sector, and always to lead him back to it, even if he becomes emotional and shows a lot of resistance to continuing. This resistance can, of course, be by-passed for the time being, but not forever.

When we can go no further, the patient should always be guided back to the point at which the resistance began. This can be done by not interrupting the patient's silence which is only an expression of an emotionally highly charged tension. If not interrupted, a patient can always be induced to stay where the psychotherapist wants him to be. The therapist has to sit out the resistance.

A more important question is the intervals between interviewing hours. They can be just as long as possible without disrupting the continuity of the psychological setting and of the psychological process. The intervals should be kept no longer than is necessary for this aim to be accomplished, and may vary with different patients.

The treatment situation becomes an entity when the therapist continually uses the words of the patient, repeats certain groups of words and thought associations throughout the interview, and then returns to those same few words and thoughts by paraphrasing them during the whole course of therapy. The emotional material connects with, and branches from a basic nucleus around which there are unconscious emotional roots. The aim of the treatment is to break up these chains of associations, a task which the patient had been unable to do. The continual repetition of the word associations and the confrontation of the patient with his own material achieve this purpose. To a great extent, confrontation substitutes for interpretation, and—as in analysis—any interpretation or confrontation on insufficient material should be avoided, because it creates only greater resistance. If, however, a patient is confronted with his own words, and gradually becomes the observer of his own behavior and thoughts expressed in his own vocabulary, we can see the unconscious meaning of the words become more and more clear to the grown-up observer part of him. Confrontation, if handled gradually in this way, saves the patient from developing too much anxiety.

The patient himself regulates the amount of anxiety he can release. This kind of approach avoids by necessity any questioning or asking questions and all questions are put back to him in his own words used in an interrogative form. This approach prevents emotional discharges which the patient cannot face and, therefore, does not lead to panic reactions that cannot be kept under control.

Another point is whether this method can be applied to all kinds of neurotic or prepsychotic conditions. It is certainly easy to use with psychopaths, in which the identification with the therapist plays such a great role. It is the method of choice in psychosomatic disorders where the associative material is centered around a symptom. Furthermore, it may be used in phobias with anxiety, because the patient during the interview cannot be overwhelmed with anxiety, since it is governed by the observing ego of the patient. It is somewhat more difficult to apply this method in a real obsessional-compulsive neurosis, because the permission to become the observer easily leads to an intellectualization of the whole process. Identification with the psychiatrist may then only aid in the production of an intellectual discussion.

Sector therapy is distinctly an active therapy. The actions chosen during the interviews aim at the activation of a specific psychological process, and do not deliberately intend to influence behavior. However, all activity of the therapist spreads much further than was intended, and has sometimes much more far-reaching repercussions than could be foreseen. This should always be kept in mind. Therefore, the question arises of how to avoid reactions which go too far beyond the control of the therapist. The limitations of the activity are:

1. It should fit into the total situation and be a part of it.
2. It should be timed correctly, and not be chosen prematurely.
3. It should guarantee the provocation and facilitation of associations which otherwise had been repressed, or for some reasons were blocked and needed this push.
4. It should not lead to wishes or demands that cannot be fulfilled by the physician.
5. It should not provoke a reaction which cannot be handled.
6. As far as possible, the patient should be unaware of the implications of the activity.

In summary, each interview should be considered as a complete entity in which an attempt is made to:

a) make understandable to the patient one of the multiple meanings of a symptom complaint in terms of both present and past difficulties in his interpersonal and intra-ego relationships;
b) strengthen the conscious portion of the ego through actively developing in the patient a historical perspective;
c) encourage the patient to attempt new solutions of old problems.

I. Introduction or Opening

1. Get a statement of the problem or problems as represented by symptoms.
   a) symptoms eventually will have to be translated into past and reduplicated present interpersonal difficulties, which the patient must be encouraged to solve himself on a reality basis;
   b) if interpersonal difficulties are immediately offered as motives for the symptoms, use them as an aid in getting into the past.
2. Expand key words relating to the symptom
   a) by repetitious re-echoing;
   b) by using them in a different sense, which will force the patient to see new meanings;
   c) by purposeful misunderstanding;
   d) by fastening onto one symptom and ignoring side issues as much as possible, i.e., pick a sector to explore in the past and present. A symptom is usually related to one key figure in the past, and that person's representatives in the present.
3. Establish positive transference
   a) by using the patient's own type of speech and words with imitative reflections; but do not play around with the transference;
   b) by alternating ego-deflating confrontations with supportive acceptance, and acknowledgment of constructive efforts;
   c) by remaining in a benevolent detachment.

II. Main Body

1. Gather material of both present and past.
   a) get into the past as soon as possible through key words suggesting long-existent patterns, e.g., "always," "never," "used to";
   b) if key words are not forthcoming, ask the patient how he was before, using words opposite to symptom words.
2. When friends, relatives, members of family, and hypothetical characters are mentioned, encourage exhaustive details—the patient is really talking about his projected self.
3. If the patient tends to remain in the remote past, get him repetitiously into the recent past and present, and vice versa.
4. Integrate historical material with present symptom and key words. The therapist must understand before attempting to get the patient to do so.
5. Attempt to split the ego by isolating a willful, envious, ignorant, spoiled, frightened, depressed, selfish, etc., child of the past, from an intelligent, objective adult in the present, who is allied with the therapist.

III. Ending

All useful material should be gathered into a symptom-meaningful relation.

1. Weave both the past and present into a continuum. Integrate, via the ego split, i.e., the adult part vs. infantile part.
2. The infantile part is not condemned, but discarded as inefficient, by expressing a sympathetic understanding.
3. The adult part is encouraged as offering the only practical solution in the long run.
4. Leave the patient with the impression of "Many battles, but only one campaign."

The factors indicating the result of the treatment cannot be measured quantitatively. It is always only the integration and harmony within the libidinal economy which will be influenced. Analysis has acquainted us with the factors that are at play and which can be influenced through the treatment. Their dynamic force cannot be judged and predicted, just as it is impossible to predict the potentialities of the patient's chromosomes. One has to rely on suppositions. However, the result of the treatment at any given time can be checked objectively by the therapist, and subjectively by the patient. But any test will only prove the ego strength within a certain sector and does not indicate the success of the treatment in its entirety. It may happen that a psychic strata which has been functionally restored cannot function effectively within the total organism due to the disorderly activity of one or several other factors.

Empirical experience has shown that so-called therapeutic successes, as well as failures, may at one time or the other change their appearance considerably, subject to the specific time at which the evaluation took place, i.e., during the treatment, at the end, or some time after its termination. However, any judgment may turn out to be completely fallacious, because what was considered in one case as a final peace agreement between the conflictual elements may later appear to be only a transitory armistice. Likewise, the price paid for the settlement of the conflicts may at one time seem very high, and at another rather low.

The adjustment to the environment in which an individual is living has so many facets, that a demand for the "spotless" total picture which deserves the name "cure" can never be fulfilled. Health in this sense does not exist—neither psychologically, nor biologically. An observation in a limited field might give the impression of health, while a more careful view may after the treatment still reveal a number of weaknesses which require many and elaborate defenses for their compensation. That is also true for the field of sector psychotherapy.

BIBLIOGRAPHY

ANGYAL, A. The Holistic Approach in Psychiatry. *Am. J. Psychiat.,* CV, 1948.

BALINT, A. and BALINT, M. On Transference and Counter-Transference. *Int. J. Psa.,* XX, 1939.

BALINT, M. The Final Goal of Psycho-Analytic Treatment. *Int. J. Psa.,* XVIII, 1937.

BERGLER, E. Working Through in Psychoanalysis. *Psa. Rev.,* XXXII, 1945.

BIBRING-LEHNER, G. A Contribution to the Subject of Transference Resistance. *Int. J. Psa.,* XVII, 1936.

BLOOMBERG, W., SILVERMAN, S., LEVINGSTON, A. G., and MURPHY, W. F. An Intensive Neuropsychiatric Treatment Program in a Veterans Hospital. *Am. J. Psychiat.,* CV, 1948.

CLARK, L. Some Practical Remarks upon the Use of Modified Psychoanalysis in the Treatment of Borderland Neuroses and Psychoses. *Psa. Rev.,* VI, 1919.

CORIAT, I. H. Active Therapy in Psychoanalysis. *Psa. Rev.,* XI, 1924.

DEUTSCH, F. Associative Anamnesis. *Psa. Quart.,* VIII, 1939.

—— Present Methods of Teaching. *Psychosom. Med.,* II, 1940.

—— Analysis of Postural Behavior. *Psa. Quart.,* XVI, 1947.

—— *Applied Psychoanalysis, Selected Objectives of Psychotherapy.* Grune & Stratton, New York, 1949.

—— Thus Speaks the Body—An Analysis of Postural Behavior. *Trans. N. Y. Acad. Sci.,* Series II, Vol. 12, No. 2, 1949.

ERICKSON, M. H. Experimental Demonstrations of the Psychopathology of Everyday Life. In S. S. Tomkins' *Contemporary Psychopathology.* Harvard Univ. Press, Cambridge, 1944.

FENICHEL, O. *The Psychoanalytic Theory of Neurosis.* Norton, New York, 1945.

FINESINGER, J. E. Psychiatric Interviewing. 1. Some Principles and Procedures in Insight Therapy. *Am. J. Psychiat.,* CV, 1948.

GARDNER, G. E. The Therapeutic Process from the Point of View of Psychoanalytic Theory. *Am. J. Orthopsychiat.,* XXII, 1952.

GLOVER, E. Active Therapy. *Int. J. Psa.,* V, 1924.

—— Lectures on Technique in Psycho-Analysis. *Int. J. Psa.,* VIII, 1927, and IX, 1928.

—— Medico-Psychological Aspects of Normality. *Brit. J. Psychol.,* XXIII, 1932.

—— *The Technique of Psycho-Analysis.* Int. Univ. Press, New York, 1955.

—— FENICHEL, O., STRACHEY, J., BERGLER, E., NUNBERG, H., and BIBRING, E. Symposium on the Theory of the Therapeutic Results of Psycho-Analysis. *Int. J. Psa..* XVIII, 1937.

GRODDECK, G. *Exploring the Unconscious.* Daniels, London, 1933.

—— *The Book of the Id.* Nerv. & Ment. Dis. Pub. Co., New York and Washington, 1928.

HARTMANN, H. Psycho-Analysis and the Concept of Health. *Int. J. Psa.,* XX, 1939.

JONES, E. Rationalization in Everyday Life. *J. Abnorm. Psychol.,* III, 1908.

—— The Concept of a Normal Mind. *The Yearbook of Psychoanalysis,* I. Int. Univ. Press, New York, 1945.

KLEIN, M. The Importance of Symbol-Formation in the Development of the Ego. *Int. J. Psa.,* XI, 1930.

KNIGHT, R. P. Evaluation of the Results of Psychoanalytic Therapy. *Am. J. Psychiat.,* XCVIII, 1941.

KUBIE, L. S. Body Symbolization and the Development of Language. *Psa. Quart.,* III, 1934.

LAFORGUE, R. Active Psycho-Analytical Technique and the Will to Recovery. *Int. J. Psa.,* X, 1929.

—— Resistances at the Conclusion of Analytic Treatment. *Int. J. Psa.,* XV, 1934.

LORAND, S. *Technique of Psychoanalytic Therapy.* Int. Univ. Press, New York, 1946.

MURPHY, W. F. Evaluation of Psychotherapy with Modified Rorschach Techniques. *Am. J. Psychotherapy,* VI, 1952.

—— and KLIGERMAN, S. Associative Anamnesis in Teaching Insight Psychotherapy. *Dis. Nerv. System,* XI, 1950.

—— and WEINREB, J. Problems in Teaching Short Term Psychotherapy. *Dis. Nerv. System,* IX, 1948.

NUNBERG, H. The Will to Recovery. *Int. J. Psa.,* VII, 1926.

OBERNDORF, C. P., GREENACRE, P., and KUBIE, L. S. Symposium on the Evaluation of Therapeutic Results. *The Yearbook of Psychoanalysis,* V. Int. Univ. Press, New York, 1949.

RADO, S. Developments in the Psychoanalytic Conception and Treatment of the Neuroses. *Psa. Quart.,* VIII, 1939.

REED, H. B. The Existence and Function of Inner Speech in Thought Processes. *J. Exp. Psychol.,* I, 1916.

ROGERS, C. R. The Use of Electrically Recorded Interviews in Improving Psychotherapeutic Techniques. *Am. J. Orthopsychiat.,* XII, 1942.

SCHILDER, P. *The Image and Appearance of the Human Body.* Int. Univ. Press, New York, 1950.

SCHMIDEBERG, M. The Mode of Operation of Psycho-Analytic Therapy. *Int. J. Psa.*, XIX, 1938.
SEARL, N. Some Queries on Principles of Technique. *Int. J. Psa.*, XV, 1936.
SHARPE, E. F. Psycho-Physical Problems Revealed in Language: An Examination of Metaphor. *Int. J. Psa.*, XXI, 1940.
STEPHEN, K. *Psycho-Analysis and Medicine*. Cambridge Univ. Press, London, 1933.
STRACHEY, J. The Nature of the Therapeutic Action of Psycho-Analysis. *Int. J. Psa.*, XV, 1934.
SYMANS, N. J. A Note on the Formation of Symbols. *Int. J. Psa.*, VI, 1925.
WAELDER, R. The Psychoses: Their Mechanisms and Accessibility to Influence. *Int. J. Psa.*, VI, 1925.
—— The Principle of Multiple Function. *Psa. Quart.*, V, 1936.
—— The Problem of the Genesis of Physical Conflict in Earliest Infancy. *Int. J. Psa.*, XVIII, 1937.

CHAPTER II

Choice of Sector

Part 1—The Envious Man

INTRODUCTION

When a patient is seen for the first time and little or nothing is known about him, the technique of the associative anamnesis is utilized for two purposes: (a) to obtain general information, and (b) to explore the most promising sector. In respect to the former, one can readily obtain pertinent information by asking questions when these are in context with the material produced by the patient; i.e., if a patient mentions a brother, we may ask him to tell us how many siblings he has, what their ages are, etc., without violating technique. Continuity of association is not destroyed.

As the interview progresses, several other sectors usually become available for exploration. It is possible to explore some of these in a tentative fashion. The choice of the most meaningful associative material will in part depend upon the knowledge, experience and intuition of the examiner, and partly upon certain unique features in each case, which include the patient's receptivity. At the end of an initial interview, one should have a fairly good knowledge of the patient's conflicts and the habitual methods of defense which have failed to ward off anxiety and/or neurotic symptom formation. In addition, the most promising sector or sectors for further exploration should have been decided upon. As a rule, it is not necessary to obtain a detailed past history, and in many cases it is not feasible. The only past that is of interest to us is that which is still being acted out in the present.

In cases of psychosomatic disease or in the psychoneurotic conditions where one part of the body is utilized as the chief vehicle for the expression of intra-ego and interpersonal difficulties, it is easy to define the sector, as the associations related to the key words stem from feelings concerning the afflicted organ, organ system or body part. In some cases with a character disorder, who complain of personal relationship difficulties or certain anxiety states, and in those whose main complaint is worry, fear, depression or some other feeling state, the chief complaint or principal symptom may be the keystone of the sector. In either case, the afflicted organ or the presenting symptom are considered merely as a kind of final common pathway for the expression of certain affective states which, when expanded into verbal material, center around a defective and conflictual personal relationship both in the past and present. The following sector interview will be an exemplification of the therapeutic approach to such a disturbed relationship.

An Initial Interview

This is an initial interview with a forty-two-year old, married postman with attacks of anxiety, depression, and restlessness—all of six to eight weeks' duration. He has lately had his postman's route changed. He told the social worker that his symptoms began about eight months ago, following the birth of a second child; both are boys. His mother died when he was four years old. He is overly talkative and somewhat prissy in manner. The interview proceeds as follows:

D. Could you tell me how you happened to come to the hospital?

P. Well, I've felt fairly good, doctor. (Pause) Much better.

[*He begins by an attempt to deny he is ill.*]

D. Much better, in what way?

P. Well, I'm not bothered with the *tightening of the head* that generally accompanies (pause), well what I'm trying to say is well, it is something that has—well, when you have a situation that calls for *stress of mind* and you, you, you, well in *my condition,* you feel that it assumes a greater proportion than it should, in my mind that is. It all resolves itself. Well, afterwards I feel *foolish,* that is, you don't think so much about it, you don't *worry* so much about it. You know it's in your *mind.*

[*The* head *and the* mind *are the chief points of reference.*]

P. For example, I have an *old car* that I drive. I couldn't get out of the yard this morning because the brakes were *frozen tight.* When I went home to lunch, I figured well, I'll try to get it out and I got it out, and I found out that the brakes were *locked tight, frozen tight.* The evening before evidently water had splashed in there. I had pulled up my emergency brake, something I understand you shouldn't do when you leave a car out where it's *cold.* The water might have gotten into the brakes. It freezes there. Then you can't use your brakes. Well, I did get the car in the alley after lunch, and I found out that the brakes were *dragging* and you couldn't drive very far in that condition, so I said to myself, well, gee now, I'd like to go over to the hospital with it.

[*The car, like the head, serves as a symbol for the whole person. A "car" should not be "left out in the cold." "Dragging brakes" means massive crippling inhibitions.*]

P. At least I want to be able to use it tomorrow, so I said to myself, I think I'll try to get it into the garage or a heated place for a while until the brakes are fixed; so I began to worry about it, you know—*little silly stuff.*

[*"Little silly stuff" means big, important things. This term is used as a key word for further associations.*]

D. What do you mean, *silly* things?

P. Well, you know—what if it doesn't, uh, unfreeze. I won't be able to use it tomorrow. Oh, it wasn't much. I didn't worry too much, but here again I think that the *average* person takes these things more in his stride. He doesn't worry about things like that. Of course, I think I'm pretty *normal* in most respects, and a few weeks ago it would have seemed larger to me than that it does now; the fact is I know I'm much better and, well, I'm more like the average person in respect to worrying about anything. As a matter of fact, I haven't noticed anything today or even yesterday. I . . . I haven't thought for that matter about what my condition is or for that matter, uh, how I am coming along. When I'm in the throes of this thing, that is, uh, as I was, well, I was afraid of *going to pieces,* but prior to that *breakdown* I would just hustle along and busy myself walking around, and I'd have a little occasional *dizziness,* but I would say to myself, it's just *nerves.* Well, anyway, I find that it has let go of me now and that I feel better. I don't feel dizzy that way at all. I feel very good, very well. Naturally, I'm a little *jumpy,* but I attribute it to the things that happen. I may be tired. Of course, the weather is pretty tough and, of course, I don't mind it too much, but it is tough and I attribute it to that. Of course, I would rather be home with my book in front of a cozy fire. The trouble is around my bedtime; around 10:30, I begin to feel a little *jittery,* not *depressed,* mind you. It's the type of jittery feeling I used to have these mornings when I felt I *couldn't* go to *work.* Well, I had this feeling last night but it is so *small*; I just want to mention it in passing, because I don't want you to think I've *lost* every particular sign of *this thing.* (Pause) Yet I was never any worse than I was last night, but I really don't think that was anything. It's just like you were recovering from a *wound* or something, and you were getting better and better, and you felt much better, and you had a *little pain* and you'd say, well, it is *natural* as you get better to have it. Well, that's the way I feel, Doctor.

[*He worries over not being "normal." What yardstick is he using to measure normalcy? Denial is obviously one of his chief defenses, which no longer is adequate: he speaks of brake failure. "Dizzy," "jumpy," and "nerves" are used as associations to abnormality. He talks as if he were being physically attacked.*]

D. As if you had a *wound?*

[*All of the underlined words lead to feelings of loss, expressed in the doubly determined word "wound."*]

P. Well, you can very well say that the *mind* is *wounded;* the body repairs itself normally, almost entirely, and likewise the *mind.*
D. Your *mind* was *wounded?*
P. Well—uh—ah—either *wounded* or a little *damaged.* (Pause) I know that it was *overworked.* I'll put it that way. It was under great *stress.* Well, I don't think it ever *broke,* that is, I don't think I had a nervous breakdown even when I had that *crying* spell and felt *prickly feelings* all over me. Even at that time I was aware how I felt, and what my condition really was. I always knew what I was doing and what I was about.

[*Al these terms are exquisitely overdetermined, and express the fear of retaliation for aggressive trends.*]

D. You felt *sad,* you cried?
P. Yes, I guess you could say that. (Pause) Of course, I was *depressed* anyhow.

[*This admission is important, and now leads to feelings of rejection for not being good.*]

D. What do you mean?
P. Well, uh, that is, uh, I was—uh, well, shall we say, pretty *down in the dumps.* Of course, it isn't a feeling of *feeling sorry for yourself.* It is just a feeling that I don't feel *good.* Not *melancholy* in the way you say a person is melancholy because he's alone, or he's *pining* for *something*—just feeling that the world, well, it wasn't a feeling that, well actually I had nothing to be *depressed* about at the time that it happened.

[*"Alone" is like the car out in the "cold." He feels inadequate as a man. This is conceived symbolically as a longing for "something" he feels has been denied.*]

D. What do you mean?
P. Well, I wasn't—uh—*frustrated.* It wasn't that I wanted *something* that I couldn't get or was *pining* for something. Well, for instance, let's say that a person wanted to buy a *home,* for instance. Now cooped up in a three-room apartment like I am, true, well for instance, I think that every *man* wants to get a *home,* and uh, well, but I don't think now for instance that I'm an *envious* person and I never was. (Long pause)

[*A "home" is more than a house. It is an extension of one's body just as was the car, and also representative of the relationship with the old or past home.*]

D. Couldn't get a *home?*

P. Well, of course not, not in my particular financial position, but—that is—I mean to say, well, we were considering that we would like to get a *home* but that it would take more of a down *payment* than we have available, and uh. . . . (Long pause)

[*He doesn't get—produce (make) enough money.*]

D. Didn't have enough *money?*

P. We didn't have enough. (Long pause)

D. Not *enough?*

[*A sensitive point: not having enough. The transference becomes apparent: he repeats the word of the interviewer.*]

P. Yes, not *enough,* and whether or not subconsciously I dwelt on that, I don't know, but I know that I never let myself, well, let it *bother* me to any extent. We would just talk about it a little, and look at the papers and the houses that were within our reach, say around $12,000, and then we considered my salary and what we could afford to carry and pay down. Well we know exactly what we can afford and what we can't afford, and we know that right now we can't afford anything like that. (Long pause)

[*He denies any worry over being in the position of a little boy whose ambition exceeds his capacity for action.*]

D. But as you said, you never were *envious.*

[*Ego support sustaining his denial. He expresses envy in terms of "car."*]

P. No. For instance, if I saw someone with a better *car* than I have, well of course, I would like to have a *better car,* but well as I have seen some people, now my own *sister* for example. She is the *envious* type (chuckles). I hate to talk about my own sister, but she—uh—she doesn't make any bones about it; either that or she can't *conceal* it. Some people just don't attempt to hide their feelings, or they just don't care. Well, she bought herself a $12,000 home and someone she knew bought a better one and she'd come right out and say to her husband, why couldn't we afford a home like that. You see what I mean now. Now I'm so different. I'm satisfied. If I could buy a home for say $10,000, I'd be satisfied. Now for instance, my *brother* just bought a home for $25,000. Now I know I can't be up in those brackets, and it doesn't bother me. I never could own a home for that amount of money, and I say to my wife, gee, we'd be satisfied with a home for $11,000 or $12,000. So you see actually I know I'm not envious.

[*It cannot be stressed too much that in talking about anyone, especially siblings, a patient talks about himself, in various aspects. A* sister *has even less than he, but gets things from someone else. He tells more about his sibling relationships in this manner than could ever be elicited through direct questioning. It gradually becomes obvious that he is envious of sister and brother, of female and male.*

He doesn't even feel up to sister, let alone brother. The sector is now chosen, i.e., rivalry with the brother.]

D. Of your *brother?*

P. Yes, of him or of anybody who could have a better home than I could afford.

[*One can easily infer the brother must be an older, and more powerful figure.*]

D. You *never* were?

[*An attempt to get into the past.*]

P. That's right, I never was. I've always maintained that I would like a *good home* but no more than the average person who has *normal* desires. They know they can't fulfill them immediately. They know that things will straighten out after a while. After all, when you've had *sickness* through the years and money has gone *up the chimney* —no sir, I don't regret it. I'm glad that I was able to give my family the kind of medical attention that they needed at the time to the best of my ability. Now for instance, the *oldest boy was sick* quite a lot, and had a number of *operations,* and the wife, too. Now these things would *worry* some people and some people would send them to the clinics and let them get it for nothing. But I always tried to see that my family got the best care that I could afford. Now, for instance, if my wife needed an operation, I always wanted to see that the proper man, that is, within my reach, that is, for the amount of money that I could afford—I didn't say for instance, you go down to the clinic and we'll save money, a 200 dollars or 300 dollars fee or whatever the thing was.

[*"Normal" has to be stressed due to his fear of being "abnormal." "Sick" means "not normal." Now he plainly reveals hostility against his old family. He uses the images of a mother and an older brother and a wife and an oldest son for expressing his retaliatory aggressive feelings by overconcern. He must be comparing himself to a sibling or representative.*]

D. You mean some people do those things?

P. Oh, definitely. Yes, sir. I know.

D. What do you mean?

P. (Sighs) Well, arr—uh—uh—(chuckles) well, for example, my brother's wife. She's the type, well, we'll put it this way, who wouldn't call the doctor to her house unless the child has a severe fever. You see what I mean—well, I'm just the opposite. I don't take chances. If the child's temperature is up in my family, I call the doctor right away. She wouldn't think anything of going into the City Hospital to a clinic, or if the kids were sick she'd wait for a couple of days and wait and see if they got any better, before she'd call the doctor. To my way of thinking, that isn't doing or giving what you owe to your family. You have responsibilities that you take on when you marry. You should give them the best that you can, so that—well, I'm not the type of person who tries to save money at my family's expense.

[*His chuckle is an attempt to deny the seriousness of his competitive and aggressive feelings toward his brother's wife.*]

D. Not like her?

P. Well, yes. I would say so in that respect. Well, she might buy them better clothes, but actually you would think that the *care of the body would come first.*

[*He had said clearly that he would be a better mother to his brother's child. The therapist's question should further provoke the denial of envy and aggression in that sector. The brother's wife is the representative of his mother and sister. (This patient's mannerisms and speech show evidences of strong feminine identifications and concern over "care of the body.")*]

D. So she saves all this money, and they have a 25,000 dollar home?

P. Well, I'll tell you, Doctor. No, it's true, she saves a lot by not spending it that way, but actually my brother could afford a home like that. See, he's a lawyer. All of my brothers are professional men, and actually he married *money* when he married his wife. Her father had the dough. He owned a small business.

D. Oh, she had *money?*

[*The repetition of the word "money" should anchor the association to it.*]

P. Well, her people had money—her father and mother. But they are not particularly happy with it. They haven't gotten along together for years. They are practically not speaking to one another, so the *money* hasn't helped them any.

D. But your brother's wife had some *money* and could help him.

[*This referral to his brother's wife serves to compare her with his own wife, as well as to obtain more relationship data.*]

P. Well, yes, well, the result of the thing was,—see there was just her and her brother, and her father is getting along in years, so to make it easier on himself, he took his children and my brother inside the business and shared it with them.

D. You didn't have that kind of luck?

P. (Laughs loudly and long) Huh, I'm not *frustrated* because he got the money and I didn't, or because he married money and I didn't. Money doesn't mean that much to me. Money is useful to get things with, but I could be satisfied with just a little.

[*His behavior is very transparent, and revealing of his true frustration: he tries to laugh off his feelings of deprivation.*]

D. You *always* were?

[*"Always" is another attempt to get into the past, which is partly successful.*]

P. Yes, absolutely. I was *always* satisfied to my knowledge, if I had a suit of clothes and I would look as nice as the fellow who had fifty suits. After all, he couldn't wear all fifty at one time. A lot of people would deride me for this attitude. Now my *oldest brother,* when he talks to me says what kind of an attitude is that, instead of three suits wouldn't you like to have twenty-five or something like that, and I would say—no, after all, what do I have to make an impression for? When I want to go out, I don't have to have a *closet full of suits,* and as far as *eating* is concerned, well, how much can a person eat, and how many pairs of shoes can you wear? And that was *always* my attitude.

[*He supports his denial of envy by claiming his disinterest in clothes and food.*]

D. How far back is *always*—you mean when you were little?
[*Persisting in the attempt to open up the past.*]

P. Why yes, I can remember. I *always* felt that way.

D. You mean as a child?

P. Well, as a child you wouldn't have reason to think of things like that. Of course, well—because then your parents are devoted to you and you get everything you want anyway, and you are *monarch* of all you survey.

[*The admission of his childish grandiose ideas of being the monarch shows the true wish of superseding his brothers.*]

D. Your brothers didn't make fun of you then?

P. *No,* and *he* went around in raggedy knee-pants then, too.

[*Denying that the brother made fun of him, since he, too, was only a show-off like himself.*]

D. What do you mean?

P. Well, I remember, well—don't forget there's only a difference of about three years between us three brothers; that is, four brothers I should say. There was a younger one than myself, then there was me, then there were two older ones.

D. They are all professional men?

[*Highlighting the competitive aspect. Now he admits they made fun of him.*]

P. *That's right.* In their conversations, of course, they would make fun of me. They would talk about how much money this one had, and how much money that one had, and to me that is boring conversation. Now take for instance the one with the big home—well, we had a little party the other night after my brother's child was confirmed, and we went out there and had a little house party. He's the one that's three years older than me, the one that has the $25,000 house, and we were out there, and of course, it's a particular kind of a society that he moves in. They're all more or less in pretty nearly the same financial state. They all own homes around that much, anywhere from $25,000 to $40,000, and my wife and I, well, suppose, of course,—well, it's no credit to my brother—after all, he didn't make the money. He didn't earn it. That's how I always feel and *I don't envy him.* In fact, I *don't envy anyone I know.* Well, anyhow, to come to the point, as we moved around in the party, and were introduced to them, oh, about a half dozen couples or more, all the conversation was how much this and that cost, and when did you buy your house, how much money did you spend, did you put all broadloom in it? As a matter of fact, we found it very *boring,* and my wife said she just wasn't going to go any more. She said she doesn't have a good time—a thing like that where they talk only about money and about their $30,000 homes and their fur coats and things like that. There's nothing there. They're not on our level. They look at things differently in life than we do. We don't do the things that they do. If they feel like it, they just pack up and go to Florida, or a trip to New York, and whereas with us, of course, by necessity we have to be satisfied with living at our own scale, but that doesn't bother me 'cause they can do it and I don't. That was not the reason I was *depressed.*

[*Father and the oldest brother, who is six years ahead of him, were too far removed to compete with, but the next oldest brother was too close to be ignored. The particular society he refers to means all the brothers. He has to reinforce it continually, i.e., his denial of envy. "Boring" means depressing in one sense, and also aids in the denial of envy and feelings of deprivation. He resents that the brothers have everything, and he nothing.*]

D. You were *depressed* over your condition?
[*Picking up the affect-laden word he has affirmed so emphatically, if negatively.*]

P. That was the condition. The condition was a *depressed* sort of condition. It's a very hard thing to describe. I just haven't been able to accept, well, that is, when this thing was at its worst you might say—once was when I was in New York. By the way, I should tell you about that *trip to New York.* That was one of the few times that I had this feeling. Well, I'll try to be brief. It seems I hadn't been going anywhere on vaction through the years. (Pause)

[*Something happened in New York connected with the "worst" depression.*]

D. Not like your brother—no Florida for you?
[*Putting the question into the negative enforces his denial of having been thwarted to a degree that his need for self-assertion is provoked.*]

P. No, I don't care about that. I never think of that. That doesn't bother me. (Pause) But I mean, a person should have some relaxation you know, well, and so I mentioned to my wife—it was around vacation time—around June or July—and I mentioned how a buddy of mine, a friend of mine, Jack, was going down south on vacation, and this fellow was going here, and the other was going there, and I said to her, look I *never get away.* Not that she would never let me, but well, there was always something coming up, some *bill* to pay or something to take the *money,* oh, you just couldn't leave, and so I decided, well that is I kept telling her that I would like to get *away* and that it would do me a lot of good. Well, I didn't right away, and then I began to feel this way, not as badly at first. I didn't get these attacks, we'll call them, well it was just a *sighing type of thing,* you know; nothing really bad.

[*He would like to break away from his passive dependency needs, but his fear of separation from his wife (mother) becomes so great that he gets the "sighing" attack (nurtured with air).*]

D. You wanted to get away?

P. No, no, not that I wanted to get away. I just felt that way, but I mean I thought *I would like to get away* and do something different for a change than just stay home. I told her I would like to get away, and she said, well, I'd like to get away too. Well, although my wife is very liberal and a very fine woman in every respect. (Pause)

[*From whom did he want to get away? Apparently from his feminine identification. He uses his wife as the target.*]

D. You mean?

P. Well, she definitely goes along in anything I want to do usually, and after all, she's right, she wants to get away too. After all, she has her work and drudgery too. Well, anyhow she knew that a year or so before this I had been feeling pretty miserable now and then, you know. Well, she had mentioned it to *her family,* and I had said to her, I would just like to go away for a couple of days for a change of scenery—something different—and she mentioned it to them and they agreed and said, why don't you let him go, it will do him a lot of good. There just wasn't enough money for both of us to go. Well, anyhow she said, uh, well, O.K., why don't you go to *New York* for a weekend? It seemed as though someone had helped her to make up her mind, and I think it was *her family* that done it.

[*The "family" should justify his masculine demands. The struggle between his feminine and masculine strivings is projected. He suggests his wife would not allow him the pleasure of the trip, but this is really himself in the passive role.*]

P. So anyway I packed up and took the train to New York. Well, I got to New York City in the morning. Now prior to this I had had two attacks, well, I call them attacks, but we'll say *two periods* in which I felt very badly, and I got to *New York* early in the morning and I felt a little tired like anyone would feel on a train, and I checked into a hotel. I took $50 with me, and I intended to bring some of that home, too. I didn't intend to go *nightclubbing,* I don't care for it. As a matter of fact, I like to *go alone.* I can go where I want, and there aren't a lot of people to say they want to go here, or they want to go there when I don't. You can do what you want to do when you want to do it, and I like to do that, especially when you have a limited time. (Pause)

[*"Nightclubbing" is going alone. He finds himself caught between both of these wishes.*]

P. Well, so I got into the hotel feeling a little bit tired, and so I thought I'd go up to my room and take a little sleep, so the bell boy showed me up to my room, a narrow little thing not any bigger than this office in width, and about half again as long with a bathroom, and he threw open the window, and I was pretty physically tired. I hadn't slept on the train and I stripped down, thought I'd lie on the bed and take a nap for a while. And then I began to feel *jumpy* and *jittery*. It just came on. It was such a small *little room* and here I was paying $12 or $13. That seemed awfully steep for a little room like that. Well, I wasn't going to argue, after all I was going to be there for a couple of days, so anyway, it seemed pretty small to me. Well, I don't know why, at this particular time—at any other time perhaps it wouldn't have bothered me. Anyhow I was thinking for $13 I should have had something better, but I never like to start a fight or argue, well, I just couldn't sleep. I started to get *jumpy* and *jittery*. Well, I never had that feeling before. It wasn't a depressed feeling; it was a *jumpy* feeling; and I got up and I looked out the window and, oh, while I was lying there on the bed, there was a rehearsal going on down somewhere along the street, and they were rehearsing a number, some song, and every time you'd hear the chorus and they'd come to this particular spot or line, I could practically see it. The conductor would stop it, and you could almost hear him rapping his baton. Then they'd start all over again and rehearse that line and keep singing that line, and it seemed to me it was pretty darn *monotonous,* the same tune over and over again, the same voices, the same words. Probably any other time I would never have noticed it. I mean it was done, well, without any exaggeration, I mean that line was sung easily twenty-five times—easily. So I got up to look out the window to get an idea where it was coming from, and all of a sudden I got the thought, hey I better get out of this room. If I don't, I'm liable to *jump* out the window. Well, now I never had anything happen in my life like that before.

[*"Jumpy and jittery" later lead to the onset of the anxiety and a claustrophobic panic. The inadequate room also symbolizes his own inadequacies and deprivations. These are numerous and overdetermined, as the material shows. He is "jumpy" and "jittery" due to the imminent danger of being squeezed into a narrow space. Finally he experiences a claustrophobic panic and the impulse to save part of himself from destruction, by flight through the open window.*]

D. You were fed up with the monotony?

P. No, no. It's a funny thing. Uh, *high places* as a rule had never bothered me. Now I remember in the last war climbing around from ship to ship, along planks, uh, *height had never bothered* me at all. At that time it didn't; but then it seemed to me it was an *awfully small room.* That's the way I felt actually. I could control myself, I knew, well, it was like a conscience, practically, like your conscience would say, "Go ahead and jump," and of course, well, I'd know better.

[*His conscience threatens him with a retaliatory punishment for his adventure into the world of men.*]

D. Your conscience?

P. Well, no, not conscience. I'm just trying to draw an analogy. It was just that *a part of me* was saying, "Go ahead and jump." Well, the position right there at the window wasn't, uh, well, it was just like you felt for a moment—here's the way it was. If I didn't get out of that room, I'm liable to jump out this window. That's the way I felt, so what I did was immediately get dressed, and I was still feeling nervous and jumpy, and I did get out of that room, and I felt if I didn't, I was liable to do something like that. Well, I never had anything on my mind before in my life. (Pause)

[*Which "part of him" is saying, "Go ahead and jump?" Is it the part which he wants to get rid of, i.e., the female part?*]

D. Not a very nice conscience to tell you to do that!

[*This remark is an emphasis of his self-confrontation. He wants to take it all back.*]

P. Well, I won't say it's my conscience. (Pause) Whether it was the high place, or looking out the *window;* whether it was the *closeness of the room.* I don't know what it was. But it was the only time—well, I never at any time said to myself, no matter how badly I felt, even with those two previous periods, and that was the first real period where I really had nervous trouble, you might say. That particular time was the first trouble, and then again when I *was at home,* just before I came in here, it was around that time, about a month ago, that I felt *jumpy.* Now I imagine it was some sort of, well, it could have been a number of things, uh, uh, put together, that causes these things. First of all it was my condition, although why *I should have been nervous and jittery, I don't know,* and why I should have even thought of jumping out that window—why truly I never said to myself I'll jump out because of this, or because of that, it was just a feeling, well, *this is a high place* and an *awfully small place.*

[*"High place" is like a grandiose fantasy of being on a "high horse." Earlier, he called himself a "monarch." It is the little part of him who is "jittery" and feels squeezed together in the small place.*]

D. Especially when you were paying so much—$13 a day?

P. Oh, no, that didn't enter into it. Of course, I felt that for $13 I should have got a *bigger room* than that. Well anyway, I never felt that way again, and I never had such tendencies. (Pause)

[*He wants not only a "bigger room" (car, house) than brother, but also than sister has.*]

D. No trouble with your conscience?

[*Confrontation with his obvious envy of his brother and hostility toward his family, while assisting his ego to master the repressed affects.*]

P. Well, I—no—I wouldn't say, well I, of course I mentioned the word, but actually it *wasn't anything inside* of me that was telling me *to jump* or prompting me to jump. I didn't have to fight with something that was telling me; it was more, well actually it was a nervous condition with the *repetition* of the song, and being up so high. I attribute it to a number of things put together. Well they all had a contributing effect—that is, put together. If one of them had happened by itself, I wouldn't have noticed it.

[*He feels at a loss because of the self-confrontations with his wishes on one hand, and the threat for acting them out, on the other.*]

D. Some song—do you remember?

[*What is symbolized in the song?*]

P. Well, now here's the pay-off. Well, first I'll finish. Well, I left that room in a hurry, feeling kind of jittery and nervous, and I said well, I'm going to take a long walk. Maybe I'll walk it off.

D. A postman's holiday!

[*A remark to lighten his tension and to reduce his anxiety which was obvious and accompanied by marked perspiring.*]

P. Ha, ha, yes. So I walked over to Radio City first. I was trying to carry out the plans that I had made, you know, and thinking to myself, gee, I'm glad I got out of that building. You see, I was fully aware all the time of what was transpiring and everything, and knowing that the room was the cause of it, and knowing that the *room was small,* well that was all my, well that was everything that was in my mind when I was there. That was all that was in my mind while I was there—what a *small room* this is.

[*Thus he was able to bring more associative clarifications as to the meaning of the "small room."*]

D. Fed up with the smallness?

[*His own feelings of inadequacy, passivity and ineptness compared with his brothers.*]

P. Uh, no, no, no, I didn't feel that way at the time.

D. You weren't fed up with the monotony?

P. No, no, it was that song, the repetition of that particular line over and over again as I lay there on the bed trying to get some sleep.

D. What line do you *remember?*

[*The appeal to his memory should lead him back to childhood.*]

P. Well, it was just that, uh, song from "Top Banana"—putting on a *top hat* and *ties* and *tails,* and like that, oh, I guess Fred Astaire was in that picture. Actually, the words had no significance to me. No, no, no, I'm pretty sure it had absolutely no meaning to me. It was just the repetition of something that grated on my nerves. Well, it's the very same thing that would happen at *home* when *the kid* would bang tin plates.

[*The song promises the top (biggest) things. The symbolism is apparent. He has condensed* two *shows, five years apart: (1) "Top Hat" a movie, (2) "Top Banana"—a play. He clearly links up the frustrations of the child with those of the adult.*]

D. Did you have that same feeling when you were out at your brother's with all that high life there?

[*Confrontation with the "brother" relationship according to the plan of the interview.*]

P. No, no, no. To me, no, well—as a matter of fact, to me, you see I'm a sort of, a funny sort of guy. They have a lot of things, well, they had hors d'oeuvres, they had a bar there with drinks; not that I don't have to enjoy it or go along with it, or drink a high ball. I drank out of courtesy, and then I went over and watched them play ping-pong. To me I didn't care what the rest of them thought or did. I just did the things I wanted to do, and I was in perfect agreement with my wife when she said she didn't think she'd want to go there any more. She didn't fit in there and to her the talk they talked, well, it was out of her class.

[*He uses "the wife" to reinforce the denial.*]

D. And is this the way you felt in New York?

[*Bringing him back to recent reality. Interweaving the present with the past to establish an over-all perspective.*]

P. No, no, not at all. In New York the thing was this. I was headed toward a *breakdown,* and on the train when you don't sleep, you know you can't sleep on those trains, and well, I don't—and you *hear a steady hum* and a *clickety-click,* and that's *monotonous.* It's tiring. It's a tiring *monotony.* Mind you, I'm not trying to impress on you that my life is monotonous. Well, it is in a way.

[*"Breakdown" is the result of the frustrated attempt to reconcile his desires and prohibitions. The abstract auditory sensation of "noise" suffices to activate the anxiety as the "song" does. It stirs up the unreconciled strivings. The noise has the same monotonous repetitive character as the "Banana" song.*]

D. What do you mean?

[*This insignificant question has great potentialities: it forces him to repetition and to further associations in the sector.*]

P. Well, it's monotonous in respect that you go to work every morning and you come home every night and you do the same things. It's monotonous in that respect. Maybe that was causing me to feel a little bit this way. *I won't deny it.* It could have a big effect on the way I feel. It may have something to do with feeling the way I do, the same as I argue about me feeling that I would like to have *more money* and all of those things; I would agree. I have those feelings—one of them being that my life is monotonous. Although at the same time I actually can't say that—uh—there are any specific things that I would like to do, and yet just this getting through work and coming home at 3 o'clock and sitting down and watching television for a couple of hours; then have supper; and then sitting down and watching more television and then going to bed, and then getting up and going to work. We don't get out much nights. You know what I mean. *My wife and I lead a very "monotonous" life.*

[*He gives up his denial of his grandiose infantile competitive wishes ("more money"). The transference in the interviewing situation encourages his masculine protest against his passivity. His last statement may foreshadow a difficulty in his libidinal relationship with her, i.e., not enough high life.*]

D. Don't get a chance to travel, go to Florida or New York whenever you want to, like your brother?

[*Back to the brother.*]

P. Well, I'll tell you. When I was little, I thought I would like to travel a lot. When I was small, *I imagined I could do everything,* that I would like to go to Europe and see those places that you see in the news reels and all of that; yeh, I really wanted to do that, but well, uh, the life I've had is good, but it is a monotonous existence. *There's no getting away from that.*

[*The infantile dream of omnipotence is revived. He reveals his surrender to passivity: "there is no getting away."*]

D. Very difficult to give up all those things that you'd like to do when you were a kid?

[*It was too near the end of the interview to exploit this opening into his past as well as the admission he made concerning the monotony. Therefore the adult part of the ego is confronted with the immature part.*]

P. Well, and then you see—and then again, I was a kid when I thought those things. Well, I thought that when I got older, I would have a family. *One doesn't know* what one's position in life is going to be, so when I was young, well, when you're young, you're very *hopeful.* Maybe in your youth you just don't like to see anything that isn't *rosy,* and you say to yourself, well, I want to be able to travel to those countries.

[*His statements refer to the characteristic patterns of his personality.*]

D. That is, little Johnny thought those things?
P. Right.
D. Little Johnny thought those things, because he didn't know that when he grows up, as you and I know—some things are more important—like having a good wife and children, and keeping them healthy and playing the role of a good father.

[*Continuing the confrontation, utilizing his own statements for the support of the adult side and a tolerant control of the infantile part. This confrontation is carefully timed as the patient is ready to accept the interpretation.*]

P. That's right, that's right. I try to be a good father, that is absolutely correct. (Beams and smiles and perks up)
D. Surely. And as you say, your brother got a wife who had some money,

but that is no credit to him. After all, she cuts corners, and jeopardizes the health of her family.

P. That is absolutely correct, Doctor, and certainly money hasn't helped, uh, his, uh, in-laws. They don't sleep together; they don't get along; they're always bickering. But I don't know, the way I felt all through that—*I never sat down and tried to analyze myself this way and say to myself, now, look, you really would like to travel.* Well, I don't know. I still would like to travel, but there are other things that have to be taken care of. Yes, I don't think the monotonous way I live is right. I think that can be helped. I still feel that I would like to travel, but I know I can't. I never thought of these things before. It would be wonderful to go to Europe, but then again here I go down to New York, and I couldn't enjoy myself, doing the things I thought I wanted to. I ended up watching a television show, and I didn't enjoy it too much.

[*The interview enters the finale; it has accomplished its goal: the patient can face one source of his conflict, as elicited in the chosen sector.—"Travel" has many important connotations as an escape mechanism, and also as a magic fulfillment fantasy. One may also expect that it is connected with a deeper meaning of going away. His masculine drives become bogged down in daydreams.*]

D. You did just like at home?

P. That's right. Getting away didn't help me.

D. You couldn't run away like little Johnny wanted to do?

[*Confrontations must be utilized at a level where they can be assimilated.*]

P. That's right.

D. Little Johnny wanted to run off, and travel, and see all those places, and seek his fortune?

P. Well, I think I can go along with you in that. (Pause) Yes, well, I'll say although it's not as sharp, that is that idea, I . . . I . . . I . . . I guess the subconscious thought might be there. Maybe somewheres way back I might feel that I would have liked to have done those things, but that's all pushed aside now.

D. You mean you now have little Johnny under control, but that he gets out every once in a while and wants to do those things he wanted to do in the past? Is that what you mean?

[*This simply shows the strength of the repressed wish and his condemnation of its masculine connotations.*]

P. Yes, it could be—it could be, but now I have him under control. I really had some monotony. Well, after all, *I've got my work, I got my home.* I guess I've got to do something that's different, even if it isn't the thing I want to do the most. I've got to upset this monotonous routine.

[*His ego assembles its resources. He stands up against his passivity.*]

D. What do you mean by different?

P. Well, at the same time there's something holding me back. Now for example, suppose I think of bowling. Well, I don't feel I want to go bowling.

[*His loss of interest in bowling means the fear of contact with people during this activity.*]

D. Bowling with whom?

P. Oh, it doesn't matter; with the boys. It *doesn't matter with whom.* (Pause) I haven't gone out, well, since the baby came, 7 or 8 months.

[*It really matters a great deal; bowling means contact with boys. Apparently the baby has revived his own infantile sibling rivalries and the trauma of the loss of mother to his younger brother.*]

D. You went out before?

P. Well, to tell you the truth, *not too much.* I was a fellow, well since I got married, well you see I did a lot of *running around* before I got married. I really did—from the time I was 16 or 17, until I was 20, I did everything I wanted to do, although, of course, I didn't leave home and travel around that age. I didn't, well, it was something you'd like to do, but it wasn't something you did do. I'd just go and see a movie when I felt like it, or did what I wanted, but I,—uh, was happy at home. I didn't mind staying at home. I was going to parties and uh, they were pretty good; *there's no denying of that.* What I can't understand and I can't analyze myself—I feel that I . . . *I don't want to continue with this monotony and yet I feel that I don't want to go out* and *do these things.* Now my wife, the only thing she wants to do is go out Tuesday nights and play bridge, and I don't mind this and don't raise any fuss because I'm *left alone all by myself,* no. Of course I'm left alone and, uh, uh, something might happen to the kids and, uh, well I, of course, I'm not a worrying type and I don't mind these things—but well, maybe that had something to do with why I didn't feel so good last night. I don't know. As a rule, of course, er, my wife is an understanding person. Of course, as far as, er, ah, my child is concerned, I feel that, uh, he was spoiled in a way by her, but uh—.

[*"I want" and "I don't want" is the clearest formulation of his untenable position in life. Wife and child represent to him a mother and a sibling rival in the present. They paralyzed his striving for independency in the present, as they did in the past. The wife (mother) spoils the baby boy (brother).*]

D. How do you mean, spoiled?

P. Well, he was spoiled. We should have trained him. When you get in that crib, you just stay there—that's what we should have done; but the first one was a sickly child. With him, we never had much trouble, but this one here, the first six months of life from then on, well the first six months of life he never cried, he was perfectly fine, so we naturally assumed he would continue to be like that, but he didn't, and he is—of course—I mean the first one. This one here, uh, he has been very bad and he's always up and always crying, and it is very difficult to get sleep. Of course, my wife does that; I very seldom get up. Occasionally she has me get up, but I don't mind doing that, although I do think I need sleep more than her, but those are little things and they do not bother me in the slightest.

[*The situation with the two children is probably a reduplication of his own infantile past.*]

D. Well, I'm glad you're feeling better, and I will see you again. Goodbye.

Discussion

This interview may serve as an illustration of how the choice of the sector determines the special nature of the content of information. Here we were confronted with a person who, in the past, denied active aggressive and competitive situations with his brothers, and attempted to utilize passive modes of mastery. The patient's use of denial up to the finale of the interview was obvious and exceptionally transparent. The oral nature of his envious wishes was equally apparent. He wanted a rich wife who would give him the things he felt his brothers received, and consequently is enraged at his "inadequate" wife. Onto her he projects not only his dissatisfaction with her as an ungiving mother, but also his hostility against her and his child as representatives of the weak and inadequate part of himself. His version of his difficulties suggests that he himself was sickly as a child. He was in a particularly unfortunate sibling position, being junior to two older and apparently more aggressive brothers who became lawyers, and senior to a baby brother who also was aggressive enough to become a lawyer.

In the interview, *he* is in all probability the sickly first child and the baby brother usurper—the spoiled one. The birth of the second child revived and intensified the infantile rage, jealousy and death wishes, which return to him in the form of superego threats (a bad conscience). His defensive economy against this threat in the past and in the present consists partly of using auditory perceptions (the clickety-clack of the train and the music from "Top Banana,") as signals against the instinctual demands. The patient denies the pain of his deprivations, and fantasies himself into a passive, feminine sexual role, in which he is damaged or wounded. In terms of the automobile (or masculine role), he feels left out in the cold, and cannot get going. His wish to escape from it all through travel is condensed with fantasies of going away, but he is threatened by destruction, i.e., dying.

The interview demonstrates clearly that this patient envied his brother to which he was passively attached. He projected his inadequacy

CHART

EXPLORING THE MEANING OF VARIOUS SYMPTOMS IN TERMS OF PERSONAL RELATIONSHIPS

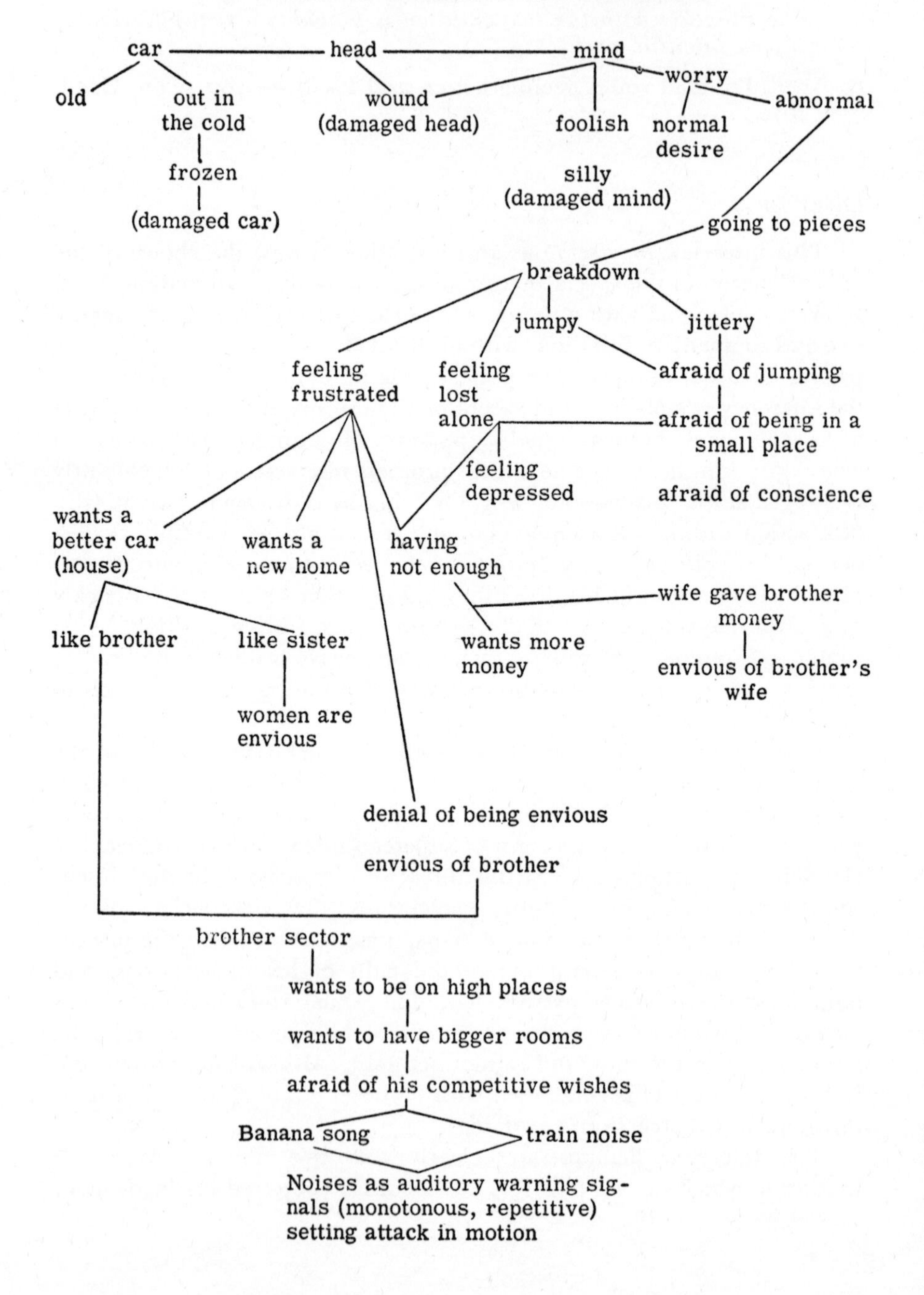

feelings to his wife, and the man in him wished to run away from his passive feminine self. The phallic nature of the envy is suggested by symbolization, and the use of denial as a mechanism of defense was clearly illustrated.

The outline of key words shows at a glance how he used *head, mind, car,* as representatives of himself at a phallic-aggressive and narcissistic-regressive level. Also plainly revealed is the deep oral nature of his wishes as well as the passive-aggressive nature of his approach to life's problems, and the ego guilt feelings and retaliation demands of the superego.

Follow-Up

In later interviews, the patient verbalized much aggression against the family of the past and his own family in the present, and for many months made life difficult for his wife. At the conclusion of seven months of treatment, he was obviously better adjusted to reality, but felt that his age contraindicated any change in his status.

His wife stated that he was "harder to get along with," but "more of a man." The patient himself complained that he was no longer his "old, happy-go-lucky self." However, he felt that he had more control of his feelings.

Part 2—The Beaten Man

Introduction

Following an initial interview, the succeeding interviews attempt to enlarge the associative material connected with the key words. Much of this material will be repetitive, but that must be considered as a necessary aid in the process of exhausting and breaking up the old association chains as they appear in the ramifications to the key words. The following illustrates a second interview, separated by a week from the initial one. In the first interview, the key word had been PAIN, with reference to the heart. Continuity is maintained in this interview, and the sector material as related to PAIN is "thinned out." This interview demonstrates the importance of affect-laden words.

Case Presentation

A thirty-eight-year-old, married shipyard worker was admitted to the hospital for O.P.D. treatment of persisting (unexplained) pains in the chest following a mild attack of coronary infarction. The heart condition began sixteen months ago, and the patient had been hospitalized for ten weeks, the EKG at that time being positive for evidence of coronary insufficiency. He had continued to complain of pains in his "heart" and "back," and appeared moderately depressed in spite of reassurances as to his physical condition by his L.M.D. and repeated negative EKG's.

The patient lived with his wife and had two children, both boys and both congenital hydrocephalics, aged six and one and a half years, respectively. The older had been placed in a State home, and the younger was in treatment for his condition. The patient was the fourth of eight, having three sisters and four brothers. His father and mother separated when he was eleven or twelve. His father was a pushcart peddler and subject to violent fits of rage during which he frequently beat up his wife and the children. Finally, he left home; the patient had missed him considerably.

During the first interview, the sector of PAIN led to his beatings by father, his feelings of inadequacy and envy of his older brothers, and to his longings for a kind father who would come to his rescue, and whom he loved in spite of the beatings he had received. The defective children were equated with a "defective" relationship to father in his childhood, and with the pains and deprivations of the past. Furthermore, the associations suggested that his "heart" condition, too, was connected with aggressive and libidinal repetitive strivings centered around the father and the oldest brother who had taken over the father's role following the parental separation. It was felt that the heart condition had served to initiate and accentuate a regressive tendency to return to the past in an effort to escape from the present difficulties, and that, conversely, his present difficulties had reopened old wounds. In the present reality situation, he confused his wife with the mother of the past, and his children with (a) himself as a child, (b) his brothers, and (c) his fantasied, defective, masculine organ.

It was apparent that he alternately played the role of his aggressive father and the kindly, ego-ideal image of father. The key words that had appeared during the first interview were PAIN—WORRY—EATING—ENVY—CRYING—VIOLENCE. The following is the second interview.

INTERVIEW

D. Well, how have things been going?

P. Well, about the same.

D. How do you mean?

P. Well, I've thought this thing over carefully, and I've come to the conclusion that the only thing that really *bothers* me is that I'm *worried* about myself. I mean I put everything in the past and like I've said before, last May when I moved into this new apartment with my in-laws, why I began to take the situation *in hand about my child,* and I began to feel *pretty good* about it. I can honestly say that any situation that has ever arisen, I mean as far as the mental attitude is concerned, well I think I was able to overcome them all right; I feel no *animosities* toward my brother *Jimmy* and my *father,* or to anyone for that matter that has tried to *do me harm* in the past. The only thing that seems to bother me is, I seem to be *worried* about myself more than anything else.

[*"Bother" and "worried" lead to his defective child who represents him as the inadequate little one in the past. He blames the bad father image for his deficiency. These words are representatives and enlargement of* PAIN *and are immediately picked up. He must deny his hostile feelings toward brother and father, although they tried to do harm to him in the past. Who is "anyone?" Is it he, who will do harm to himself?*]

D. How do you mean, *worried?*

P. Well, worried about my *condition.*

[*"Condition" refers to more than the heart.*]

P. I'm afraid that it is going to come back on me. What I'm really *afraid* of is, I haven't got any *money* and in case I do have to be hospitalized again with *this thing,* why I don't know what my *wife* is going to do. It was fortunate that last time I had red leave and a lot of sick leave coming from the shipyard and, therefore, why I was getting a weekly salary. I was getting all my benefits that were coming to me; but, like I said, I'm really *worried* about this thing more than anything else. Because you see, I never *worried* about *pain* in my life about anything.

[*If the "male" part gives up, what is the remaining part going to do? "Wife" is the projection of his feminine passive self. Worries and pain are the key words to the past.*]

D. What do you mean, never?

P. Well, I mean, like I spoke to you some time ago about *my brother beat* me, why *they* used to *beat* me; of course, I didn't mind the *pain* at all.

[*He has to specify clearly the multiple father images who beat him, before one can proceed to the key word* PAIN. *Why should he not mind the pain?*]

D. They?

P. Yuh, my father and my brother.

D. You never minded the *pain?*

P. Well, of course, if it was too bad, why I uh, I used to *worry* a little bit about it. That's about all.

D. *Worry* about the *pain?*

[*The main associations are fed back to him.*]

P. Yuh.

D. How do you mean?

P. Well, my brother caused my *nose* to *bleed* or *something like that,* why I'd *worry* about it for a little while and then I'd forget about it an hour or two later, or *something like that.*

[*The nose as a phallic representation.*]

P. But before I took sick, why, I used to have little *jabs* here and there, for example, waking up in the morning, then I'd find that my shoulder is a little *sore* from probably sleeping on that side too long or *something like that;* and that never used to bother me; it never did. But it seems as though I get these very same *pains* that I used to get before and I really *worry* about them.

[*He tried to deny his "condition." "Jabs" had been used referring to the "heart," then to the "shoulder," and then to "something like that." What causes the pains?*]

D. You get the *pains*? What pains do you mean?

P. Well, a *pain* in the *shoulder* or I get a *twitch* in my *arm* or something like that, but that's *normal* though for anybody to get anything like that, isn't it? A *twitch* in the arm or something like that.

[*He wonders whether he is "normal." "Twitch" is a defensive movement against the imagined danger of being beaten. It is a warning signal: the forerunner of pain.*]

D. You say you got those before?

[*He is guided back to the past for more light on the present.*]

P. Yuh, I did.

D. What do you mean? When?

P. Oh, during the morning, in the morning when I'd get out of bed, or sometimes at work I'd get a *twitch* or *something like that.* It never used to bother me.

D. And the pain when you got beaten—you say it didn't bother you?

P. No, I didn't mind it too much.

[*Should he have liked to be beaten, using father or brother as the executors of his masochistic fantasies?*]

D. But I thought you said he sent you to the hospital?

P. Yuh, I did. My father did. Of course, I was a youngster then. I was about, oh, nine or ten, ten or twelve years old, *something like that,* but I, well—I took some *buttons* to *play* with, some lead buttons that he had, I took them to play with. He used to save them because he was a junk man, and I took *five or six*—I think to play with. He came home that night and saw me *playing* with them, so he just laid me down on the floor and sat on me and *beat* me, until blood started to run from my nose. Then my mother stopped him. Well, she started to stop him before he started to *beat* me, but it wasn't any use.

[*The confusion in ages means it happened repeatedly. He was beaten for playing with "something" forbidden. A highly charged screened memory of passive feminine fantasies. In the female role he identifies himself with mother.*]

D. Quite a bit of *pain?* Where did he *beat* you?

[*Indirectly the interviewer praises his past endurance.*]

P. Yuh, in the *rear end,* yes.

D. Beat you on the *rear?*

P. Yuh, he sat on me and *beat* me on the *rear* with a strap.

[*Father beat him on his "rear end," i.e., the feminine side.*]

D. Just for *playing* with his buttons?

[*The associations to "buttons" are searched for.*]

P. Yuh, just for playing with the buttons.

D. You didn't mind the *pain?*

[*"Pain" is repeated to link up the past and present.*]

P. Well, yes, it did hurt. And as I said, in thirty-two years I haven't had a sick day in my life. I haven't been in the hospital.

D. No *pain?*

P. Well, yes, I'd get these little *pains,* a *twitch* here or there, but I never used to mind them. I still get the *same pains today* I was getting before all this happened, and I mind them more today than I ever did. I seem to mind them more today than I ever did.

[*"Twitch" is "little pain," foreboding the danger of damage or loss.*]

D. What do you mean?

P. Well, it seems to *frighten* me, and uh, but those things are harmless. I'm perfectly fine when I don't get these *pains.* I'll be working along, and singing and talking with the boys, enjoying myself as much as I possibly could, and then all of a sudden I start getting these same little *pains* that I used to get before, and they seem to *worry* me somehow, 'cause all last year I had *pain* in this *elbow,* in the *left elbow,* and I'd get it every day. I never *worried* about it. As a matter of fact, I didn't even want to go to see a doctor about it because I just thought it was nothing at all.

[*The defenses are not entirely effective against his anxiety.—The left arm and elbow are representations of other protruding limbs in the body image.*]

D. Like when you got the *beating?* You didn't *worry* about it then?

[*Returning him to the past with father.*]

P. No, no, I didn't *worry* about it then.
D. You didn't think it was so much?
P. No, of course I probably didn't understand it because I was only a youngster about nine or ten years old.
D. But after father threw his *knife* at you?

[*The knife incident of his childhood refers to material from the first session. It is related symbolically to being beaten on the rear, which was also a painful event.*]

P. Well, I was about fifteen then. As a matter of fact, I don't think I was too *worried* about that. I just picked up my bundle and ran, that's all.
D. You weren't *worried,* but you ran? What do you mean?
P. Well then when I got out, I said to myself, what the heck was he trying to do. I mean, I had forgotten that. That was a long time ago. I mean, I, I (pause)—

[*He forgot what he was afraid of: What father might do to him.*]

D. But you had some ideas or you wouldn't have *run?*
P. Yes, I certainly did.
D. He had given you reason in the past to believe that he was a *dangerous man,* hm?
P. Yuh.
D. Sent you to the hospital?
P. That's right.
D. So you had some reason for running?

[*The interviewer harps on the theme of father's violence.*]

P. Yes, I did.
D. You did mind?
P. Well I, uh, not too much.

[*He admits and at the same time tries to minimize his anxiety.*]

D. Really?
P. I didn't mind too much. I didn't know what it was used for. I honestly think he was going to *cut up* the bundle of *clothes.* That's

what I think honestly. Because I don't think he—he got violent yes—but I don't think he ever got *violent* enough to *kill* anybody.

[*Castration anxiety becomes rationalized in this memory.*]

D. But you said he was pretty *violent* with mother?

[*His indulgence in these "violent" fantasies leads by necessity to an escape into the female role.*]

P. Yeh, he was. But I don't think he ever got *violent* enough to want to *kill* anybody. None of us. There were eight of us. Of course, I think he—my oldest sisters got some of the treatment, but not quite as bad as I did.

[*He groups himself with the sisters.*]

D. You mean when they were little?
P. Yuh, I don't think he ever got *violent* enough to want to *kill* anybody.

[*These negative assertions express his underlying fears.*]

D. He lost his *temper* though, huh?
P. My older brother Jimmy didn't want to, or didn't try to I should say, to live up to my father's standards. It seems as though my brother Jimmy and my father could never—that is could never, the way I feel about it, he *couldn't take it out* on my brother, so he used to take it out perhaps on mother. That's the way I used to look at it.
D. Couldn't take it out on—?

[*This unfinished question refers to his "violent" fantasies. What happened to mother could happen to anyone in the mind of the child, including himself.*]

P. On Jimmy, because my brother Jimmy was quite a *big* boy and he was always ready to *fight* back. In other words, my brother Jimmy inherited the same *temper* that my father had.
D. But Jimmy wasn't always big!
P. Well, he was a pretty *big* boy.
D. Even when you were a *little* boy?
P. Yuh, I'm the *smallest* one in the family. I'm the *littlest* one, I mean. All my brothers are over five feet five. I'm just about five feet five. And so—.

[*"Big" means "man"; "little" means child or "female."*]

D. So he could *beat* you easily?
P. That's right.
D. You were the *smallest?*
P. That's right, that was easy.
D. But you minded when you were a little boy?

[*Size is related to phallic masculinity. He is the smallest. This material is given with reluctance and frequent long pauses.*]

P. Yes.
D. When he *beat* mother?
P. What? When my father beat mother? Yuh, I did mind it.
D. Because as you said, you were *frightened* he might hurt her?

P. That's right. I *stepped in* once, I think to stop them.

[*He was protecting the mother against father. Unconsciously he wanted to take her place, and to share her being beaten.*]

D. You stepped in?

P. Yuh, in between them. That's the last time, the next to the last time I've ever seen them. No, no, wait a minute, that's wrong. That hap—, yuh, that's when he left, that's the second time he had left. He left us and went back to B——, and that's when I stepped in between them. Then I do remember he was walking down the stairway and he was cussing and swearing to beat the devil. I do remember that.

[*Father left home more than once, as is revealed now. Swearing is beating with words.*]

D. You were *afraid* he'd *hurt* mother?

P. Yuh, because she was a very *little* woman anyway and I couldn't stand seeing even—.

[*He and mother are little: another feminine identification.*]

D. She was little?

P. Yuh.

D. Like you?

P. Yuh, she was *shorter* than I was, a very small woman. Stood about five feet. I mean four feet eleven or something like that. So I just stepped in between them. Well this was the first time I think I have ever seen him try to *slap* her face.

[*A "slap" in the face is like a "jab" in the head. He shares the fate of a woman.*]

D. Didn't do it before?

P. I don't think he ever did. I think this was the first time he ever did try to *slap* her. But as I said I don't think he was so *wild,* he didn't want to *kill* anybody, but he did have an awful *temper,* though. My mother and he couldn't agree on any one particular thing.

D. And Jimmy?

P. And Jimmy didn't either.

D. He had a *temper* too?

P. Yuh. In other words, I think my brother Jimmy's temper, he *inherited* that, my father's temper, more than anybody else.

[*The older brother is a father equivalent.*]

D. Did mother mind being beaten?

[*Again he is reminded of his feminine identification.*]

P. I don't remember, well I guess she would mind, yes. I don't think anybody likes to be *beaten.*

[*He is not sure whether a woman likes to be beaten. This contradicts what he has been saying all along about not minding the beatings. Therefore, the confrontation with his passive wish is repeated.*]

D. Of course, that's what I thought, but you said you didn't mind the pain.

P. Well, I, for myself, well I didn't like to be *beaten* either for that matter, but I didn't mind the pain so much and, of course, when I was in the—when he put me in the hospital—why I was only there for two or three days, that's all.

[*Women who are "beaten" have to go to the hospital. This is a disguised birth fantasy.*]

P. But like I said I am *worrying* too much about myself, and my *child*—I'm not concerned about him any more, because even though the ailment he has, well I still, I treat him as a *normal* child. I've *accepted* him. This is honestly and earnestly. I've accepted him just the way *God* wants to give him to me, and I've made up my mind that I—.

[*Now he identifies with the child who has the defective head. Treating his own defective child as normal, he tries to annul the past. Mother had a defective child (himself), and so does he. God is the Father Almighty, i.e., more powerful than his father.*]

D. Not like *father* who wasn't satisfied with your behavior?

[*A crucial confrontation with his fear and wish of being violent like father.*]

P. That's right.
D. You don't lose your *temper?*
P. No, I don't lose my *temper.*
D. Any more?
P. Of course, I did have a *little temper* at one time but there is no need of losing tempers; there is no need of it. I mean you can straighten things out in a nice sort of way rather than lose your temper.
D. You used to have a *temper?*
P. Ah, not quite, not too much of a temper.
D. What do you mean?
P. Well, I mean I would *brood* rather than fight back.

[*He settles his aggressiveness in daydreams (brooding).*]

D. Brood over—how do you mean?
P. Well, if I'd get involved with someone and I couldn't make them see my way, why I'd begin to brood over it and I'd say to myself, what a darn fool I am. And then I'd begin to think about it and so on, but I never had much of a temper, never did, because I never wanted to be like my father as far back as I can remember.

[*Instead of fighting actively, he turns to being like mother. This is the only alternative he had.*]

D. How far back is that?
P. Oh, that's quite some time. Since I was fifteen, or something like that. That's when I said to myself, I hope I never turn out to be like him, and I can honestly say that from that time on I didn't have as much of a *temper.*

[*After his surrender, he repressed his aggressiveness.*]

D. From then on?
P. Um.
D. Before you had?
P. Yuh, I used to get them. When he used to *beat* me, I used to get awful mad but there was *no need* of it.
D. Really?
P. Yuh, I thought there was *no need* of it, *beating* me like that. Of course, I probably wouldn't have been in the state of affairs if they had done something about it—*talking* to me in a nice way and *teaching* me the proper way—rather than *beat* hell out of me for something I can honestly say I don't think I was responsible for. Like I told you a week ago I was mostly *envious* rather than anything else.

[*Father is responsible for the sacrifice of his masculinity. Envious of what the other boys had, and what was* more *and* bigger *than he had.*]

D. What do you mean?
P. Because I, we were poor, and all the kids used to wear nice *clothes* going to school and I didn't. And they used to have *candy* bars in school, and I never had them, so I was actually *envious* more than anything else. That's why I used to *steal* all this money that I told you about the last time I spoke to you. So I was mostly *envious.* I can remember one promotion day—I still remember it though. The only thing I had to wear that looked clean was a boy scout coat that someone had given to me because I was a boy scout when I was about *twelve;* and I was really *envious* that day too, because I could see the way all the kids were coming to school and had all *nice things* where I didn't; so I can honestly say that I was always *envious* of anybody that had *anything nice* up until the time I was able to get these things myself, and I *still* am *envious* as a matter of fact, because I feel as though there is no reason why we couldn't have a *well child* as anybody else. This is the *second one,* you know, with the same thing. So like I said, I'm still a little bit *envious,* but as far as my *son's condition* is concerned, why I put that in the back of my mind, and I try to treat him like a *normal* child, and I try to act toward him like he was *normal—talk* to him and *play* with him.

[*He took over the female role, but also wanted to have what a man has. The "nice things" are representatives of the wish for more manhood like his father and brothers who were bigger, taller and more aggressive. He then fuses the past with the present, and reveals again the identification with his son, treating his son like he wished father had done with him.*]

D. But you wish, of course—?
P. Yes, I do wish.
D. You *envy* these men who have *normal* children?

[*He is being talked to symbolically.*]

P. Yes, that's right.
D. You didn't get these *things?*
P. That's right.
D. Did Jimmy get them?
P. Yes, he's got his *little boy,* and he was always able to do what he wanted to do.

[*An ambiguous statement suggesting that with the proper "tools" one can do anything.*]

D. And you couldn't?
P. No.
D. What do you mean?
P. Well, he used to chase me around from one *job* to another. He'd get me one *job* today and I'd leave it tomorrow because I didn't like it. I just wanted to get *something* for *myself.*
D. You didn't want to *work?*

[*Highlighting his passivity.*]

P. Well, I didn't want—I felt—the whole thing was this. I felt it then, and I still feel it today. I don't like *anybody* doing *anything* for me. I like to do *things* for *myself.* Then I know when I do it for myself I'm really proud of it. And I felt then as I do now about it.

[*The masculine side we are dealing with now rejects the wish to get things the easy, passive, feminine way. At the same time he is denying the persistence of his passive wishes.*]

D. Felt then, what do you mean?
P. Yuh, well, I mean when I do something, I mean I like to know that I did it, and say to myself well I think I did a pretty good job.
D. So you mean he tried to get you to work—?
P. For jobs that I didn't care for, like being a *coffee boy* in a restaurant, and working in a print shop, things like that. I didn't care for those jobs at all.

[*Either side of him will always feel frustrated, since he can be satisfied only if he is bigger than any other man, and a woman like mother.*]

D. Not enough *money?*

[*He had mentioned this previously.*]

P. No, there wasn't much money in them. If I could have gone out and *sold myself* to somebody, that is, what I mean to say is, if I had gone out and seek my own job and had been able to *talk* to my employer, you know, I think I could have done much better than he had done for me, see. That's the way I always felt about it; I still feel the same way about it. I don't like *anybody* doing *anything* for me. I'd rather go out and *do things for myself,* and know that I can honestly say that I earned it. Just like this situation now: this is what *frightens* me—in case I go back to the *hospital.* If I had another *attack,* I don't know what I will do, because I don't like accepting anything from anybody.

[*His expression, "I don't like anybody doing anything for me," betrays the unconscious wish of taking "something" from a man (father, employer), and acting as if it were his own. That provokes and exposes him to the "attack" of which he is afraid.*]

D. I thought that you were *envious* of other boys who got from their parents *bicycles* and *toys* and *suits*. . . .

[*Confrontation with his envy of other boys.*]

P. That's right.
D. You wanted them, too?
P. Yuh, when I was able to—when I was old enough, I used to be able to go out and buy those things.

[*He reveals his boastfulness.*]

D. You mean, then, you wanted father and mother should give you those things?
P. Yes, it would have been nice.
D. But they wouldn't?
P. They didn't have the *money*. And father never earned much, that is, never earned much money to get anything like that.

[*Father could not give him anything, because he never had enough for himself.*]

D. What was the matter?
P. I guess he didn't have any—what you might call "know-how" to make a dollar. He used to give my mother so much, and that was all there was to it. *I don't know what was wrong,* but we seemed to be always *poor* somehow. It wasn't my fault, or my mother's fault, but I *blame* it on to my father.

[*Was father the victim of mother's attack, or was he a weakling? He identifies himself with the weak father.*]

D. What do you mean—it wasn't your fault?
P. Well, I was a *little kid* at the time. I mean I couldn't go out to work. I do remember, though, that I started to *sell* papers when I was *twelve* years old, so I could earn fifteen or twenty cents or something like that for myself.

[*He said before symbolically, "I sold myself."*]

P. The only thing that he used to know about was horses and wagons; so, like I said, in a way I still am *envious* of other people in one respect—that they have *healthy children* and I haven't, but in another way I think I'm the richest man in the world, because I have a wonderful wife. I don't think there's anybody—I think she's one out of ten million people. I don't think there is anybody that is like her out of ten million people!

[*He blames father for his envy and for producing defective children. Mother's (wife's) value rises, as father's goes down. He begins to swing back to his identification with the mother.*]

D. That's a lot of people!

P. A lot of people! So I think I'm very—I can honestly say that I have done a very *good job* in selecting a wife for myself. But—of course —I still am envious of people having well children, and I love children very much. As far back as I can remember, I *used* to *love to play with little children.*

[*The phrase, "I used to love playing with children," gives more meaning to his identification with mother.*]

D. Do you remember?
P. I *used* to watch out for my children and see that they weren't *abused* in any way.
D. Abused by whom?
P. Other boys in the neighborhood. I *used* to watch over them. That was when my older brother, Jimmy, wasn't around. I mean when he *used* to go to work. I'd be with them most of the day. We went to school together and I *used* to see that they weren't *abused* or try to keep them from being *abused* by other kids in the neighborhood. So you see I always loved children and people younger than myself.

[*He watches the children to prevent their being abused, or abusing themselves. It sounds like an alibi when he speaks of himself as "using," while of others as "abusing."*]

D. You were like a good *mother* to them?
P. Yeh, I used to watch over my cousin, Freddie. He *used* to have a funny habit "of going off" at nights somewhere and going to sleep in some doorway, and his *mother* would say, "Who would go out and find him?" and I'd go looking for him and I'd find him sleeping in a doorway. So I always loved children, and I still do to this day.

[*"Loving children" versus "working."*]

D. But Jimmy went out and worked?
P. Yuh, that's right.
D. He took over *father's* role?
P. Yuh.
D. And you helped *mother*?
P. Um, as much as I could; of course, when I was old enough, I used to do a lot of housework for her. As a matter of fact, I *used* to do most of the housework in my own place for my wife. Every Sunday morning I'd go over the house thoroughly, mopping, *washing windows, making the beds, washing the dishes.* Even when we took this place —it's the dumpiest place I think we've ever lived in—and I *used* to go over that floor at least two or three times a week just to keep it looking clean. And of course I've always liked to, that is, have things neat and clean around the house, and if anyone walked in, I'd like to have them say, "Well this person has a nice home." I have a nice home anyway. And—so I wish I could get over this *worrying* business somehow.

[*He confirms the strength of his tie to mother (his feminine identification). He is leaning over backward in his pride over his feminine effi-*

ciency, practically saying, "If I can't have a man's satisfaction, I can have a woman's." "Worrying" means being concerned over the sacrifice of his masculinity.]

D. How did *Jimmy* feel about your doing that?

[*The interviewer uses "Jimmy" as the representative of masculinity.*]

P. He wasn't around. He was in N—— at the time, that was when I was old enough to do it. Because he went to N—— when I was about eighteen, seventeen or eighteen, about that age, and I was up in W——. Then when I found out that he had gone to N——, that's when I came back home again. Then things were a little bit more pleasant for me except when he used to come here on visits.

D. What do you mean?

P. He used to visit my mother two or three times a year. Then we'd get into an argument somehow, and I'd say, "Ah go to the devil." I'd just *walk out* the door and I wouldn't come back to see him again until he left. But today he seems to be acting, seems to act a little different toward me. He is a little nicer to me than he has been. I guess he's, well I think I can blame that on one thing. He had quite a discussion with my brother, Herb—I told you about it and, of course, he was always looking after my brother, sending him clothes and *things like that,* and until recently they had some little income tax discussion which they didn't agree upon. So my brother Jimmy called me up that night and told me about it, and then he said to me, I guess I've been *favoring* the *wrong one* all these years, and the last couple of times he has been here, why he seems to act —ever since this has taken place he seems to have a *different attitude* toward me. It was quite a discussion too. Of course, I've always been trying to bring a *reconciliation* about with my brother Herb and my brother Jimmy and my brother John, but you see, my brother Herb had been sick for eight or nine years and he, of course, was dependent upon my brother John, although I used to give him a few dollars a week too, just as much as I possibly could, but it seemed as though he was never grateful for what was being done for him. Of course, when this income tax thing came up, my brother Jimmy thought that he was able to get $250, because he was supporting, he was helping to support my brother and his wife and his two children; why, then there was a big question about it, and so that was when my brother Jim called me up and he was telling me about it—that it seemed he had been *favoring the wrong brother* all these years. Why, I don't think that's so. I think Jimmy had too much of my father's temper. You couldn't *talk* and you couldn't reason with him in any way possible. The first thing you know he'd be *all over* you like that—handful of *wasps,* I mean bees. I remember you never could reason with him, you could never—he's even that way today. He'll never take any excuse from anybody, even from his, the people that *work under him.* He's oftentimes told me that. He says he's not going to take any *excuse* from anybody, but there are some times when people have a good *excuse.* He doesn't seem to remember that. Don't you think so?

[*The older brother was the competitor in his relation to mother. The patient walked out on brother and mother: father had done the same to mother and him. He became the ally of his older brother against the younger one. The older brother should turn away from the other brothers and favor him, as he wished father had done. He would like to reconcile the opposing forces (brother images) in himself. Then he would not have to worry any more. He does not say who would have been the "right" brother whom the older one (father) would have favored.—He would be stung—a good symbolic enactment of his fears. Like father sitting on him and beating him on the rear, or throwing the knife at him.*]

D. You say *father* was like that too?

[*Excuse for what? For taking away? For stealing? For abusing? With this confrontation leading him back to the past, the summarizing of the interview begins.*]

P. I beg your pardon!
D. You say father was like that too? Like Jimmy?
P. Yuh.
D. The same way?
P. Yuh, he would never take any, any *excuse.* I didn't lose any of those things. I took five or six and I gave back five or six. I didn't lose *anybody,* I mean any of them.

[*There were six siblings altogether. A slip, probably showing the identification of the buttons with the children. The brothers are father's "buttons." This is a denial of the wish to lose or get rid of them as far as the masculine side is concerned, and a longing for babies of his own as far as the feminine side is concerned (like mother.)*]

D. The buttons?
P. The buttons. I knew what would happen if I had lost any, but I was awfully careful that I wouldn't lose any.
D. He just didn't want you to play with them?
P. That's right. I wouldn't take anything for, he wouldn't take an excuse.

[*A confusion of identity.*]

D. And is he that way with mother?
P. Yes, he was that way with mother too, and he wouldn't—my brother Jimmy, my father would never take any excuse from anybody.
D. But mother took it?
P. That's right.
D. She didn't leave him?
P. No.
D. She didn't mind?
P. I don't know. I don't remember. I guess, I suppose she did. After a while, she *got fed up with it,* I suppose she was glad to see him go, because she took an awful lot of *abuse* from him.

[*Mother didn't mind being beaten, when taking the "buttons" of father. Mother got "fed up" with (by) father. Father abused mother, as children "abuse" each other, as he "abused" himself.*]

D. Otherwise she might have left him?
P. Uh huh. But tell me this—I've always had a *thought in mind.* Of course, my brothers feel as though it's—when he passes on, it is a custom that we pray for their souls, but my brothers say that they will never do it. I say to myself, well, it's a duty, he is still my father. But I still, I feel that way too, that when he does pass on, I I think I would go pray for his soul. (Here tears come to his eyes.)

[*Sons are not sorry when they "let" father die, but they have guilt feelings.*]

D. You mean you loved him in spite of his beating you?
P. Um, that's right. I think I would.
D. Because as you say—.
P. I would, I know I would, because I think it's a,—I like to think that no matter how bad a parent could be: when they pass on, I think that they should pray for their souls, because *what else is left?* Am I right?

[*He tries to ward off the murderous thoughts against father by re-creating the pain of being beaten. Thus* pain *becomes for him: (1) a gratification, i.e., father beating him; (2) punishment: he will be left defective; father will go away.*]

D. You really loved him a great deal?

[*He is encouraged to make full use of the transference, and to mourn for father, as well as to relieve himself of the guilt for his death wishes against him.*]

P. Yes, I did.
D. You missed him?
P. Yes, but I, that's when I was a youngster. Of course I didn't realize it then; but I do now.
D. How much you missed him when he went away, you mean?
P. I missed him when I was a youngster even though with all the beatings he used to give me.

[*The little boy weeps freely: a kind of abreaction with insight, though.*]

D. How was that?
P. I don't know. Maybe it's because I looked too much like him. That was one thing. Maybe I'm beginning to think that my *brother used to beat* me because I used to look too much *like my father* and uh, ah, he couldn't, I mean he wasn't around so he could take it out on him, so he used to take it out on me. I just look like him *a lot,* the *spitting image* of him.

[*He sees in himself the image of father whom he "let" be killed. He wanted to kill (beat) father, and at the same time surrender passively, as he still needed him. Here we are mainly concerned with his passive longings. Brother was jealous of him, as he was jealous of mother.*]

D. Really?

[*Does he cry being afraid of retaliation?*]

P. Yuh, except for the moustache. He used to wear a moustache.
D. Didn't you want to have a *temper* like him?
P. No. When I was fifteen years old and I saw all that took place, I say I don't want to be anything like this guy. He's not for me.
D. I thought you said you do have a *temper*.
P. Well, it wasn't a *violent temper* like his. Well I mean, it is a common thing for anybody to get *angry* once in a while.
D. As you get *angry* with your wife?

[*Confronting him with the present: he acts out on the wife and son the conflicting strivings of the past.*]

P. Once in a while. I mean not too often, because we get along like *two lovebirds.*
D. Now?
P. Always did.
D. Always?
P. Well, of course, it wasn't too *bad*. I mean just a normal thing between two married people, that's all. I mean we would have a *disagreement* once in a while about something, but it was never *violent* like my father's. I never used to get *violent* with my wife the way my father used to get *violent* with my *mother*. I mean he'd really lose his temper. If he had *something* in his hand, I think he would have really thrown it.

[*This refers not only to the knife, but indirectly to his fear of his masculine aggression, with its consequences.*]

D. You mean he might have really *hurt* her?
P. Yuh, but I mean of course with my wife and I, I mean we never, I mean anything like that never happened to us, just a *disagreement* and she would *brood* for a while, and we'd forget about it. It was all over. But never like my father—heaven forbid. I was never as *bad* as that. I don't think I ever could be because I found out, I've said I think that I'm one of the easiest-going people there is, because I'll never try to get myself involved with anybody in any kind of *disagreement* if I can help it—I try to avoid it just as much as possible, because I want people to think of me as a *nice fellow* and not as a violent person or a person who loses his temper.

[*Now his wife is the "brooder," as he called himself before, when he referred to his way of acting out his destructive tendencies in daydreams. Putting on the façade of a nice fellow, he tries to screen his aggressive feelings. A behavior such as this in an individual with a vulnerable ego leads either to massive crippling inhibitions and/or the body itself becomes the target of the aggression.*]

D. Never were *violent?*

[*For a confrontation with this pathologic conflict solution, the key word "violent" is repeated. It should lead to an admission of his own violence.*]

P. No, I don't—no, I was never *violent,* never. The only time I, of course, well, even when it came to a fist fight when somebody else in it was *violent,* I just used to laugh it off, that's all. Of course, if a fellow hit me a little bit hard, why, then of course I'd get a little bit *mad* and then I'd go right after him as hard as I possibly could, but it never came to a stage where I would get real *violent* because I saw that, I saw what it had done.

[*He admits his "madness" when attacked. But the price for being aggressive was too high: he would have lost either father or mother.*]

D. What do you mean?
P. It *broke up* two people like my father and mother. If he hadn't had that nasty *temper* that he had, I'd say my mother would live with him.
D. So you mean you were afraid you—?
P. That's right.
D. If you showed your *temper* to your wife—?

[*Now he fears losing his wife who must play the role of a kind father as well as a mother for him.*]

P. No, I couldn't have shown any *temper* because I never had that kind of *temper.*
D. But I thought you told me that you had a *terrible fight* with her.

[*Using material from the first interview.*]

P. (Laughs) No, I, I. . . .
D. You said that you had stopped yourself. You were afraid of losing your head.
P. Well that was just once, just once.
D. Tell me about it. What happened?

[*He has to be confronted with the hate for his own femininity which he projects onto his wife.*]

P. It was on a New Year's, on a New Year's night, and uh, uh, I went to bed early that night. I was getting over a *cold* and I went to bed early that night. I didn't want to stay up to wish her a happy New Year, because I was tired and I wanted to go to bed. I don't even do it to this day. I never bothered with staying up New Year's. I said happy New Year and I said well do you mind if I go to bed, I'm rather tired. She said, okay. Well, this was the first time this had ever happened, because previously she had been, we had been out on New Year's and on this particular time, why, I had a *cold.* This was during the war—1942 I think it was—and uh, I had been out *sick* for a few days, and of course New Year's fell on one of those days I was out *sick,* and I went to bed. I said do you mind, and she said no, so I went to bed. So she figured I'd wake up about twelve o'clock to wish her a happy New Year, so when I didn't she started to *rave* and this and that—so she woke me up and I said what's the matter with you? She said the least you could have done was to have stayed up and wished me a happy New Year. I said look, I've got a *cold.* I told you I was *tired.* I said why is it so important. So I said all right, I'll wish you a happy New Year tomorrow, why, what's the difference? So I began, I was quiet, I didn't say nothing, I *was just lying in bed,* and she began to *rave* and *rave,* and I said, look, now cut this out, this is enough; and she wouldn't stop. So she kept on and I just leaped out of bed and said look, now that's enough. So I got dressed and I *went out,* and that's all that was said, but I was really, really *mad* about it, and I walked around for a while and I cooled off. When I came back, she was still *raving,* so I said, you can go ahead and *rave* all you want to, I'm still going to bed, I'm not going to let you bother me, and I did. So she *brooded* for two or three days—but I never got violent though. That's when I said I'll never get as mad as that again. I'm never going to let it happen again, and I didn't.

[*"Cold" also refers to deprived and unloved feelings. Being "cold against" the wife is his expression of aggressiveness and abuse. Wife reacts with raving. When confronted with his wife's demands on his masculinity, "he" gets "real mad"; but then "he" is afraid of his anger and runs away. The "cold" against the wife "cools off," and he returns. The wife becomes the "brooding" one. He had said previously that he was fearful of losing control of himself and striking her.*]

D. You were *afraid*?
P. I wasn't afraid; there was nothing to be *afraid* of.
D. But as you said, you didn't want to let that ever happen again.
P. That's right.
D. Why?
P. Well, because there was no need of it. It was all foolish, that's all.
D. I wondered if you were *afraid* she might *leave you* like father and mother split up.

[*With the reminder of the parents' separation, the material of the past is connected with the present.*]

P. Well, I had that in mind, yes.
D. That's what I mean. You thought of that!

[*For therapeutic reasons, it is necessary to make him admit what he is afraid of.*]

P. I thought of it, and that's why I said this is no good. This is the last time this will happen, and it was the last time. Of course, we've had a few *disagreements, I'd say quite a few since then.*

[*Now things are more out in the open. In the previous interview, he had told about his rage and hate directed at the sister-in-law at the same time when he had resolved never again to lose his temper and quarrel with his wife for fear of what he or she might do.*]

D. What do you mean?
P. Oh, like for example, uh, I think I told you about this last Thursday, I told you last Thursday that when my sister-in-law came down, the Wednesday night before, she asked us what we were going to do New Year's, and I said I think I'll go out in the afternoon sometime. She said swell. So she said, well what time do you think *you'll*

go? I said: about three or four o'clock, and I started to explain to her that I have to go when I feel as though I can go. I just can't get up and run any minute. When I feel as though I was rested, I'd be able to go, and I figured I'd stay home all day and rest all that day Monday, because we had the whole week end off—Monday and Tuesday—but we had to work the following Saturday to make up for the Monday that we were given off Christmas and New Year's; so I said to my wife: well, I think we'll leave about three or four o'clock, and we'll get back in time to let your sister go out. I figured that they would go out about nine o'clock. I figured we would have lunch and then go over to her younger sister's house and play poker or something like that, because that is generally what we like to do.

[*This part of him represented by the feminine identification, projects the urge of turning to men (father-brother images) on his wife. He is sensitized to "madness" by the repressed wish of leaving wife (mother) as father did, and losing her to the competitor (sister), of whom he is jealous, because his wife might prefer her to him. (According to the wife, he was extremely irascible over the smallest of provocations and had always been anxious over controlling his temper.)*]

P. So my wife says to me, on Thursday she kept asking about it and I said well, we'll go out about three or four o'clock. The same thing happened Thursday, Friday, Saturday, Sunday and Monday, so Monday morning I got *real mad* about it. I said: look, why do you insist on asking me all the time. I said I know what's in back of your mind. You're thinking that we ain't going to get back on time to let your sister go out, oh yuh, and then I found that they wanted to go to a burlesque and I said, you're worried about that, you won't be back on time to let your sister go out and your sister is going to give you the devil for not getting back on time, so I says now look, cut it out, that's enough, I don't want to hear any more about this thing. I'll go out when I feel as though I'm ready to go out, and if it's too late I'm not going to go at all. So I said, "Look, you've got to understand my condition." I says I just can't fly out of the house like I *used* to do, so the result is that was all that was said. I just said: look, I don't want to hear any more about it. So I had my breakfast and went back to bed until one o'clock and around one o'clock I started to get dressed and left the house by 2:30. We went to a place at C—— Street and had a nice lunch, and from there we went—and while there she brought up the subject again. I says, look, I says, now wasn't this foolish, you *nagging me* since last Thursday.

[*In the first interview, he had stated that mother had nagged father many times and hinted that she was to blame for father's leaving home.*]

P. She said: yes it was. So I had a drink or two and I started to get a little giggly because it doesn't take much to get me giggling anyway (laughs).

[*He puts on an act to laugh off with great verbosity the "violent" side of him.*]

P. And we laughed and I thought of a few things that were funny, and you know, just try to forget the whole thing and make it much more pleasant, and I laughed, and when I laughed my eyes began to water and she looked at me and she started to laugh, so while we were there we both had a laughing good time. Then we went to see "Quo Vadis" and were home by eight o'clock. So you see there's nothing to it. I didn't get *violent* or anything like that. I just told her, and that's all. So she understood after a while. That's the way it is. So you see I'm not as *violent* as my father was. Isn't that right? But then I should have been smart.

[*He cannot fully decide with which parent to identify.*]

P. I should have said: we'll leave when we're ready. I told—I thought that that would be, that was the best thing to say: we'll leave when we're ready. But that would be no good either on the other hand because she would ask me: what time is that? and I'd still have to say around three or four o'clock, so that wouldn't be any better. But anyway, it all turned out for the best, and nothing ever came of it. I didn't get *violent* or anything like that. And that's how things are. We never get violent at each other. The only time, of course, she did, she *threw something* at me when she came back from the hospital when she first had the *baby*. Something was *bothering* her, I didn't know what it was. Of course, I had done every possible thing to please her, I mean I cleaned up the whole house, cleaned down the walls, washed the windows, hung the curtains. This all took place in the ten days she was in the hospital *having the child.*

[*Father threw knife at his rear (at his female side). Wife did the same. In the wife's absence he took over the woman's role (cleaning, washing). In this role he let himself be treated by his wife, as father treated mother. She threw the ashtray at him, when he disappointed her by not being a man after she became a woman with a defective child.*]

D. Which one?

P. When she came in, she was very pleased, but then I noticed that she was *sulking* about something. I kept asking her what it was. I said, tell me what it is and I'll try to do something for you, but she wouldn't tell me. So the last night this happened—and she was in this condition she *threw an ashtray* at me. Well she didn't *throw* it at me, but no, she, I don't think she *threw* it at me. She just got so *mad* about *something* that she threw the darn thing on the floor and it broke into little pieces. And I said, now, look, what was the idea of that? If you will tell me what is wrong, I'll probably be able to help you. She got over it right away and then a few days later she apologized for throwing the ashtray. Then she started telling me what was bothering her, that she didn't have any *confidence* in herself as far as you know taking care of the baby, since we had lost our first one. She thought she wasn't going to have any confidence in herself to take care of the second one.

[*He pretends not to know what his wife expected of him. He becomes aware that he distorts reality to suit his fantasies. He let his wife have no confidence in herself as a woman, to cover up that he had none in himself as a man.*]

D. And that made her *mad* at you?
P. Well, huh? What?
D. And that made her *mad* at you?
P. Well she was mad at the world I guess, not at me. I mean I tried to help her because I thought I did what I possibly could by cleaning up the house and making it spotless for when she'd come home with the baby. But my wife was *mad* at the world and she took it out on me, but as far as she is concerned I mean, like I said, we get along like two lovebirds. Of course we have disagreements here and there or something like that. I guess that's just the way of living of two married people.

[*Doing housework as a good deed, to excuse himself. He let his wife be mad with the reality world, in which she looks for a "man." She got mad at him for not being a man. He projects his disappointment with himself on her, as she does on him.*]

D. But as you said, even though *father beat* you, you still loved him very much.

[*The "father image" is introduced to let him verbalize the present conflict in terms of the past conflicts. He takes the "bait," as the following associations show.*]

P. Yeh. I don't know why. I guess it's because I wanted to have a father. I never saw him much—I wanted to have a father. I knew the other children had, but I didn't have any; he wasn't here. He was up in M—— somewhere most of the time.

[*He loved the beating father.*]

D. You thought about him?
P. Recently?
D. I mean then.
P. Yes.
D. You used to think about him?
P. Um. He used to do some *awful things* to make me, to make us, that is all of us, my brothers and myself, *mad*. I remember he used to have us get our *hair cut*, and cut all the hair off and just leave us a little bit of it right here, right there, just a little bit of hair hanging, you know; and all the other kids used to laugh at us. My God, he was such an awful *fanatic*.

[*The meaning of madness is now clarified: everybody is mad, being afraid of having everything cut off. He is longing for the "mad," "beating, "cutting" father. Father was a "fanatic" cutter.*]

D. But you missed him?
P. Yuh, I still missed him.

D. You still miss him?
P. Yuh. What, today?
D. Yes.
P. No, not today, I don't miss him now. I don't miss him at all. I don't even, well I think about him once in a while; I say to myself, it's too bad it had to happen, that's all, between him and my mother.

[*He denies that he misses father, but contradicts himself in the same breath, by being sorry that father left him (mother).*]

D. You mean that he ran away and you lost him?
P. That's right. I mean, uh, I do think of him quite a bit, I mean, the few years my mother did spend with him, why, she wasn't happy with him at all, and, well I say to myself, it's a shame that had to happen, because I know my mother was a *nice woman.*
D. A boy needs a father?

[*The ambiguous remark, "A boy needs a father," stirs up the opposing passive and masculine drives.*]

P. Naturally, a boy needs a father. And perhaps if he hadn't been a *fanatic* the way he was, we might have had a different life.
D. What do you mean?
P. Well, probably brought up different. It was hard for my mother to bring up, well my sisters were gone, two of them were married and one was single, and then my brother Jimmy, but he was never around, and when he was I used to hear about it. But it's nice to have—to go to a synagogue with him, go to the baseball game with your father, go to a football game with your father, go to a movie with your father or something like that. A boy takes pride in his father if he's good to him. I never had one, and I think my life would have been a whole lot different if he had been, if he hadn't been so *violent,* with a temper, not willing to accept an excuse. I think that because, I can honestly say it was because of the fact that we never had anything, why that's why I used to *steal* money, not much, just ten or fifteen cents or a quarter, or something like that, because like I said, I was envious of what the other children had. I just wanted what the other children had and I never could get it. Well, that's about all. *How am I going to get over this feeling of worrying about myself?* That's what I'd like to find out, because nothing else bothers me now, I mean, *I've put that all in the past,* and *it's there.*

[*The imagined danger of having something cut off by father let him feel as if it had already happened and he never had anything. Therefore, he tried to restitute the imagined loss by stealing. He understands now, in part, the problems of the past.*]

D. What do you mean, worrying?
P. Well, like I said, I mean, I worry too much about myself. I know it. I mean there are people that have *heart conditions* and they don't worry half as much as I do. Maybe on the other hand, I really do have something.

[*The meaning of his worries about the "heart" condition is now clear, as seen in this sector: he still worries about what the "mad" father might do to him, the little boy. To be safe, father had to leave.*]

D. You mean worrying about something happening to you? And going away and leaving your wife?

[*He wishes to leave his little boy and wife, as father did, to help his heart condition.*]

P. That's right, that's right; because I feel as though I've got a job which I want to do.
D. But a *wife* needs a *husband*?
P. That's right, and I don't want to *leave* my wife.
D. And *children* need a *father*.
P. That's right. I think my *boy*—(pause). (Weeps)
D. You don't want to have happen to them what happened to you?

[*To arouse the patient's repressed emotional reactions, the interviewer confronts him again with his fears of the past. He weeps like the little boy who felt threatened that father might leave mother and him, too.*]

P. That's right. I think that, I believe in miracles and I believe a miracle can still happen with my son although they have told us that his *head* has *stopped growing* and the *fluid* has left it *soft*.

[*"Head" and "heart" conditions are equated.*]

D. You mean if he had a father who can do magic?
P. That's right, and I want to be around to take him to football games and stuff like that.
D. You want to be able to do to him what—?
P. That's right.
D. What you never got yourself?
P. That's right.
D. And then he'll grow up right?

[*The repetition is necessary, as all this painful material tends to be quickly denied and isolated.*]

P. That's right. Well I don't expect him to be normal, that's why I feel about my son.
D. But you said you believed in miracles.
P. Well I expect a miracle, yuh, to take care of him, but I don't expect him to be a hundred per cent or ninety per cent normal as far as, uh, intelligence will be concerned.
D. What you mean is, you are afraid it may happen to your son and your wife what happened to your mother and to you?

[*This statement formulates again the meaning of his problem.*]

P. That's right, that's right. I don't want my wife to be left without a husband even though I'm insured for $4,000. I have made every provision for other things that are needed after I'm *gone*, but I still would like to see my wife. (Weeps)

D. But as you said before you are *afraid* if you lose your *temper* it might affect your *heart.*

[*It is obvious that he lives in a pseudo reality in which the past and the present are one and the same. In the first interview, he had talked about how the doctors told him he must keep calm to avoid future heart attacks and high blood pressure. (Present B.P. 160/100). The interviewer confronts the patient with his "madness" and his worries of retaliation.*]

P. No, I don't lose my *temper,* just a *disagreement,* but it doesn't get to that stage where I get *violently mad.* I mean I don't do that; I've very seldom done that. As I said, the only thing is that I'm worrying too much. That's all. I just want to have peace of mind for a while, that's all. Not to have to worry about this and not to have to worry about that because this thing doesn't seem to leave me alone somehow. Like I said, all these *little pains* I used to get when I was well—Dr. H—— for the past ten years has told me that I'm a very well person—but it happens that, like I said, in the morning you get up and you get a little *twitch* here and a little *twitch* there, and you never used to mind it, but the same thing *still happens* today and I mind it more now than I ever did. I'm more *pain conscious* now than I ever did, I mean than I ever was, and I worry about it, which I mean I never used to let it *bother* me, and even the doctors at the hospital and Dr. H—— have told me that I'm doing remarkably well. The lines are beginning to straighten themselves out, and the only way anybody will ever know that you had a heart attack, if I take another EKG. So what's *frightening,* or why am I *worrying* about it? That's what I want to find out. I mean these other things that have happened to me in the past with my father and my brother Jimmy and uh—. (Pause)

[*The pains become unbearable when reality events make it seem as if "Now it will really happen—what I have always feared!" Pain becomes laden with anxiety when the forbidden wishes, terrors, and fear of punishments of the past are revived. In many ways, the doctor substitutes for father. He should tell him that his heart is all right, i.e., that there is nothing "cut" in him.*]

D. You didn't mind the *pain* then?
P. No, I used to laugh them off then; it was nothing.

[*He denied and repressed wishes, thoughts and feelings, which now return.*]

D. You didn't know that father was going to go away and leave you.
P. That's right. I didn't mind it then at all.
D. But after father went away and left and you missed him so much—?
P. What you're trying to say is, if my father would beat me I wouldn't mind the pain, is that it? (Laughs)

[*He brings out the unconscious meaning of his symptoms himself. This will be used again and again in later interviews.*]

D. You would rather have your father then.

P. Huh?
D. Maybe you would rather have your father then.
P. No, I don't think so. I can do without that too. (Laughs)

[*The reality principle asserts itself.*]

D. Do without it, huh?
P. You ain't kidding. I can do without those beatings.
D. You mean you did mind the pain.
P. Well not so much. I was a pretty tough youngster anyway. I mean there isn't anybody who could hurt me physically or anything like that.
D. But as you said, the big pain, the heart pain that you had when father went away and you—.

[*One of the manifold meanings of heart pain is now interpreted, as he has been prepared for it.*]

P. That's right, that, that's the biggest pain although it don't hurt sometimes. That's the biggest pain. It's a grieving inside you, I think.

[*"Grieving" is the reaction to the painful, real loss of the cutting father, and to the imagined loss of what has been cut off (beaten).*]

D. And you still are grieving?
P. Grieving about myself.
D. About father?
P. I've forgotten about him.
D. Really! But you cried last week because you missed him so much.
P. I was emotionally upset, I guess, but of course I've gotten over that.
D. But you told me before that you really still thought of father.

[*Confronting him with his own words.*]

P. Well I still do once in a while, and I say to myself, well, when he passes on I'll still go pray for his soul because he was my father.
D. So there's a little ache there still?
P. No, I don't think so. No, I'm just doing it because it's in the Laws of God and it's the proper thing to do.

[*The feelings are too passive and overwhelming to be accepted.*]

D. So you mean you've cried about him in the past though?

[*A more round-about approach is needed.*]

P. It's a good many years ago.
D. You used to cry then?
P. When he'd go away.
D. And now you—?
P. Now I don't care. I just—.
D. Now, since you feel like crying, you feel like crying about you going away.

[*The core of his problem.*]

P. Myself, yuh, because I know what I'm leaving behind; I'm leaving behind something I thought was very beautiful.

[*This is his narcissistic overvaluation of the loss.*]

D. Father didn't know that.
P. No, but I do.
D. You mean having a son?
P. Having a son.
D. And a wife?
P. A wife and children, and all wonderful children.

[*He can only accept wonderful children.*]

D. He didn't mind going away?
P. No, he didn't care. He was just one of these fellows who didn't care, I suppose. He didn't want the responsibility.
D. Never cared for you, you mean?
P. Hm, it seemed that way. If he had cared, why, he would have stayed home and done his best, regardless of the fact that whatever—how shall I say it—um, well I mean disagreements that he had with my mother. We all have a few. That doesn't mean—we don't have to leave home because we have a disagreement with our wives. You don't have to leave home because your son doesn't want to pray out of a prayer book, like you do. He isn't going to become the same *fanatic* that you are.

[*He avoids the feelings that father left for other reasons also; i.e., as if his sons were unloved and inadequate. His wording shows clearly the double meaning.*]

D. We hope not.
P. Well, I hope you can tell me how I can get over this *worrying* thing.
D. Help you?
P. Well, what is bothering me, I mean, can you tell, I mean—you spoke to me before, I mean what's in the back of my *head* that makes me feel this way?

[*He asks for the magic word of the father (interviewer) instead of using the insight—limited though—into his worries. This sort of "pretended" ignorance as a defense appears often at the end of an interview which seemed to have been so enlightening to a patient. It shows that this "insight" could not be sufficiently integrated into his consciousness. However, he has to be confronted with his own statements.*]

D. As you remember, you said you don't want to go away and leave your wife and your child the way father went away. You don't want to get mad the way he did. You don't want to be a fanatic like he was.
P. Well, those things don't bother me any more. I want to get away from this worrying about myself, keep my mind on other things.

[*The task remains, to aid him in the chosen sector in dispensing with his protective denials and anxiety-laden longings.*]

D. I'll see you next week.
P. O.K. Thanks a lot.

CHART

ASSOCIATIVE MATERIAL SHOWING RELATION OF SYMPTOM PAIN TO THE FATHER

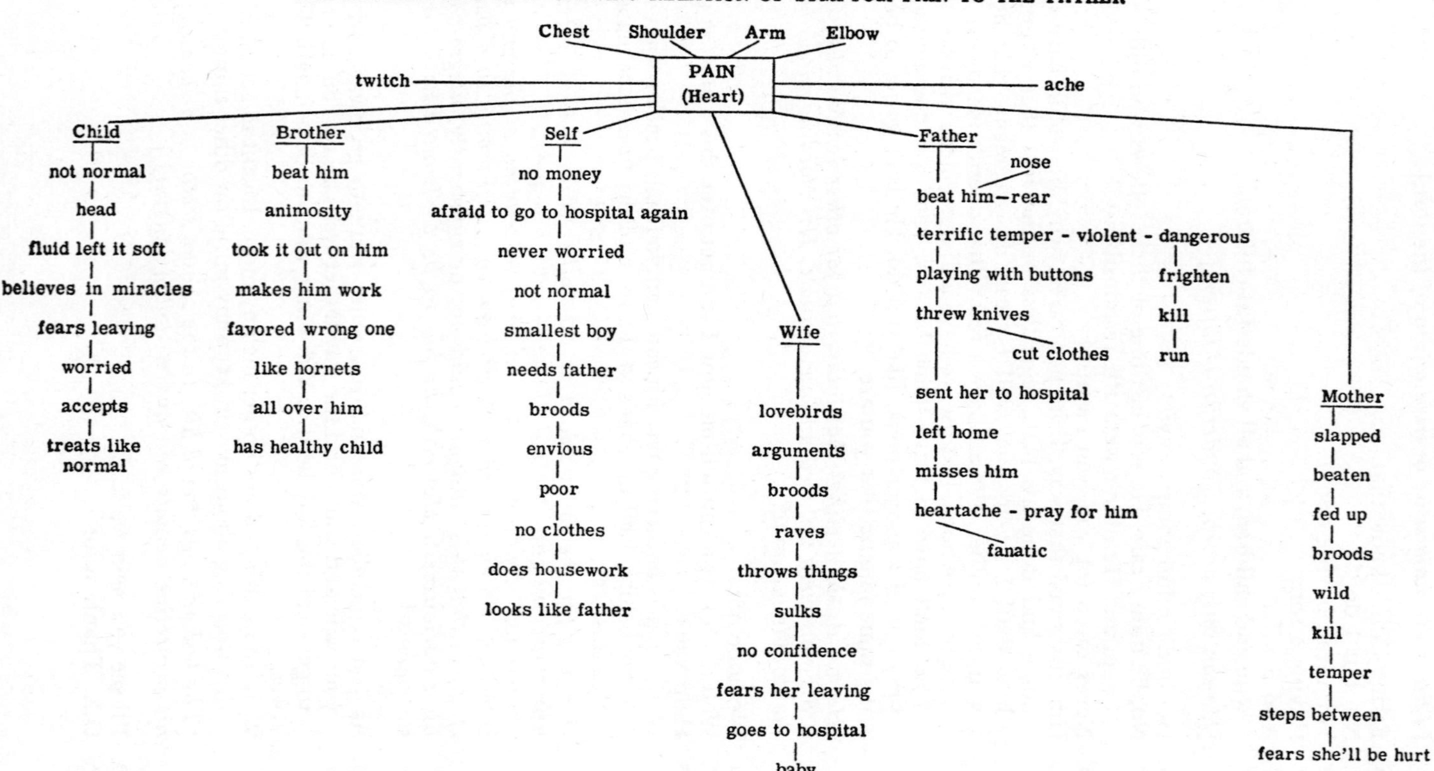

Final Discussion

The stimulus word PAIN led in this interview to a series of associations connected with memories and fantasies centering around aggressive behavior between:

a) Father and mother;
b) Father and himself; } in the past
c) Brother and himself;
d) His wife and himself } in the present.

There were also feelings of loss and deprivation concerning the patient's relation to:

a) Father in the past, leaving mother and him;
b) Himself in the present, leaving wife and child.

This material was obvious and presentable to the patient at a conscious level. The symbolism showed guilt and inadequacy feelings in relation to his brothers, and failure to work through his oedipal rivalry situation with his parents. That led to strong, repressed passive feminine wishes toward his father, alternating with identifications with him as a dangerous, aggressive phallic figure. The key word PAIN opened the chain of associations related to the endangered phallic representations: heart, shoulder, left arm and elbow. An outline of these associations clearly demonstrates the painful material both in the past and present.

Follow-Up

The patient was seen twice a week over a period of twenty-two weeks, with complete symptomatic relief from PAIN. According to his wife, he was at this time making a very good adjustment at home, and they were planning to have another child. Blood pressure at the time of discharge was 140/90. He has continued to be in this good condition over a period of four years.

CHAPTER III

Establishing A Sector

The Weak Feet

Introduction

A symptom is usually considered as the symbolic representation of an intrapsychic conflict solution between irreconcilable wishes and prohibitions. It can also be looked upon as an attempt to postpone or evade the painful recognition of a reality situation which implies an unbearable loss or injury to one's narcissism. Moreover, it attempts through utilization of secondary gains to make good for the loss which may be real, fantasied or threatened.

The dissolution of a symptom as a symbolic unit will occur only when the patient is able to abandon defenses against the painful affect-laden material of both the past and present, which is responsible for its appearance. The following interview will illustrate how a symptom with an obvious meaning can be undermined, and its usefulness to the patient eventually be destroyed. Such an event can happen only when the interview serves to support the ego in finding a better conflict solution.

In contrast to the loquacity of the previous patient who freely produced associative material to cue words, this interview will demonstrate how to apply the sector therapy to a reticent, negativistic patient.

Case Presentation

The patient is a twenty-six-year-old, plump, aggressive man who entered the hospital shortly after becoming engaged to marry. His father died a few years before he entered the Service from which he had received a medical discharge. He had been living with his mother who babied him considerably. He had an older and much envied brother who was married and successfully established in business.

At the time of this interview, the patient had been in the hospital for a period of over six months, complaining bitterly of pains in his feet and demanding barbiturates. The residents assigned to this case felt that he was so aggressive and unco-operative as to make treatment impossible. He continuously demanded to return to an older therapist who had allowed him to have barbiturates, and who had given him a great deal of sympathy, without an appreciable change in the clinical picture.

The interview will demonstrate how to remain in a chosen sector, how to guide the associations of a resistant patient, and how to give him some understanding of the meaning of his conflicts within that chosen sector.

INTERVIEW

P. (Knocks on door).

D. Come in. Sit down, please. You wanted to see me.

[*The patient had requested an interview due to difficulties with his therapist.*]

P. I haven't been feeling so good this week. (Pause)

D. This week?

[*His complaints had been loud and consistent for six months in spite of all attempts to help him in individual and group therapy, by changing therapists and prescribing all the ancillary aid programs—most of which were refused.*]

P. It's the same most every week. I pick up a little and then I seem to go back. I don't know what it is.

D. Sets you back, in what way?

[*Awaiting an opening.*]

P. I can't stand on my feet. They send me down to the *foot* doctor. I sweat all day.

D. Can't stand on your own *feet?*

P. I've got no strength in my *feet*. I've got no strength in my body.

[*Feet are paramount in the body image.*]

D. It isn't a nice position to be in, not to be able to stand on your own *feet*. You weren't always like that?

[*It was decided to take the symbolism of "standing on one's own feet" as the core of the sector.*]

P. What I'd like to do, I don't know. It might be me; it might be my doctor. I don't know why I don't seem to get anywhere.

D. You mean you're not *getting anywhere* on your *feet?*

[*Connecting his own words; he needs feet to get somewhere.*]

P. *Getting anywhere! I got a certain problem.* I go in there and tell him. It hurts me a little. Maybe I start to cry. I still don't *get anywhere*. I don't understand it. I want to go back to Dr. B.

[*"It (feet) hurts him," and he cries.*]

2152

D. What do you mean, a certain problem?

[*Dr. B. was kind and sympathetic and allowed him barbiturates. The patient is pinned down to the key word relating to feet.*]

P. I'd like to get back to Dr. B.
D. What *problem* are you talking about?

[*His plea is ignored. It is important to remain consistent.*]

P. Well, like the other day. I go in to talk to him and I told him how I felt. I started talking about the Army and how they used to *drag* me, and how I'd start crying. So I cry. Then I go off and I feel just as bad, and I still don't understand it any more.
D. You went in the Army and they started to *drag you?*

[*He was dragged when his feet gave way.*]

P. That's right. They used to drag me *and things,* and so I'd tell him.

[*"And things" seems to contain the important material.*]

D. They used to *drag* you?
P. That's right. Two people, one on each side. I want to go back to Dr. B.
D. Two people dragged you, you mean like you'd drag a *kid* along?

[*"Kid" is used here to get ready for splitting the ego into a childlike part that faces an adult portion, and to stimulate thoughts connected with the past. Was he ever "dragged" before? It is assumed that his problem is not knowing how "to walk and to stand like a man" without fear.*]

P. That's right. Two people, one on each arm, drag me, and *things.*
D. Why?
P. Because I couldn't walk. They thought I was faking. I want to go back to Dr. B. I've tried four months here and I don't know whether I'm wasting my time. I think Dr. B. knows my problem and I want to go back to him.

[*He was two months with Dr. B.*]

D. They said you could walk, but you mean you really couldn't walk?
P. I'd like to go back to Dr. B.

[*The interviewer ignores the patient's childish request and insists on his sector approach.*]

D. What was the trouble that you couldn't walk?
P. *Bad feet.* I'd like to go back to Dr. B. He knows my *problem* and perhaps he can help me.
D. Could you tell me about your *problem?*
P. I don't know. I've got so many *problems* that I'm getting all confused. I want to go back to Dr. B.

[*Walking and being dragged, feeling bad and bad feet, all have infantile roots and problems in the past, and this is shown in his admission concerning "confusion." The interviewer's insistence begins to pay off.*]

D. You've got so many *problems?*

P. No, I've not got so many *problems.* I've got a few basic things that bother me and I can't clear them up here.

[*This is too dangerous an admission. He resents being pinned down.*]

D. (Interrupting) Would you tell me what they are? What are the basic things that bother you?

P. *Tired. No strength.* Can't walk on my (pause), I can't walk. (Pause) And sweat.

[*He is aware that this admission highlights his main problem.*]

D. You mean this is what keeps you from walking on your own two feet?

[*A deliberate distortion to bring home the meaning of the symptom. Standing on his own two feet is a physical task, so he cannot deny the statement.*]

P. I've got bad feet. I went down once to see the foot doctor, and he said my feet are so bad they can't do anything for me.

[*Now he needs a testimonial. "Me" and "my feet" are equated.*]

D. How did you get those?

P. What?

D. Bad feet.

P. I got them in the Army. They were second degree then. Now they are, I don't know what they are. I can't stand up.

D. They were second degree? And what did that mean?

[*"Second degree" is overdetermined. He has an older brother to whom he had to play second fiddle all his life.*]

P. I don't know. That's what they said, but they never bothered me.

D. They said when you went in the Army that you had second degree feet?

[*This is pinning the patient down so he will not be able to deny his statements later. He wants to retract his words.*]

P. I think so, or maybe first degree. I don't know.

D. They said you already had bad feet?

P. No, I didn't have *bad* feet then.

[*This retraction shows: (1) Secondary gain: It is the fault of the Service, and I want recompense. (2) Once I was a wonderful man. The interviewer uses the second premise.*]

D. You mean, then you felt they were all right, good enough for you?

P. They were all right for me.

D. How do you mean? You mean you could stand on your own feet then, before you went in the Army?

[*We are pointing toward getting this difficult patient back into the past.*]

P. I could always walk, ride, hike and do different *things.*

D. You knew that because you had done those *things,* you mean?

[*Pinning him down in the past. What are different "things?"*]

P. Yes, I've done all those *things*. I want to go back to Dr. B. There's no sense in talking to you about it. He knows my problem and I think he can help me.

[*This means, "I don't want to talk about it, as I suspect a trap."*]

D. You could walk and you could ride?

[*Continuing in the sector.*]

P. Bicycle ride.
D. Use your feet?

[*The cue word "feet" is put in to preserve continuity.*]

P. Yes, wonderful. I was strong.

[*Now he brings up the superman, ego ideal from the past.*]

D. How so?
P. Oh, strong as anybody. I could go and play basketball.
D. You have always been so strong?

[*"Always" should lead to the past.*]

P. Yes.
D. How did you know?
P. How did I know?
D. Who told you, I mean.
P. What do you mean? I used to run around the track on the Fourth of July. I'd run around as much as anybody else in Lincoln Field.

[*Running is closely connected with walking and means competing by using the feet. Now we have a definite opening.*]

D. You mean in those competitions? When was this?
P. Almost every year I used to run.
D. You were a runner?
P. Not a runner; I used to run with the fellows and play football and baseball. That's what I came to see you about. I want to go back to—
D. (Interrupting) You mean when you were . . . . that is, before you went in the Army?

[*We pin him down to the past and quickly break up the other train of thought.*]

P. That's right.
D. How old were you then?
P. When I went into the Army? Seventeen.
D. When did you start *running* at Lincoln Field?
P. Well, since I was—well—every year they have it.
D. Since . . .?
P. Since I was a kid.

[*An opening into the past is available at last.*]

D. When was that? How old were you when you started *running?*
P. I wasn't *always* running. I played football, baseball and basketball.
D. But I mean at Lincoln Field?

P. Well, maybe eight years old. . . .
D. You started running when you were eight? So you must have been in the second grade in school at that time.

[*This repetition aims at enabling him to hear himself, and to fix him in the past from which he continually wriggles, trying to escape. The interviewer tries to establish the age and to evoke more memories of the past.*]

P. Oh, I was eight years or nine years old at that time. I used to go down there to watch them run.
D. You watched them run then, when you were eight. You weren't big enough to run yourself?

[*"Eight" and "big" are linked up.*]

P. Oh, yuh, they used to have kids' races.
D. Oh, different classes?

[*This is one of his problems. Classes are brothers at a different age.*]

P. That's right.
D. How did you happen to get interested in running?
P. Oh, everybody else did, all the kids did.

[*Everybody is a runner.*]

D. All the kids in the neighborhood, you mean, around there went up to the field to run?
P. We all used to play, run, get ice cream. They used to give us ice cream.

[*Then he could run, and was orally rewarded.*]

D. Oh, yes, that's right. It was a big holiday and you kids would all go up there and compete?
P. Yuh.
D. And you would win?
P. Well, almost, maybe I'd come in second.

[*Now we see what second degree means, i.e., second degree feet. There must be somebody who came in first.*]

D. Second? You wanted to be first?

[*The interview proceeds on a symbolical level, on which the interviewer can back up the patient's immature ego.*]

P. Naturally.
D. But second is good, too. You were competing with all of those other children.
P. They came from everywhere. Why ain't I getting better? I want Dr. B.
D. You could run then anyway.
P. Why aren't I getting better? I'm not a *jerk*. I go in there and talk and I don't seem to be *getting anywhere*.
D. What do you mean, you are not a *jerk?*

[*"Jerk" is overdetermined and is connected with a denial of being *"bad." A "jerk" is someone with "bad feet" who can't "walk," also one who "jerks" or masturbates.*]

P. I've got a brain in my head.

[*At least the "head" is good, if the "feet" are bad.*]

D. You mean, you were good in school as well as in running?
P. No, I was not a genius in school, just good.
D. How did you happen to get interested in running?

[*With whom has he been racing?*]

P. Just like you play football, just like you play baseball, just like you play basketball.
D. But I wondered how you got interested in it. Did you have anyone else in the family who ran?
P. No, no one in my family.

[*The following questions are not asked to ascertain facts, but to get the competitor into the picture, who has the "first degree" feet. Leaving the sisters aside, he turns to the brother competitor. (Actually, he also had two older sisters.)*]

D. Who was in your family?
P. I've got a brother and three sisters.
D. Older or younger?
P. An older brother.
D. How much older?
P. He's thirty-five.
D. How old are you?
P. Twenty-seven.
D. So he's eight years older?

[*The number "eight" appears in connection with running. The brother was eight years old when the patient was born.*]

P. That's right.
D. Did he run, too?
P. Oh, we used to play, play in the playground, all of us together. We used to play in the playground during the summer.
D. And did your brother run at the Fourth of July races?
P. Oh, sure.

[*He drifts deeper into the competitive spirit, and this is exploited by further emphasis on racing against the brother.*]

D. And was he a good runner?
P. Oh, he was all right.
D. So did he show you how to run?
P. Oh, no, no. We were just a gang of kids.
D. He didn't teach you?
P. No.
D. He wasn't interested? He was eight years older and you were only a small fry then.

[*The confrontation with his competitiveness is enforced.*]

P. I wouldn't say that.
D. But I was wondering if he was interested in showing you how.
P. Listen, I think a lot of Dr. G. He's a nice fellow, but Dr. B. knows my problem, and I think I can clear it up through him.

[*Why does he turn from brother to Dr. G.? Why has he had such difficulty with his therapist? It shows the transference relationship plainly. Dr. G. is the brother he wants to beat, and Dr. B. is the kind, indulgent father.*]

D. What problem?
P. Problems, plural.
D. You mean the problems related to your standing on your own two feet and being able to walk and run and play?

[*This confrontation by using the cue words feet, walk, run, comes close to being an interpretation, but it is diluted with walking, running and playing.*]

P. (No reply)
D. Is that what you mean?
P. (Hangs head down and looks as if he was about to cry—(long silence) I can't run any more.

[*The defenses have been overwhelmed momentarily, as he admits his defeat.*]

D. What kind of running have you got in mind?
P. I've got no running in mind at all. I don't want to run from anything. If I was going to run, I wouldn't stay in here.

[*He recovers.*]

D. You don't want to run from anything?
P. No, no. I've done too much running now. I ran for nine years, and I'm not running nowheres.

[*Nine from his present age leaves us with seventeen, the age he went in the Army. Also, nine plus eight is seventeen. In the Army, he could not even come in second, and was "dragged."*]

D. You mean you've had enough running from your problems?
P. I mean I want to stay in here and get cured. I'm not going to run no more. I'm going to stay here and figure myself out.

[*He cannot be pinned down too much at this stage of the interview; it would arouse more resistance.*]

D. But this is a different kind of running.

[*More emphasis on the meaning of "running." It is not obvious to him.*]

P. I want to stay. I don't want to run nowhere. I want to stay here, and I don't know whether I can do it through Dr. G. I want to get cured.

[*The competition with, and hate of, the older brother prevents any positive transference relationship with Dr. G.*]

D. What do you mean by cured?
P. I want to understand myself, get peace of mind.
D. You haven't got that now?
P. No, I don't think so.

[*Now he agrees to a shift in his complaints and problems.*]

D. If you had—could you walk?
P. That's right. I'd feel strong, and I don't feel strong.
D. By feeling strong, you mean able to stand on your own two feet, and being able to run in a different way, I take it.

[*The continual emphasis of the feet should undermine their usefulness to the ego as a symbol.*]

P. I'm not interested in running. I'm going to walk the rest of the way. I don't want to run nowhere. The only thing I want to do, is get better.
D. By "walking" the rest of the way, you mean you want to run against people of your own age and class, and be able to compete with them in your own field? Is that what you mean?

[*Confrontation by continuous repetition.*]

P. No, what I mean is, I want to go on the outside. I want to get married and I want to be able to live peacefully.

[*His denial is contradicted by himself. Painful and inadequate feet are thus more clearly sexualized symbols. He wishes to use his "feet," but has no confidence in them and is afraid they might get hurt.*]

D. But that's what I mean. You want to get married and be a man among men and *stand on your own feet. . . .*
P. No, no. I just don't want to feel sick any more; don't want any more *headaches;* I don't want to feel weak. I want to be strong.

[*"Head" and "feet" again become equated. "Being strong like men" is unattainable for him. Why?*]

D. Of course, I'm taking that for granted. You mean, you don't want to feel weak in comparison to the other fellows of your own age; you want to be like the rest of them.
P. I just want to be all right.
D. That's what you mean: be all right like the rest of the boys on the outside.

[*It would have been more adequate to say, "like brother" instead of "boys," but that might have been too large a dose at this point. However, it sufficed to stir up his masculine protest.*]

P. What do you mean? I'm just as good as anybody.
D. But you said you feel weak.
P. That's right. That's the way I feel.
D. Is that being as good as anybody?
P. My vote is as good as anybody's.
D. In what way?
P. In every way. My vote's as good as anybody's.

D. Just as strong?
P. Yes. The only thing that is wrong with me is, I have certain things that bother me, and I want to clear them up.

[*The confrontation with his contradiction increases his self-assertion.*]

D. You mean if you could get rid of those *headaches* and that feeling of *weakness,* then you could go out and *run?*

[*Bringing him back from his problems to his symptoms. He must be made to understand that his symptoms are symbols of the fearful withdrawal from unknown (unconscious) dangers.*]

P. Maybe.

[*"Maybe" is almost a confirmation.*]

D. Maybe? How do you mean?
P. I'm not running any race. I'm not running from anything.

[*All his negatives are emphatic affirmatives.*]

D. But everybody is running a race in one sense—aren't they?
P. No, I'm not.
D. You mean you have given up?

[*The painful alternative!*]

P. No, no, no, I've not given up. I'll never give up.

[*His reaction shows how close he is to complete passive surrender. This would imply giving up his masculinity, represented by his feet. The pain is thus a warning signal.*]

D. Of course you won't. There's no need of that, but you feel like giving up.
P. No, I don't feel like it. There's something strong in me.
D. What you mean is that you feel like *giving up* only when you don't feel strong enough to run?

[*The associations to his self-assertion are enforced by confrontation.*]

P. What I mean is, the only thing that I mean is, that I've been through so much that I want to go back to being like I was. I want to stay here until I get like I used to be.

[*He obviously refers to the little boy's dreams of glory.*]

D. How do you mean—like you used to be?
P. Like I was, strong, nothing bothered me.
D. That's when you felt you could walk, and you could run, and you could compete with the other boys—even come in second?
P. (Loudly) Come in first.

[*Now it is out in the open: he wants to come first, which is an impossible goal in the sense he means.*]

D. Did you ever come in first?
P. I don't remember.

[*He does not want to remember that he never was first.*]

D. But you mean you could have, if you had stayed *strong.*

P. What do you mean by *strong?* I feel strong. I am strong. I've just got *emotional problems* that I've got to get cleared up.

D. What *emotional problems* have you in mind? What do you mean by an emotional problem? What is your emotional problem?

[*He is not allowed to evade the issue, and is pinned down.*]

P. I think I met up with a wall, and I bounced back,—and I reverted back to my childish ways.

[*He does not retreat and is able to face the child in him.*]

D. For instance—what childish ways do you mean?

P. I'm sorry, I just can't think of any.

[*The mature part of his ego is still defensive. He becomes resistant.*]

D. Of course, this is *painful* to remember.

[*This remark calls indirectly upon his claim of strength.*]

P. It's not painful. I want to get it cleared up.

D. Surely, but that's not easy, and it is somewhat painful.

[*The theme of the painful feet is replayed.*]

P. It's not easy when you've gone as long, uh, for instance, I was in one hospital from March 28th to July 10th, and I know the progress that I made then, and I don't know the progress that I am making now. Then I felt I was getting somewhere.

D. In what ways do you feel you are immature?

[*"Immature" refers to his feeling like a child, as he had used it before.*]

P. When I get feeling *bad,* I get frightened. I don't accept it for what it is. I like my own way. I don't like people to boss me. It upsets me.

[*"Bad feeling" now substitutes for "bad feet." He objects to being forced to use his feet. The interviewer uses the patient's own words in a different sense to aid in the split of the ego.*]

D. You mean by liking your own way, that you never had people to boss you back in the past when you were immature? By immature, you mean when you were a kid, don't you?

P. I don't know, I mean, uh, well, like somebody, uh, who was happy.

[*He cannot deny his own words and is puzzled as to how to avoid the past, where he was happy in fantasy.*]

D. When you had your own way, you mean?

P. What do you mean, when I had my own way?

D. Before the war. When you were a kid.

P. I didn't always have my own way. I used to get everything I wanted. I never even thought about it. If I wanted a bicycle, my father would get a bicycle for me. If I wanted something else, he'd get me something else.

[*He contradicts the obvious, referring to the magic, all giving father. Here the overtones are obvious. His words are repeated so he can hear himself and not deny them later.*]

D. You mean, whenever you wanted anything, all you had to do was to ask father?
P. That's right.
D. That would be nice, if you could only keep on being that way, huh?
[*This confronts him with the present reality.*]

P. No, I'm not going to keep on being that way, and I've worked since I was a kid. I had to. When I wanted a thing, I went and worked for them.
[*The strong, self-sufficient ego ideal; the opposite of the passive take-all person.—The words he has used are woven together to new patterns.*]

D. Surely, and that's a form of *competing,* isn't it?
P. I did all right competing.
D. You were able to work and get those things.
[*Another "pin" for later use.*]

P. Oh, indeed, that's right. I got all the things I wanted.
D. What do you mean? If you went out and earned money and bought them yourself, you didn't have to go to father.
[*Confrontation with the contradicting parts of his ego.*]

P. That's right.
D. You went to yourself.
P. That's right, and I had the power to go to myself and I don't have it now. (Long sigh)
[*This is because father died, and he can't find another.*]

D. So this is what you mean by saying you feel weak and too tired to stand on your own two feet?
P. No, the reason why I feel weak is, I have emotional conflicts within. (Pause) I'm looking for a key . . . (Loudly) a key to my problems, and a psychiatrist is supposed to give me that key, and I can't get it. (Breaks into tears)
[*He shifts from one defense to the other—"emotional conflicts" means "painful feet." Now he no longer has the wonderful father who nursed the megalomania of the little boy who could get himself anything he wanted. A key symbolizes a magic wand, a sorcerer's hat. A psychiatrist for him, the child, means an all-giving father.*]

D. What do you mean by emotional problems within?
[*Problems substituted for conflicts.*]

P. There must be conflicting forces within me. That's why I'm so tired. (Pause) (Loudly) I have as much strength as anybody else if I could use it, but I can't use it.
[*This astonishing piece of insight is not as deep as it appears.*]

D. What's conflicting with what, is the problem then, isn't it? You mean there is an immature part of you which wants to get things from father, that is conflicting with a mature part which wants to go out and get them for himself. Isn't that what you mean?

[*The interviewer clarifies the issue for the patient, using his words.*]

P. No.

[*This means "yes," as the next reply shows.*]

D. What do *you* mean?

P. I don't know what I mean. You've got me so confused that I don't know. (Long pause)

[*"Confused" means that the adult and the immature are fused.*]

D. Then what do *you* mean by saying that you are immature?

P. That's right, that's what psychoneurosis is. It is the immature part taking hold of you.

D. What do you mean—immature?

[*"Immature" to him means inadequate; he hates this part of himself and wants to get rid of it rather than control it, i.e., self-destruction. In any interview, the therapist integrates by going from the general pattern to the specific detail, and vice versa.*]

P. I've got childish ways. A lot of my thinking isn't mature. That's what I mean.

[*This is not insight as much as incantation.*]

D. For instance, what are some of your childish ways?

P. If I knew that, I wouldn't be here, if I understood it.

[*It is true and illustrates well the fallacy of accepting a patient's statements at face value.*]

D. If you understood it; but there is only one way to understand them.

P. What way is that? That's the way I am looking for.

D. And that is by discussing them with your doctor.

[*He must make his peace with brother.*]

P. And I do, so help me God, I do.

D. By telling him that you are immature and childish?

[*The problem has been stated, i.e., to show him how, why, when and where he is immature and childish.*]

P. That's right.

D. And telling him how you are immature?

P. I tell him everything that I can think of, everything that comes to me, everything. I, uh, uh, they say this thing is based on having a problem in your childhood and you have it, the same problem, as an adult. You meet it as a child and you can't meet it as an adult and you revert back to your childhood and childish ways, and you have a psychoneurosis.

[*While this is all "patter," it is useful when* he *says it, and must be translated and illustrated specifically in everyday incidents and trifles.*]

D. What you mean is that an adult tries to get things and act in an adult way, but when he doesn't succeed, he might try to go back and get them in a way that succeeded back in his childhood?

[*His childish behavior was appropriate, with his family.*]

P. Uh, I don't know, that may be, uh, that's uh, the definition, but it is not my definition.
D. But we want your definition; what it means to you—that counts.
P. What it means to me is that when I came out of the Service they marked me "psychoneurosis." It was right in my hand. I saw it in the folder, and he took me in there and he tried to talk to me. I asked, what does this mean, and he says it means you're nuts, so I went in there and I denied everything, and they sent me to the Red Cross girl to put in a claim. I got CDD'd. The only thing I told her about the fact is I had a twitching in my eye and I was always tired and my feet were flat, and when I went home, I don't know. I started going to the VA. They gave me *arch supports.* And I went to the Memorial Hospital and still *my feet* were bothering me, and they told me psychoneurosis, so I told them to go to hell and I walked out.

[*It is now apparent that he has many meanings attached to "psychoneurosis," all very important. An entire interview might be devoted to going into the meaning of "psychoneurosis," but the sector of the interview was centered around the "feet."*]

D. Because you didn't believe your feet were second degree?

[*To keep him in the sector.*]

P. I, uh, no. I'd something I didn't want to accept. I didn't want to accept this thing here, and I kept fighting it.

[*He cannot accept what he feels is his inadequate self; thus feet-phallus-self are all equated.*]

D. No one would.
P. No one would, well, anyway I kept fighting it. I know an adult would fight it. Maybe I'm too proud.

[*A request for some praise.*]

D. You mean that you were always an adult kind of a guy who went out and got things for yourself and worked for them. But then you also said, when you wanted things you turned to father, and father got them for you. He got you a bike.

[*The material is summarized for him and repeated in a way so that he will not have to use his "feet" symptomatically.*]

P. He got me a bike for my Bar Mitzvah present.
D. When you became a real man, he gave you a bike. He was a real good father to you.

[*The adult part is encouraged.*]

P. Yes. He was wonderful.

D. He gave you everything you wanted?

P. Yes, that's right. Maybe, maybe that's why I want to go back to Dr. B. I think he's wonderful, too.

[*A partial insight which can be used now; the strength of his passive wishes must be made apparent to him.*]

D. You mean he was like your father and you expected him to give you everything, too?

P. No, no, no. I just expected him to guide me right.

D. Like a father would guide a boy right?

P. Certainly. He's somebody who knows my problem and understands me.

D. You mean you need a father now?

[*The transference reaction is out in the open. No doctor can play the role that he says Dr. B. played, if he wishes to be the man who goes out and earns things himself.*]

P. I don't know what I need now. Right now I need mental stability. I have been here six months.

D. It is not easy?

P. No, it's very difficult. Only I know how difficult it is, and I know something is wrong with me. What I want to do, is get better.

D. You want to be helped so you can stand on your own two *feet,* is that what you mean?

P. I tried. I went down to occupational therapy this morning. I couldn't work. I was too tired, so I left. That's not right. I've been in a sweat all week. I perspire, and just before I came in here, I was. I don't like to bitch. I'm afraid of bitching, and I feel a pressing feeling over here (puts his hand on his heart).

[*He accepts the confrontation with the meaning of "feet" without any objection. It has become conscious in its true meaning. His ego now turns to another organ, the heart, and presses it into use for its defense. The interview has to be terminated now. He is afraid to bitch (a female figure symbolically and actually).*]

D. Over your heart?

P. Yuh.

D. Before you came in?

P. When I was lying down, just before coming in here.

D. And you never liked to bitch?

P. No, I'm afraid of bitching. I'm afraid if I bitch something is going to happen to me.

D. What?

P. Oh, I don't know. People drive me into a fear. If I bitch, they are liable to court-martial me.

[*Here the interview is entering another sector.*]

D. You mean in the Army?

[*The Army personified his aggressive fantasies.*]

P. That's right. I'm afraid of a lot of things now, and I've tried to understand them. I don't know. Maybe I'm doing it all wrong. Maybe I'd like another doctor to sit in and see how things are going, to see if I can't be straightened out some way, tell me what I am doing wrong.

[*His remarks show the strong transference. The interviewer has been taken over as the all-powerful good father.*]

D. Well, I'll see you again and we'll try to help you.
P. Thanks. I hope you will help me.
D. We will try to get you to stand on your own two feet, because I know that is what you want to do.

[*The parting promise which summarizes all.*]

Final Discussion

This interview is an example of the application of sector psychotherapy. Here the patient plainly revealed his hostility and competitiveness toward his brother; his yearning for an all-giving, motherly father who will give him what he needs in a magic, easy way; and his despair, frustration and rage over his inadequacy feelings. His defenses through denial, somatization, reversal and isolation are plainly demonstrated, and the information vouchsafed is pertinent to the complaint and is readily demonstrated.

Follow-Up

In the course of further interviews, the symptom modification was such that the patient abandoned the feet and used various other portions of his body as symbols. During that period he was depressed, bitter and resentful toward his young therapist, and ingratiating toward older men. However, forced to face his problems upon a more interpersonal level, he decided six weeks later to leave the hospital, go to work and be treated on an outpatient basis. He continued to pursue a pension, but was able to resume work and applied for job training at a local school. It was felt that the patient's approach to reality living had improved considerably, and that from the point of view of a goal-limited therapy, the therapeutic result was satisfactory.

After a trial period at a Mental Hygiene Clinic, this patient consulted a private doctor whom he has been seeing once a week for two years. Six months ago he appeared at the hospital where the recorded interview was taken previously, and asked for a job. At that time he seemed moder-

CHART

ASSOCIATIVE STRUCTURE OF THE SECTOR CONCERNING PAINFUL FEET

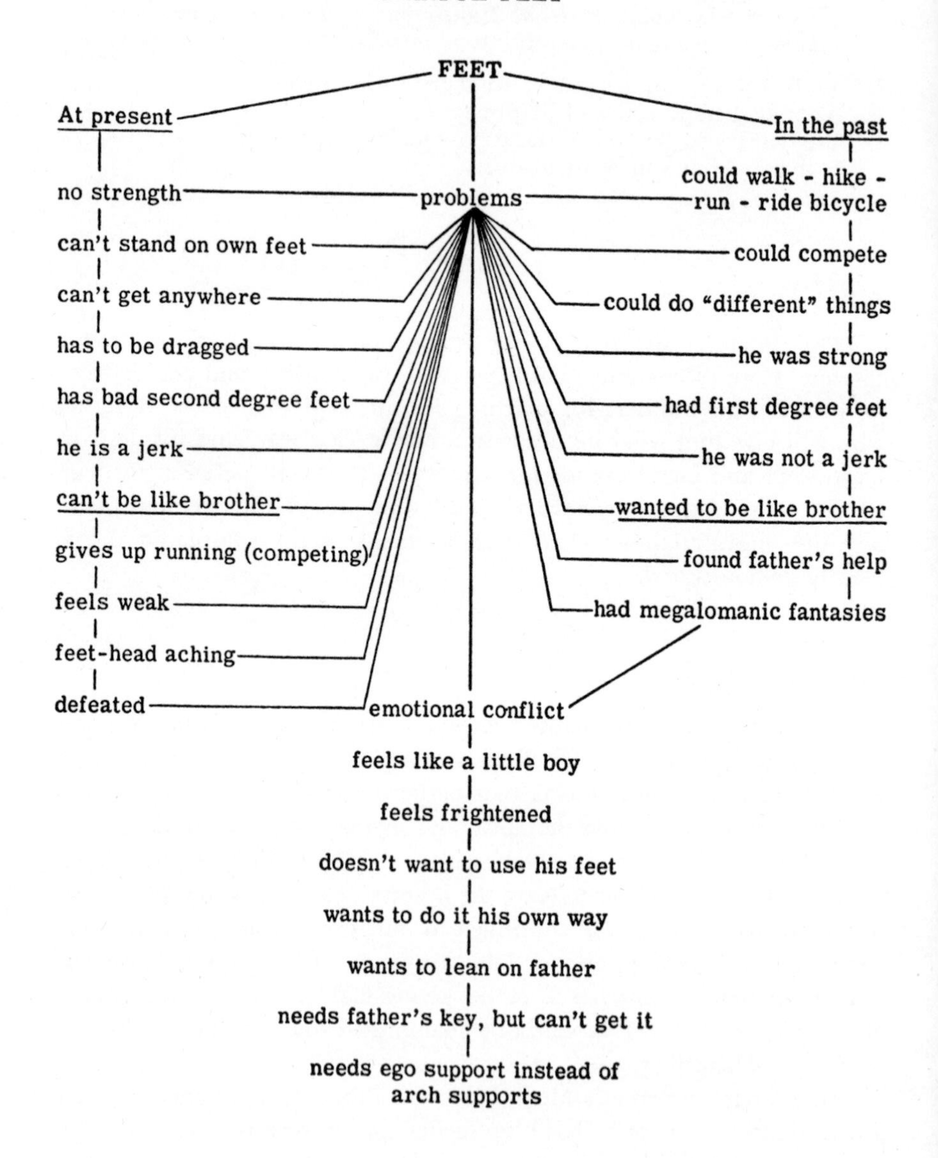

ately depressed, but had no physical complaints other than being 40 lbs. overweight. He was still single, and talked in terms of his feelings of discouragement and getting no place, expressing doubts as to his being helped in psychotherapy, because he didn't feel "big enough."

CHAPTER IV

Sector Continuity

Part 1—The Bad Conscience

Introduction

In aiding a patient in one sector, repercussions occur in all other segments of his personality and sectors of his life. However, a psychotherapy such as sector therapy which works essentially in one sector, disregarding other differences, cannot substitute for psychoanalysis which approaches the total personality.

In psychoanalysis—to mention only a few facts—the working through from all angles, and the transference itself, are analyzed and resolved. In sector psychotherapy the transference is, as a rule, maintained on a positive level, if possible, without actively manipulating it. With this goal-limited therapy and its unresolved transference, however, relapses and recrudescences can and usually do occur, and the patient may reappear for further treatment, as it was already pointed out in a previous chapter. Symptom removal is achieved without marked personality changes, and very often with by-passing the resistances. When the patient has a relapse and appears for further treatment, it is often because of a reactivation of some insufficiently resolved conflicts or because of a life situation which has stirred up those conflicts again. Recurring symptoms or anxieties of this type can usually be eliminated if the interval since the last interview has not been too long.

Successive interviews in a chosen sector have to be carried out by employing again the key words, phrases and contents from previous interviews. In this way the patient will be confronted with his conflicts which had been approached before, and into which he had gained some insight. Thus establishing a sector shades off into maintaining the sector, i.e., the sector continuity.

The interview which follows here demonstrates how an almost hypochondriacal complaint concerning a body part, i.e., the neck and back, a compulsion to *bow the head,* and an infantile masturbatory conflict, are combined and interwoven into a sector, and how the resolution of the symptom in this phase of sector psychotherapy was carried through.

Case Presentation

The patient, a twenty-five-year-old white male, came for treatment because of a severe anxiety neurosis with compulsive obsessional features that had been present for at least fifteen years. For the past four years, his symptoms had become so severe as to cripple all his efforts to make a social or work adjustment. He was the seventh and last child of a family of six girls, and his mother's favorite. His chief problems were numerous compulsions and obsessional thinking concerning looking at himself, and being looked at. The historical material continually revolved about masturbatory guilt and castration anxiety feelings. Infantile masturbation—according to his parents—began at three, and lasted until the age of nine, in spite of many attempts on the part of his parents and himself to stop it. Up to the age of ten, he anxiously, sensually and aggressively depended on his mother to awaken him, feed him, and dress him. He would become panicky if his mother left the house without his knowing where she had gone. Numerous threats were continuously made to him by his parents and sisters with regard to his masturbation, and all members of the family took it upon themselves to sneak into his room and pull back the covers to see whether or not his hands were on his genitals. The patient was frequently threatened with the loss of this organ, and it was readily apparent that his masturbatory practices were connected with hostile, defiant impulses against his parents, as well as with castration anxiety over his unfortunate sibling position, and libidinal pleasure elements.

From the ages of seven to nine, he gradually and successfully warded off his masturbatory impulses and rage reactions against his parents and family, and developed numerous compulsions and obsessional thoughts. At nine, he had to step on cracks in the pavement, perform a counting ritual before going to the toilet, and to touch many objects. He was also filled with obsessive doubts concerning religion, and became increasingly concerned with the size of, and feelings in, his body, and no longer concerned with his penis. He went through many rituals to prevent a stunting of his growth or his becoming a girl, and to protect his parents and siblings. Around nine to twelve, he would ward off fantasies and sexualized play with mother and sisters by snapping his fingers and making the sign of the cross. These symptoms persisted up to the time he came to treatment. Sexual relationships were attempted at eighteen with tremendous anxiety and impotence which lasted until the termination of treatment.

At the age of eighteen, the patient had entered the Air Force. In addition to the previously mentioned symptoms, he had at that time strong fears of going insane, pressure feelings in his head, and constant compulsions to recheck all his actions. He was discharged from the service as a neuropsychiatric casualty due to his compulsive rechecking of everything he did. When he began therapy, he was restless, tense and agitated. He feared losing his hair, was sweating continually, looked at his tongue, watched the color of his cheeks, took his pulse, was unable to sleep, had mild tics of his eyelids, and played constantly with the end of his belt. All the time observing himself, he used to daydream on a bed. He would put enormous bandages over small scratches he had suffered. From his reading he had numerous formulae which he kept repeating to himself to ward off illness, e.g., "This is all psychosomatic."

At times the patient suffered from headaches, temper tantrums and disturbances of eyesight necessitating rubbing his eyes violently. Some times he feared developing cancer of the hand or a venereal disease. He claimed to be furious, but did not know against whom his fury was directed; he could not "put his hand on it." He did not smoke or drink for fear of injury to his body, and his social relationships with girls were minimal. At times he indulged in genital masturbation "without feeling," "purely as an experiment." He had to sleep with his hands above the sheets, and had numerous nightmares in which "terrible things" happened to his father and mother. However, his symptoms and anxieties were completely ego alien to him, and he put up an excellent front, making friends readily both in and outside the hospital. At no time did he show any evidence of impaired reality testing. He was seen three times a week for a period of ten months. At the end of treatment, his symptoms were minimal and consisted mainly of transient attacks of anxiety over his relations with girls.

The patient entered college, completed four years, and received his degree with honors. While in school, he was seen once a year, always at his own request and, as a rule, due to a mild recrudescence of his old symptoms. The following interview took place around the time of his graduation from college. He had been last seen one year before. During the interview, he appeared anxious, pale and sweating. He tried hard to appear at ease, licked his lips frequently and laughed in a forced manner. His physical symptoms of anxiety appeared directly related to material concerning his masturbatory guilt and castration anxiety. Aside from the use of a small amount of material from the patient's known past, this interview differed little from previous ones. There we can readily see the patient's ego cast in many roles: the threatening parent who watches and tries to catch him doing wrong; the rebellious bad boy; the good little boy striving to make amends; and the weak, anxious but rational, and more adult part striving to integrate and control.

The sector chosen for this interview revolved—like many previous ones with this patient—around looking and being looked at, catching and being caught. Essentially it was concerned with aiding him to face and master his anxieties in regard to his infantile masturbation, so that he might act more mature in his handling of the reality situation. The problem in this interview was to establish a sector revolving about his infantile masturbatory anxieties which would demonstrate to him the relationship between his symptoms, feelings and modifiable behavior tendencies. By making this conscious to him, his ego was able to discard certain defenses and feel aided in its adaptation to his reality world. This interview will also demonstrate a type of problem encountered chiefly in behavior disorders where one deals with an inadequately developed superego, and acting out occurs in the field of sexual relationships.

Interview

P. Well, how are things going, Doctor?

[*An ordinary introduction. The patient plays the doctor's role: transference is already obvious.*]

D. (Smiles and nods) How are things going with you?

P. O, comme-ci, comme-ça, as they say—oh, so-so. Well, anyhow, I'm getting along OK, I guess. Oh, I'm *anxious* at times in *certain situations.* I *understand* things rather than get *panicky.* I *catch myself* every now and then *doing things, you know,* these compulsions.

[*He, the adult, catches himself (the little one) doing things. Here in "doing things" is expressed the compulsion as well as the defense against it. "I understand" is self-reassurance.*]

D. What do you mean?

P. Well, it seems of late, anyway, every time I go by a church—now this is part of my early training, you know, etc., etc., *you know.* It was supposed to *bother me* then, *you know,* out of respect for *religion.* When I'm riding down the turnpike and when I pass some of these *churches,* I have to make sure before I approach it; well, that is, it's on my mind; I must *bow* my *head* very meticulously.

[*He is ashamed to admit the little one's fear of mother church, and wants to appear as an adult who understands everything and is in control. The phrase "You know" is typical for compulsive neurotics and is used to offset the objections to "I don't know." Bowing head is a token sacrifice, warding off a feared punishment for carrying it erect.*]

D. You *bow* your *head?*

P. Yuh, very meticulously. I make sure that I bow my head and not just go by.

D. You don't take chances; is that what you mean?

[*A new word, but an obvious inference.*]

P. Yuh, of *passing* by without *"doing it,"* because—oh, I *don't know* what; perhaps because of what might happen, or *something like that.*

[*Little ambiguous words have an importance of their own; here: "something like that." The meaning of it has to be established.*]

D. What do you mean?

P. Well, I *don't know.* I guess when I was a kid I *used to do it* and *I did it* in a similar way; that is, conscientiously.

D. When you were a kid?

P. I mean when I was younger, when I was about—oh, 10,—9 or 10, or *"something like that."* I guess I was all wrapped up in the church or something like that. *I'd bow my head.* Then I figured I *didn't do it* right, so *I'd do it again;* of course, making sure that no one could see me, but then as I'd go by, I'd bow my head again, and maybe two or three times *you know*—make sure I *had done it,* and *done it right.*

[*It is easier for him to talk as if the child existed only in the past. It was around this age his masturbation stopped and concern over his body appeared. Church has both maternal and paternal aspects, but the paternal ones are pre-eminent in this interview. The phrase "something like that" reappears. Likewise "doing it" and "I know," but they have their negation, "I don't do it right," and "I don't know."*]

D. Walking by?

[*This substitutes for "passing by," but it is more active.*]

P. Oh no, I wouldn't walk by the church again. I'd walk by the church once. I'd never have to go back anyway. It wasn't that *overwhelming,* but I'd do it, *you know,* while walking by. I'd say, maybe *I didn't do it right;* maybe I'm not as *religious* as I should be, so I'd *do it* like this. As I was walking by, I would bow my head again. I never let myself know why: perhaps *hypocritical,* or something. *I don't know.*

[*"Religious" means "bowing the head." "Hypocritical" is pretending not to know what he does know.*]

D. Hypocritical, in what way?

P. Well, toward the church. I mean like even today, I sort of—well—*you know* it isn't really *agnosticism. You know,* I go to church, and all that, but I mean—it just doesn't mean *too much,* or *something like that.*

D. How do you mean *"too much?"* In what way?

P. Well, it doesn't have the meaning for me that it did at one time. *You know,* it used to be that I was all wrapped up in it—in church, in religion, etc., etc. I wanted to lead a very *virtuous* life.

[*He wants to rebel but doesn't dare. "Virtuous" is "doing it right."*]

D. What do you mean by "virtuous?"

P. You've got me there. I suppose when I was at a young age trying to overcome things like—*you know—masturbation,* or *something like that,* and then there was *obeying* your mother and father, and not swearing or not having *bad thoughts,* and so forth and so on. You understand what I mean?

[*He himself begins to link up things. "Something like that" refers to masturbation, but also to "bad thoughts" in other respects.*]

D. About having bad thoughts?

P. Ha, ha, that's right. Of course not, unless they were subconscious. I didn't seem to have any *bad thoughts.* I guess I repressed pretty well. But I wouldn't want to pass that church unless I was absolutely sure. I always concentrated *on what I did* at that *particular moment.* It seems like I'm doing that now. I *catch myself.* I catch myself doing it several times when I'm not thinking about it.

[*Bad thoughts themselves have become equated with masturbation. Note the contradictions. He has to be on his guard not to do wrong, and if he had done it, to make good for it.*]

D. You said part of you doesn't quite believe?

[*The adult part is encouraged, so he will talk freely, as he has begun to perspire.*]

P. Well, yuh—well—I *believe* now. I still believe and everything like that, but I don't believe the way I used to believe. *You know,* I used to be quite wrapped up in church. Now, I accept more than *believe* certain things. I believe in God and the life hereafter, everything like that, but I mean—I'm not as devout as I had been, or *something like that,* or, perhaps it's that feeling of *hypocrisy* that makes me want to feel sure. *You know* (chuckles) that God Almighty is *watching me,* or *something,* and I have to *bow my head. I don't know why* I *do it.* I remember I *did it* when I was a child. I noticed myself in doing some of these compulsions, that's one of them. Or another thing, is like . . . that is . . . of late I've been saying my *prayers* before I go to bed. Now it's a funny thing—I don't concentrate on my prayers in a sense like I used to. I mean, I concentrate on every word. Like "Our—Father—who—art—in Heaven . . ."—that is, I concentrate on every word. Right now, for instance, I *concentrate* on the blessing. In other words, I have to bless myself every two or three times. I have to *do it right.*

[*He pretends to "believe," but he is "agnostic" or "something like that." "Something" is a parent, i.e., not quite "God Almighty." "Bowing head" too has a masturbatory implication. "Prayers" stands for head bowing. Concentrating on every word is like counting the number of words as he counts how often he blesses himself. It is a compulsive ritual, and expiation. The words themselves are almost meaningless to him.*]

D. How do you mean, *"right?"*

P. Well, rather than saying it fast, "In the name of the *Father, Son,* and *Holy Ghost," you know,* just like that, I like to think, "In—the—name—of—the—Father—Son—and—Holy Ghost." *You know,* I think about it, and I dwell on each one for, *you know,* just a second or two.

D. How do you mean?

P. Well, I don't say it fast, "In the name of the Father, Son, and Holy Ghost," like people generally do. I say it *reverently,* "In the name of the Father, Son, and Holy Ghost." I think about it. (Pause) I still feel very tense. I still get *tensed* up, and I was going to ask you, by the way, (Pause) I *don't know* whether I'm going too far on this business of *snapping my neck. You know,* every time I get tensed up, I can bring *my arms back.* It's a kind of physiotherapy. I can hear a *snap right back in my spine,* and it makes me feel good, you know. (Pause—laughs) Well, *I don't know;* I can *snap my own spine out,* you know, and it *bothers* me. If I feel very *tense* and I go to bed, it bothers me. I just shift around, and I can hear crack, crack, crack. (Pause) So I was *wondering,* what could that be?

[*The masturbatory conflict appears in disguise. It is displaced onto the neck and spine. He cracks his neck and laughs with relief because nothing has happened. Laughter betrays his anxiety by denial. He turns the infantile anxiety tension into a fear of a reality which he can master. This stimulates uneasiness and guilt feelings.*]

D. You say it feels good?
P. Well, (Pause) it releases the tension, or something like that—the *tension* that I do have. *I don't know* anything about the physiology of it, but I imagine that perhaps the *muscles* which are grouped around the spine, they get tense and in so doing they *dry up the fluid* that is around the *joints* in the spine, *you know;* I imagine, and that's what makes the *noise* when you snap it.

[*This is really concern over loss of a different kind of fluid.*]

D. When you get tense, the fluid is *dried up?* What do you mean?
P. Well, isn't that true, the joints or bones, or something? *You know,* I'm very *stiff.* I can do *an awful lot* of *this* (cracks his knuckles). I can move my *neck* around in such a way that when I do that, anyway, it *relieves* me, *you know.*

[*"Cracking knuckles" and "snapping neck" relieves the "stiff" bones.*]

D. It gets stiff and you snap it. It feels good and you feel relief?

[*In combining his own words in such an obvious manner, the therapist gives no indication he is aware of the conflict. It is much better to have the patient himself become aware of what he says.*]

P. Well no, I mean, that is . . . it feels stiff. (Long laughter) *I know* what you're getting at.
D. What do you mean?
P. Well, because of what you're getting at. Do I have a *guilty looking* smile?

[*He has to be on his guard not to reveal his guilt.*]

D. How do you mean, "guilty?"
P. Well, I thought, of course, about *masturbation* when you said that; *you know,* when you *snap it,* you get relief, *you know. You know* the jargon that kids use, "snap it," or something like that. So—ha, ha—that's what made me think of it. But I mean that my *neck* just gets *tensed* up. It gets very stiff, and I can feel it—the muscles bulging, or something like that. If I can kind of *rotate* it, *you know* what I mean, I can feel the cramps, and it relieves them. It relaxes the muscles.

[*Here the obvious is ignored. His apparent insight is defensive and needs more associative material for confrontation. "Snap it," means to him "masturbating." "Tension" means to him "tense neck" or "stiffness." The secondary meaning of the key words is obvious. He changes the words "snap it" to "rotate," out of guilt. "Rotating" may be substituted by "relaxing."*]

D. And you relax after you snap it, but the cracks worry you because you feel there isn't enough fluid in the joints?

P. Well (Pause—laughs) I said that, I suppose.

[*He wants to, but cannot deny his own words.*]

D. Why do you laugh?

P. (Laughs loudly) *I don't know* really. It seems silly to be laughing at something, but I guess I made a *slip of the tongue,* or something; that is, *I know.* But anyway, what does it mean when it cracks like that?

[*"Slip of the tongue" is like "snap the neck." The amount of laughter reveals the degree of anxiety (tension) he must ward off. He screens his recognition of the obvious by asking questions.*]

D. You mean you don't feel you should have to *snap it?*

P. No—I mean—(Pause) What do you mean, snap what? (Pause) My neck? Oh, I don't want to do it. I wish there was some way that I wouldn't have to do it; that is— maneuver my neck.

[*He feels trapped!*]

D. You mean you wish it wouldn't get *stiff?*

P. I wish . . . I wish that I. . . . I mean . . . well, you know, I get that stiff neck, *or something like that.* I guess it's *tension* that makes me get that way, *you know,* and in order to relieve it, *or something,* I generally—put my hand behind my neck and bring it up, and you can hear, *creak, creak, you know,* all the way up—from the middle of the spine up, and, as I say, I can feel it right down here, and I get kind of, *you know,* like when I'm *laying down.* I can turn very slowly, and I hear *crick, crick, crick,* and it *feels* very *good, you know,* but it seems, for *Heaven's sake,* that a guy wouldn't have to do that.

[*"Or something like that!" He adds to it more ambiguous words the meaning of which he has made transparent before. "Using hands on the neck," leads to "crack," "creak," "crick" and finally to "snap it." "Feeling good" apparently is the orgastic feeling. He is asking himself why he has to displace the masturbatory activity. "For Heaven's sake" means: a good person should not do such a thing.*]

D. You wish it wouldn't get *stiff?*

P. Well, I wish I wouldn't have to *snap* my back.

D. When it gets *stiff?*

P. I wish it wouldn't get *stiff*—my back. (Long pause) Yeah, there's a correlation there somewhere.

[*Insight can be admitted on a conscious level. He understands the meaning of the screening words.*]

D. What do you mean?
P. Oh well, between the words, or something like that. Naturally (pause). My back feels very *stiff,* and so on, but I used the word "snap." I could have said "maneuver" or so forth, or something like that, you know.
D. But you, yourself, connected it with *masturbation.* How about it? Do you wish that it wouldn't get stiff?

[*It is now safe to talk more openly.*]

P. (In a low voice) I haven't *masturbated* in a long, long time.

[*For the time being, he accepts the implication of his words.*]

D. It hasn't gotten *stiff?*
P. (Slowly) Well, it does; I mean, well, that is (pause) well, I'm living—not a promiscuous life, but I have a little girl, (laughs) well, I mean a girl anyway. *You know,* once a week or so.

[*Here comes the present acting out which the symptom foreshadows. A little girl means "a child."*]

D. What do you mean by "a girl anyway"?
P. Just a girl, no strong feelings, or anything like that. It isn't that I'm *degrading* her because of her, what it is, *nymphomania* or tendency like that.

[*He degrades his genital activity to a child's play without feeling. He admitted the "good" feelings when snapping the neck.*]

D. How do you mean?
P. I think she is. *Oversexed.*

[*A projection of his own sexual condemnatory trends.*]

D. *Oversexed?* What do you mean?
P. Just by her actions, and so forth, and so forth. She'd rather do that than anything else.
D. Do what?
P. Have *relations.*
D. She'd rather do that?
P. So it seems. Yeah. Sometimes I say to her, let's go somewhere else tonight, and then she says, why don't we go parking. She's just one of those gals.

[*He tries to put himself in a good light, but is easily persuaded.*]

D. She would rather go parking?
P. Parking, yeah, and have *intercourse,* yeah. She wants it.
D. And you?
P. Yuh, I do it, naturally, but she seems to have an abnormal drive for sex.

[*He is natural, but she is abnormal.*]

D. Abnormal?
P. Well, I *don't know* what's *normal.* I suppose, I mean, I really could do it more than one time if I wanted to. But once is enough for

me, anyway. I feel very *rested* afterward and *relaxed*. We do it about once a week or so, or even less than that. It will be two weeks tomorrow since I did it.

[*To admit sexual needs is abnormal. Any sexual activity is only "snapping" and therefore "relaxing."*]

D. You feel she's *abnormal?*

P. Well, yeah. Well, here's the story. I've got the low-down from other guys. Maybe it's a *homosexual* thing, but I know other guys who have taken her out, and she is a *push-over,* sort of speaking *you know.*

[*He uses the term "homosexual" as a defense and an intellectualization.*]

D. You mean she's doing it with other boys?

P. Yuh.

D. What do you mean by "homosexual things"?

[*The interviewer disarms him by questioning him about the term. He wants to intellectualize, because it is a trap from an economic point of view, even though it deals with valid material.*]

P. Well, for boys to be talking that way with each other—isn't it? Isn't it so when boys discuss with each other their sexual doings? It's kind of a homosexual thing. In other words, they derive some sort of a pleasure in talking about it and telling their friends how *virile* and sexually *potent* they are. Isn't that a form of homosexuality?

[*He betrays his attempted escape into "homosexuality."*]

D. And you tell them how *potent* you are?

[This *is part of the sector connected with fluid loss and drying up, and affords a chance to return to the masturbatory problem.*]

P. Oh no, I haven't; I don't say anything. Anything that goes on between that girl and I, that is a strict secret, but other guys have said to me, I hear you're taking out so-and-so, and I say yeah, and they say she's easy. (Chuckles) Oh, *I don't know.* I have "no feelings about it," *you know.* Of course, I *just use the girl.* (Chuckles) Really, it's probably an *abnormal* thing. (Laughs louder) Or is it? I *don't know.*

[*Denies again the "good" feelings. He only "uses the girl" instead of himself, as he does in masturbating. The girl is only a projection of his feminine part.*]

D. How do you mean?

P. Well, *you know,* it's just a release—a relief.

[*He equates it with masturbation.*]

D. So it makes you feel *bad,* is that what you mean, when you go by *the church*—you have to make sure you do things right? You feel guilty that you're doing something bad?

[*A confrontation that is practically an interpretation.*]

P. Well, yuh. (Long pause. He is sweating, mops his brows, and lights a cigarette).

[*His bodily symptoms substitute for words.*]

D. By *abnormal,* you mean you're doing something like masturbation?
P. Yuh, I suppose that's about right. I suppose *you* would call it like *masturbation.*

[*He doesn't wish to accept what the interviewer verbalizes for him.*]

D. You mean you're *masturbating* in using this girl?
P. (After a pause) Well, I suppose so, but—of course, not consciously.
D. But you said . . .
P. Yes, yes, *I know!* Well, isn't it *masturbation* if there's no feeling of love?

[*The continual confrontation leads to his own interpretation of what the interviewer had proposed before.*]

D. Just *using her,* as you said.
P. (Louder) Yes.
D. And you feel guilty?
P. Not consciously—I don't. That is, I said I don't feel it, but maybe—underneath it all (pause).

[*He apparently stuck out his neck too far (on the adult level). To take the pressure off him, the interviewer addresses the little one. This gives courage to the adult part of the ego, and takes sides with the interviewer.*]

D. Anyway, little Dick used to feel very guilty about masturbation.
P. Yuh. (Pause) And, as a matter of fact, he really didn't. (Pause) I guess when I was young, he did. That's when his *mother* used to slap his *hands* and pull down the sheets in the morning to see if he was playing with it. Yes, sure, to see if my hands were down there, but then I just about gave it up.

[*Where were his hands when mother slapped them? On his neck? "Just about" means "not quite." He straddled and denied the issue and never solved it.*]

D. And so when you go by the *church,* you feel someone is *looking* at you?

[*Weaving the past with the present.*]

P. Uh, huh. (Pause) There's a lot of that *wrapped up* in there no doubt, but I guess it's not on a conscious level.

[*Before he said "wrapped up in church."*]

D. You mean that *little Dick* who feels someone is always *looking* at him when he *masturbates,* that little Dick is still with you?
P. Could be. You see, consciously I don't feel *guilty* about it. I keep saying that it is a *heterosexual* relationship, and I look on it at an *adult* level, rather than *masturbating,* or anything. But there's no love.

["*Masturbating" means to him on "a mature" level.*]

D. And you said if there's no love, it's just using her and is just like masturbation.

P. Aren't most people that way? Of course, I could tell her that I love her, but. . . .

[*He doesn't dare; he is too little, and the situation is too laden with guilt.*]

D. You mean you feel the way toward her like you feel toward religion —that is, others do it in love, but you feel a little agnostic? You say, "Maybe I'm supposed to feel that way, but the other boys go out and do it. Why shouldn't I, and, after all, it's a *heterosexual* thing; it's not as bad as *masturbation.*" However, little Dick really feels it's just like masturbation, because you're just using her, and there's no love. And little Dick feels it's like those games you played with the *little* boys and "little girls" when you were young. So you still feel when you go by the church, that someone is looking at you, and you have to make sure you do things right, and you still feel bad.

[*Knitting together the meaningful phrases of the interview for a confrontation. Reinforcing split in ego and taking role of kind but firm parent who is allied with the adult part of him.*]

P. Yuh, *it's true.* (Pause) And another thing I found out about this girl. She's an extremely uninhibited girl. She'll do anything, *you know.*

[*"It's true" is the confirmation of the confrontative material.*]

D. What do you mean?

P. Well, I mean, she'll *let herself go.* I cannot do that.

[*He now shifts the guilt to the feminine demands on him.*]

D. How do you mean?

P. Well, I mean she'll—oh, *I don't know,* I just kind of sense it in her. She just enjoys it and very much. Whereas, *you know,* with me— I'm always thinking of maybe someone's coming, or—(pause).

[*"God the almighty parent" is watching, as he said in the beginning.*]

D. That someone is going to *see you?*

P. Oh yes, I guess I really feel like that. I guess I'm a *hypocrite.*

[*Hypocritical refers to everything that he knows but does not want to know.*]

D. You feel like a *hypocrite?*

P. Yes, I can't quite really *relax* and *let myself go.* I feel *tense.* I do feel that way on an intellectual level; that is—that it is all OK—on an intellectual level. I can't feel that way though—even if I say all these guys go out with girls and do things and what not, and they go to church, but I think about those things. I say to myself, here I am horsing around with the girl. *What a damn hypocrite* I am! I just don't try to restrain my feelings, or anything like that. I go out with the girl, and *I know* what's going to happen.

[*He has not yet fully accepted that intercourse for him equals masturbation. "Relax" means now "snap it" with feeling and without guilt.*

The guilt feeling forces him to put up a façade. What is going to happen if he let himself go? If he knew, he wouldn't be afraid. The harmlessness of the cracking of knuckles is not a sufficient guarantee. Reality tests don't protect against "Heaven's" threat.]

D. And you can't let yourself go?

P. Yuh, that's right. I mean, I can't let myself go completely. *You know,* I'm *stiff. You know,* I only do it as much as I possibly could, but I don't get as much enjoyment as I should get. *Heaven knows.*

[*"Stiff" has genital and inhibiting components like his compulsions.*]

D. Because you feel that Heaven knows and that God is *watching* you?

P. Yuh, and also because I feel that it's wrong, that big *superego* there. It says it isn't right. I think of *cops* and things that are tangible. but there's also this feeling that you can't fool *God,* and that kind of stuff. He sees everything. That strict *superego* is always with me. Perhaps it was all due to my upbringing, *you know.* Sex is bad.

[*He has learned the term "superego" in college psychology courses, and uses it here for "God." You can't fool God by being a hypocrite. Trying to wriggle out from under guilt feelings.*]

D. They said so?

[*Ego split encouraged and enforced.*]

P. Well, *you know,* they implied it; my *mother* did. (Laughs) She never used the word *"sex"* but we had to tow the mark and so on, and so on. Now here's the story. (Begins to talk hurriedly) I realize it when I'm with the girl. Now when I go out, *I know what's going to happen;* that is, with that particular girl. It's funny—but this girl is such a *satisfying* girl that I just don't feel like looking around for anyone else. Whenever I feel like it, I can call her up. Sometimes she has *other dates* and it's no soap; but, of course, with other girls I just don't try to touch them at all. Now, *you know, I don't know* whether I'm *degrading* this girl subconsciously or not. I don't feel guilty about it consciously. With the others, I just look for companionship.

[*You can't fool mother even. "Superego" also means "mother." As far as the mother image is concerned, he knows "what's going to happen." This situation evidently revives a conflict-laden, unsolved dependency relationship with mother to whom he was excessively attached up to the age of nine or ten when he attempted to turn to church and father. The mother relationship makes "love together with sex" incompatible. Therefore, he has to degrade "the girl" to a masturbatory object. In masturbating he loves himself, but has to hide it.*]

D. What do you mean?

P. Well, I really go out with *two girls.* I just go out with her for companionship. I haven't been out with her very many times—just two or three times. I've only known her about three to five weeks; that is, this girl I have relations with. Previous to that I was going with a girl who was really no good, that is, I mean really.

[*He is now dealing with two mother figures: (a) the pure one he cannot touch; (b) the bad one he, the bad boy, fantasied about with the aid of his infantile masturbation.*]

D. In what way?

P. Well, for Heaven's sake, she had been married *three times.* She has about four kids and she does a lot of bouncing around and, *you know.* (Laughs heartily) I mean socially and every other way, but the one I go with now is a younger girl.

[*There is an old saying concerning masturbation, "the widow thumb and her four daughters." This female is the "bad" mother with whom his masturbation fantasies were concerned.*]

D. How do you mean?

P. Well, the other one, she was older. She was around thirty or thirty-two. But this one here is only twenty-five or twenty-six.

[*These ages and the women could well have been related to sister figures who took mother's place, as one was thirty and another thirty-two. As he himself is twenty-five, it suggests that the little girl is himself in his masturbating activity, i.e., a narcissistic solution.*]

D. And you feel you're *degrading* her?

[*He confirms it when he equates satisfying her, with satisfying himself.*]

P. No, I don't want to feel that way. I feel that I'm sort of *satisfying* her whims; at the same time *satifying my own.* It's a funny sort of relationship. We understand one another, and I said to her, let's not let this go any further than it has already. If at any time things get any stronger, it's just no dice; that is, if at any time things get *out of hand.*

[*Again fear of being overwhelmed by the little boy's bad wishes. What has he got in his hands?*]

D. *Out of hand?*

P. Ha, ha, ha. I mean if things ever get into the serious stage we'd just break up. I said to her, and she says OK; that is, we have that understanding, ha, ha.

D. So you keep things *in hand?*

P. No, no, that is, of course. I wouldn't want to marry her, to tell you the truth.

[*"Marriage" would bring "the bad things" out into the open.*]

D. Because?

P. I just don't want to get *married.* That's the way a lot of other boys feel, too. I wouldn't want to be married to someone like that, anyway, because you could never *satisfy* her.

[*How can a little boy handle a little girl like a mature woman whom he cannot satisfy, as he cannot satisfy himself?*]

D. You couldn't?

P. No, I don't think I could.

D. What do you mean?

P. Well, for Heaven's sake. If you have, well, that is, when you do it, she wants to go back and do it again. (Laughs) Twice, *three times,* but I don't; I feel completely *relaxed,* that is, after once. Well, oh *I know,* I've tried it twice, and I *strained* the hell out of myself. Of course, *things finally did happen.* (Pause)

[*The main question: "What is finally going to happen?" has the answer: "I strained myself."*]

D. What do you mean by *"strained"*?

[*This word might be used for neck, joints, or knuckles.*]

P. Oh, what I mean is, it's worse for me the second time. The first time is fine. I just feel relaxed after. The second time I have to force myself. I mean, the first time is spontaneous. I love her up a little bit. Everything is just as it should be, *you know.* The second time she fools around; she gets in heat or something. (Laughs uneasily)

[*"The little girl" plays the role of the "hand."*]

D. What do you mean?

P. Oh, she gets excited, or something, and hell, I'm not even excited. I say to her, well, you'll have to help me along with the *hand, you know.*

D. Is that what you mean by keeping things in *hand*?

P. Well, that is, no, maybe if I let it go for an hour or so, or even after a half hour; if I don't have a hard time. I can't do anything. I still, after the first affair, feel very relaxed, and I'd just as soon not bother with it again; in fact, many times I don't. I simply take her right home. But, sometimes I sit around or something, and she just starts getting all warmed up again, and sometimes—really this happened—where I have felt the same way spontaneously. It just came up automatically, but most other times I just don't feel like it. Well, and so just to make her happy (he chuckles) I say, that is, more than anything else (laughs again uneasily); I don't know whether I'm a *frigid male* or not, but just to make her happy, *you know,* I'll do my damnedest and hope she'll get some pleasure. Sometimes it takes an awful long time before anything happens, and well (laughs heartily) *you know* how it is. Once is enough for me.

[*The past is being relived, and mastery attempted in the present. His inadequacy feelings break through in spite of efforts to deny them. "Frigid male" is a male without feeling.*]

D. You mean . . . ?

P. (Breaks in) Well, you see, I just have to force myself.

D. To do what?

P. Oh, to uh, (Pause)—to reach the climax or something like that. I can just go and go and go and there's *nothing there. You know,* it takes a long time, about twenty minutes maybe.

[*He is already symbolically "dried up," as he called it referring to the joints.*]

D. You say there's nothing there?
P. Yuh (pause). What do you mean there's *nothing there*?
[*The anxiety is plain.*]

D. You just said there's *nothing there.*
P. Oh well, I mean, well, *you know* how it is, the first time it's a perfectly normal thing. You feel excited and everything is beautiful, and then you relax. The second time I just don't feel much.
D. So you think you might be a *frigid male*?
P. Well, no, not particularly, but oh—well, if I were, she would go out looking for it elsewhere. She's an attractive girl. She wouldn't have any trouble. (Pause) This *other* girl, she's sort of a nice girl. Of course, I don't want to be egotistical or anything, but I think if I forced the issue I bet there would be something there too, probably. She's a very, very good-looking girl. She's a DP, by the way. She's German, a real Aryan who came over from Germany, a nice, *blonde* Aryan. (Laughs) She's about twenty.
[*The "three girls" is also symbolic and a common figment of dreams in this type of patient. He turns to the nice girl as an incestuous figure. Aryan means pure and untouchable.*]

D. You say she's a nice girl.
P. Yes, and with her I just don't want to do it. I just haven't had any desire. Oh, if I love her up a little, it will come up and all that, more or less—*you know* why, now I'll tell you. She's just living with her mother. Her *father is dead.* They haven't got *anything,* although I guess they were pretty well to do in the old country or some damn thing. But this girl is in the market for a *husband.* I don't want to sound egotistical. I don't think exactly that she picked on me for this reason, but I guess she could get a nicer-looking guy, but she's a real good-looking girl and all that. But when you get with something like that, suppose there was a *slip* or something, *something might happen,* you never can tell, and then you'd really have to marry her.
[*He means desire toward the incestuous figure. Having those seductive thoughts, he plays safe and lets father be dead. Earlier in the interview, he already mentioned "slip or something," and what might happen.*]

D. You don't want that?
P. No, no, I'm not ready for that.
[*He had already revealed the dangerous meaning of marriage: he would be exposed.*]

D. What do you mean?
P. Well, I'm trying to be a realist. I can't afford wedding bells at this time. Of course, I'll be getting through in school in August now. I'll get my A.B. Of course I should have graduated two weeks ago, but I'm taking an extra course.
[*The other aspect of the reality situation: he would like to remain a "schoolboy."*]

D. Hanging on?

P. (Laughs heartily) Ha, ha, that's right. I hate to leave. Around July 7, I'll really be all done, but I did very good. I made the Dean's List. Of course, I don't feel I did as good as I could do. I guess that's good enough, though. I've been *taking it easy*.

D. You mean if you didn't have this trouble about feeling the eye of God upon you?

P. (Quickly) Yuh, I'm *tense*; is that what it is? I just feel tense. I *stiffen* up. What do you think it could be?

[*Being graduated means being an adult with all the obligations of doing what grownups do. This aspect makes him "stiff" and "tense" and forces him to "crack the neck." His own castrating and inhibiting tendencies frighten him.*]

D. If this thing didn't get stiff, you wouldn't have to go out and then you wouldn't have this trouble concerning marrying or masturbating. You then wouldn't feel that *God* was looking or "Heaven knows."

P. Yes, like for instance, *you know* what I say, I rationalize a lot. I say it isn't right to be *promiscuous* or *something like that*. You shouldn't have affairs with girls when you are not married. Society condemns it.

D. You feel you should be married? *You condemn it.*

[*He must become aware of and face his needs and condemnations.*]

P. Yuh, well, you know, *you know,* after all that's part of the mores. Here I am—I'm almost twenty-six.

[*This self-asserting tendency is encouraged by confrontation.*]

D. And you're a college graduate and you feel you shouldn't be acting like a little boy who *masturbates*—who *snaps it*.

P. But I don't want to get married. Of course, if I get a job and I get a few dollars salted away, then I, for instance,—what *the hell am I going to be married on*?

[*He balks when put on the spot.*]

D. You mean you haven't got *anything*? There's nothing there?

P. (Laughs loudly) That's it. There's *nothing there,* and I mean *literally*.

D. And in other ways too?

[*So he cannot evade the issue.*]

P. No, no, well—that is—I mean I'm not like other guys. Some guys are rabbits. They can hop on and everything, a couple of times a night.

D. Once a week is enough for you?

P. Well, yes,—no, that is, once a week is enough for me. Of course, with some people it's that way. It's once a week; with others, it's once an hour.

[*Yes—no—shows his ambivalence plainly.*]

D. But as you said, you were afraid you might be a *frigid male*?

P. Well, I was really only *kidding* (Pause), although there may have been some *seriousness* to it.

[*A weak denial. He cannot take one side or the other.*]

D. How do you mean?
P. Well in order for me to say that. I don't think that I am, *you know, oversexed* or things like that.

[*This was applied before to the "little girl."*]

D. You are not a *rabbit?*
P. No. I mean if circumstances were such, well anyhow, once a week is good enough for me. Anyway I just call this girl up once a week. The reason I don't call her up any more is that if I did, she might think I'm getting serious or something like that. I don't want to give her the wrong impression.

[*His conscience is the practical one of a little boy.*]

D. You don't want to be *caught?*

[*"Caught" more ways than one, referring to: (a) being watched doing bad things; (b) being punished (castrated) for it; (c) being married (being unafraid of doing it openly).*]

P. Yuh, that's right. Hey—what do you mean by being caught? You mean being caught doing things? I'm really just afraid that she might be considering me her steady boy friend.
D. That you might be expected to *marry* her?
P. Yes.
D. You feel there *isn't enough* there yet to get married?
P. Well, of course, I mean just *money.*

[*Of course.*]

D. You mean, all you need is just money and a job?
P. Well, it is just that I can't *see* getting *married.*

[*In one sense, he cannot see being a man. Only men work and make money.*]

D. You can't get a job?
P. Oh well, maybe when I get out of school I'll look for a job. Of course, I've been looking for one in a couple of places. Oh, I'm going to *get a job, by God.* After all—a guy getting out of school should be working. *My God,* a guy almost twenty-six years old. Right now it's sort of a transitional period for me, going to school and what not, but I realize now that the vacation is over and it's time that I took myself by the scruff of the *neck* and got to work.

[*A constructive ego tendency to be encouraged while its more severe aspects are discouraged by the therapist's benevolent detachment. He takes himself by the neck, but not for "snapping" it—rather for "stiffening" it.*]

D. You mean you have been a little boy long enough?

[*It is necessary to take sides, although in a questioning way.*]

P. Yes.

D. And it's time you went out and thought about serious things—like jobs and marriage?

P. Well, sure. Don't you think that's right?

[*This attitude represents the more mature and constructive portion of himself. He behaves as if he himself had made the suggestion of taking a job and marrying.*]

D. Certainly, but I wondered how you felt about it.

P. Oh, I want a job. I really do. I would like to get a job. I would like to get a good job, of course, like everybody would.

[*Be a* normal *man.*]

D. And then?

P. Well, and then I'd make a few dollars, buy myself some nice *clothes* and maybe a *car,* maybe I'd even put a little away.

[*His courage runs away with him.*]

D. And then you would have *enough?*

P. Ha, ha; maybe I'd meet a girl some day who *felt* like I did and *saw* things the way I do. Maybe I'd even get *married.*

[*A narcissistic reduplication of his feminine self.*]

D. You mean a "girl" who wasn't *oversexed?*

P. Well, yes, *I know,* there are some cases, for instance, this other girl that I had an affair with. That girl is a *nympho.* She'd rather do it than *eat.* It is *impossible* to *satisfy* her. Yes siree. She had a hysterectomy and she can't have any more kids, so it was kind of a good deal, ha, ha, in some respects. Well, of course, I think I did all right. She was *happy.* Of course though, she was going out with a lot of other guys in between. After all, I'm not the *biggest* man, but then again—I'm not the *smallest,* ha, ha. I guess I'm average. No, sir, I wouldn't want a *nympho,* and I wouldn't want a *frigid gal.*

[*He is torn between his own concepts of good and bad. At one time, he had turned to eating as a solution of his problem and had become very obese. He is the one who cannot be satisfied.*]

D. You mean like yourself, you don't want to be a *frigid male* and you don't want to be a *rabbit?*

[*Placing the problem where it belongs.*]

P. That's right. I'd like to be this *pseudo normality,* oh what the hell, there is no such thing anyway. Who knows? How can anyone decide? But I would like to find a girl like myself and yet I . . . I don't consider myself frigid either. I just want to find someone who falls in that particular category, but then *I don't know, I don't know* how I'll ever find out what that is. Chances are that if I had something to do with a girl, I'd well—with that kind of girl I'd marry her (Pause). And yet I wonder if I would.

[*"Pseudo normality" is used as a cynic defense and escape from reality. To love a girl like himself would be a step forward for him. Such a bold step is still frightening. This would be a neurotic acting-out solution.*]

D. What do you mean? You wouldn't mind going out with this nymphomanic girl, and at the same time going out with this nice Aryan girl?
P. Yes, that's it exactly.
D. But then, of course, you will feel guilty, and when you go by the church you feel God is looking at you, and you try to be so good and you say your prayers so carefully because Heaven knows what might happen. As if you were still a little boy.

[*The interviewer is again probing the little one's guilt feeling.*]

P. (After a long pause) Yes, I suppose that's true. It is really not on the up and up. There's no love.
D. As you say, you're just using her, and you feel guilty.
P. Of course, consciously I don't feel that way at all. Ha, ha, I don't even think about it.
D. But you have this *funny feeling* and you wonder if something can be wrong with your *back* and your *neck.*

[*Therefore, the interviewer again confronts him with the feeling in the neck. The reaction is significant: it shows how deceptive the previous exhibition of insight was.*]

P. Oh no, that is a fact. *By the way, what causes that, though? You know,* when I get that way, I can hear the *snap,* the *cracks* right in my *back.* You know I think it is this, like I told you. I think that there may be *muscles* around the *bones* and that when they *tense* up for some reason or other, there's an excess of *adrenal secretions,* or something, *you know.* It causes the *muscles* to *tense* up, right—that perhaps there isn't enough *fluid* in between the *joints,*—isn't that so, or is it, I *don't know.*

[*He desperately tries to displace the conflict to the somatic area again, and to straddle the issue once more. The ego is still too anxiety-ridden as to give up the defense expressed in the symptom. To keep it up, he exhibits a pseudo ignorance and reiterates and enumerates compulsively the former "words" like empty shells: bones, joints without fluid—as if in a learned lesson. He knows more than he is willing to admit.*]

D. You mean, when you feel *guilty* about this *masturbation* with this girl, and not being a *man,* you *tense up* and begin to *worry* about whether you have enough *fluid?*

[*A rewording of his own terms.*]

P. (Laughs heartily) Maybe it's just my imagination.

[*He wants to stop right now. The confrontation continues with "As you say. . . ."*]

D. As you say, when something gets *stiff* and *tense,* it makes the *fluid* dry up. Then you worry over *snapping* it. Do you mean that you're still acting like the little one who did it because it made him *feel so good,* but always felt mother's eye upon him and was afraid of being punished?

P. But the deal I have now is really kind of a cozy deal.
D. But you're not *satisfied* with it entirely?
P. Yuh, well no. I'm not *satisfied* really.
D. *As you said,* you felt it was about time a twenty-six-year-old boy got a job and had some serious thoughts in life instead of playing around, being satisfied with cozy deals, huh?

[*The adult ego is confronted with the immature part.*]

P. Yes, definitely. All my life I've been *dependent* on *Mama* and *Papa,* and I still depend on *Mama* and *Papa* right up until *today.* I really feel *guilty,* yes. My father gets out and he works hard, and here is his God damn lazy, good-for-nothing son going to school, a man who should actually be kicking in and helping to support the family.

[*The bitter truth is faced temporarily. Now the other side of the coin shows up.*]

D. You mean you don't want to be a fellow who is just looking for a cozy deal?
P. Yuh, that's right.
D. He doesn't want to just go out with this girl and snap it?
P. That's right. I really want to get married, yes.

[*He accepts "snap" in a different sense.*]

D. So there's a part of you that wants to be independent, grow up and really get married; and then there's a part, little Dick, who wants the cozy deal, stay home, be taken care of, and continue snapping it?
P. Yuh, ha, ha, ha, I guess that's right. (Long pause) You know the trouble is I don't think I'm capable of love, i.e., in the real sense of the word, i.e., if anyone knows what the hell love is. I can take them or leave them.

[*He is too anxious and narcissistic to love.*]

D. You mean you don't feel you can be big enough or have enough to do such a thing?
P. Well, yes, that's what I mean. I don't know what the score is. It's uh, uh, uh, it's a psychopathic stage, isn't it, being so much engrossed in yourself, uh, uh, well, I just never felt that way.

[*Apparently rationalization from reading, yet closer to the truth than he intended. He quickly denies it.*]

D. You're too much engrossed with little Dick?
P. Right, yes. It's just what I was going to say. I love myself. *I watch myself* and *see* how I *act* and try to *impress* people. Why do I feel that way?

[*He gives a correct characterization of himself, admitting his narcissistic love. Then he tries to turn the tables.*]

D. That is the way the little one feels.

P. How do you *choke* this little one? Jesus, there's an awful lot of the little one left in me though. (Pause) Too much, because yes, I don't feel I could make a go of married life; that entails an awful lot of responsibility. You've got to work hard and you've got a lot of responsibility. You've got a wife and your family.

[*He shrinks from the adult task.*]

D. Little Dick doesn't feel big enough to work hard?

P. No. The little one has big ideas. He don't want to *work hard* like my old man, with a pick and shovel, or something like that. How many guys who take care of a family have to work with a pick and shovel? A whole lot of them do—right? And I'd like to get a good job. *You know*, I can rationalize. I can think up some beautiful arguments, though. They are lulu's. Now *I know* a kid who just got married, who went to school with me a while ago. I said to him just the other day, "Hey, you God damn fool, what the hell did you want to get married for?" I said to him, "Listen here, you could get all you want for nothing, and not only that, you're going to have a wife and kids and suppose there are no job opportunities and you want to go out West, say to Colorado, for example. You won't be able to do it. You'll have to stick around and find an apartment to live. Maybe kids will come along." For Heaven's sake, if *you're all by yourself*, you can live in a "Y" and save your money, and then you can *eventually* come back and marry the girl. I thought I was doing the kid a favor. Of course, that's the way I look at it, and really that's the way I do. Now is that realistic or isn't it?

[*He joins the interviewer in the confrontation. His dilemma is, he would rather be an infant than a hard-working father. His ambition up to the age of sixteen was to enter a religious order, which he saw as an easy life where he would be taken care of and avoid sexual and competitive masculine strivings. He preaches self-love against object love. "Be all by yourself," as a prevention against "giving away something," is the defensive slogan.*]

D. You mean *little Dick* feels that way, but also pays for it by feeling very guilty, and always God, the *Father's* eye is upon him, and he looks at his *father* who works hard for his money with a pick and shovel, and he looks at himself and feels very guilty about taking money from him and, as you said—being a *good-for-nothing.*

[*Again the tie-up begins, and the guilt feelings from which he is trying to escape are reinforced in an attempt to uproot the symptom.*]

P. Yuh, I guess so, but it would be pretty tough having a wife tagging along all the time. *You know*, when you get married, aw, *I know* guys who got married and they say they wished the hell they hadn't got married. They've got responsibilities, maybe a kid comes along or something like that, or they want to change gals and they can't do it, and they're just *stuck* for life.

[*"Guys" who wish to leave their wives, may well refer to his fantasies concerning father, as his parents quarreled frequently.*]

D. You mean, they have to work like father did all his life with a pick and shovel, with his nose stuck to the grindstone?

[*This confrontation with his own statement is a strong dose. He admits his parasitic wishes.*]

P. (Gives a nervous laugh) Yuh, and he's still working, *supporting me.*
D. Supporting you?
P. Yuh. (Laughs again nervously)
D. And you don't want to be like father?
P. No, by God I don't—I don't want to work that hard. He really works very hard. Of course, I admire him for it. I really think an awful lot of him.

[*He admires father, but only for his own good. His need for narcissistic defense is greater than the guilt feelings.*]

D. You admire him and you look at this little boy who wants to be supported, take it easy and have a cozy deal, And you really feel guilty for not being a man like father. Are you *ashamed* of yourself, huh?
P. Yes, definitely.
D. So when God, the father, looks at you, you don't feel so good?
P. No, no I don't. I just don't feel good, and then when I pass by the church, I've got to concentrate on bowing my head, and then when I pray I have to say it very slowly, "In the name of the Father—Son—and Holy Ghost."

[*The confrontation with father's condemnation stirs up the compulsive trends as antidote against the guilt.*]

D. The son concentrates on these words so he won't have to think about how guilty he feels?
P. Yuh, other people can do it without thinking about it—but not me. I have to think about it all the time.

[*He means he thinks about it instead of doing it.*]

D. You mean, instead of thinking about: "Here I'm almost twenty-six years old, and I still feel like a kid. I feel I haven't got enough, I feel like taking it easy and going along looking for cozy deals when I should be out working, being a man with responsibilities, getting *married*?"

[*The term "married" is chosen for giving up hypocrisy and exposing the "bad" doings. Can he face it?*]

P. (A long pause) *You know* that really bothers me a lot. Whew! It's a lot of responsibility. People get married every day, but you wonder if they realize it, i.e., what they're getting into. Maybe if you stop to think, you think to stop. *You know* the old proverb.
D. Afraid of getting into things, or might get into when you get *married?*
P. Oh, yuh, yuh, I guess so. Oh, I suppose I just don't want to get *married.* I mean, not yet. I *just can't see it.*

[*He wants to delay the decision of giving up to be the "little boy."*]

D. You're not *big enough* to get into these things?

P. You said something there that's probably a lot of it. (Pause) *I don't compete very much.* If I have to go to a dance, I sometimes, well, I pause in what I'm doing; rather than go up and ask a very attractive girl to dance, I say—oh, well, she'll probably refuse me anyway, so I just don't try, ha, ha, ha, but I *put on the attitude that I don't give a damn,* but really I look over there at her with *longing* eyes, ha, ha, like the poet says.

[*He admits his feelings of inadequacy and fears of competition. He uses "hypocrisy" as a defense when he feels uncapable to live up to the demands of the girls.*]

D. You mean you really want to be a man and be able to do the things that other men do, but you're *afraid* you aren't big enough.

[*Supporting the adult ego.*]

P. (Long pause) Well, I suppose that's a lot of it, but I just don't want to *marry* the girl yet.

D. As you said, you look at her *longingly,* but become *fearful* and say, I don't really give a damn. As you said, you don't like to *compete* with these others, the other fellows?

[*Confrontation with his "hypocrisy."*]

P. Yes, I feel that way.

D. But it is sour grapes.

P. Sure, ideally I would really like to be married, and work, and have a job, I mean a good job. What I mean by a good job, I really *don't know.* Oh, say, a job that pays, well—I'd be very satisfied if I could have a job that pays $5,000. Then I could perhaps have a wife, see, and a nice little home and a car.

[*He needs a big salary, or "something like that," to feel "big enough."*]

D. You don't think you can do that?

P. Not right yet. I can't anyway under the present circumstances. I'm still in school.

[*Wants to prolong being a school boy.*]

D. But not any more.

P. Oh yes, I'm going to school now.

[*Immaturity as defense.*]

D. But you're finishing up very soon.

P. Too soon. Holy God, only two more weeks.

[*He dreads facing the inevitable.*]

D. Little Dick is very much afraid now that there's no more excuse left, huh?

P. That's true, I do, I'll admit it. I'm not afraid. I mean, oh well, everybody feels that way, I suppose. They all want to go out and get a good job and something like that, but what the hell, I feel I'm ready to tackle it. I'm no different from anybody else in that respect. I'll go out and plug along, but I'd hate like hell to end up as a clerk in some office. That's why I say I don't want to get married, because if I do get a job and I see there's no chance for advancement or something like that—of course—I don't mean that I want to get a job and *right away become vice-president.* I'm not being unreasonable in life. It depends—but if the road seemed to be *blocked* and there is a lot of competition or something like that, then I want to feel *free* to leave. I don't want to be *tied down* and have to accept a lot of *responsibilities.* I just couldn't. I have to make sure that I know where the next *meal* will come from—that it is there. I *want to know* that I will be *taken care of.*

[*He faces reality and gives himself a pep talk, but the little one is clamorous: he runs for shelter on one hand, and has megalomanic demands on the other hand. This conflict is an exaggeration of one faced and solved by every boy.*]

D. But then you feel *guilty* and feel it's about time little Dick stopped being *taken care of,* and is able to take care of himself.

P. That's right. There's that oscillation. I do and I don't. I will and I won't. But it is really nice while it lasts. You can understand me what I mean, don't you? It's a nice feeling.

[*He wants to have his cake and eat it, too: "I do and I don't; I will and I won't." The ambivalence is impermeable.*]

D. Certainly, but at almost twenty-six.

[*Re-echoing his own words.*]

P. That's right. It's about time the vacation is over. It can't go on and on, but little Dick would really like it to. A lot of guys go out at seventeen and get married.

D. They do?

P. Yuh, I know a guy who is now about twenty-four, two years younger than me. He got married at seventeen and divorced at twenty-four. He's even had a kid. That's a hell of a note, isn't it?

[*Pleads for the interviewer's agreement that it is inadvisable to take on responsibilities prematurely.*]

D. But you feel it's about time you did something, too?

P. Well, yes. Don't you think it's about high time I started to do something. In the past, I just used to want to change the world all around like everybody does.

D. Like all little Dicks?

P. Yuh, I guess that's right.

D. But you know you won't start at $5,000 a year.

[*Testing his readiness for facing reality.*]

P. Of course I won't. I'll be damn lucky if I start at $300 a month—(Pause) damn lucky. Most of the places start you off at about $50 a week. (Long pause) But, doctor, *what makes your back crack, i.e., creak so? Is there anything that I can do to stop it?*

[*It seems as if the interviewer had overplayed himself: the pseudo-ignorant questions appear again.*]

D. To stop snapping it?
P. Well, I figure it this way: I'm always tense. My head hurts back here perpetually. I can't get rid of that *old pain in the neck, you know.*

[*The head and neck are too vulnerable to be left unprotected.*]

D. You mean this of little Dick?
P. Ha, ha, I guess that's really it; but this *tension* has undoubtedly caused some *bodily changes.* Maybe it has made my *bones brittle.* What should I take—*cod liver oil?* Is there anything I can do?

[*He had a swelling in the breast resected in the Service. The idea of "brittle bones" reveals the "brittle" ego. Infants take cod liver oil.*]

D. How do you mean, brittle?
P. Ha, ha, I mean brittle, weak, *cracked.*

[*Brittle—weak—crack—creak—crick—snap.*]

D. You mean your bones are too *dry?*
P. Well yuh, that is undoubtedly what makes the, no, I've really got enough fluid.

[*The reminder about lack of "fluid" is too anxiety-provoking.*]

D. But you are not sure?
P. (Laughs heartily) If I'm not sure, I could take an *egg* in my beer.

[*He suggests "egg" in beer to have more "fluid," to be more of a man.*]

D. How do you mean?
P. Well, *you know,* there's that old saying, *you know yourself* how they say, an *egg in your beer* really gives you the *old stamina.*
D. Gives you lots of *fluid,* huh?
P. Yuh, ha, ha, ha (pause).
D. So you feel you ought to take cod liver oil or an egg in your beer?
P. (Laughs) Yuh, *you know,* every now and then I do take an egg in my beer. (Laughs loudly) It's really good for you, *you know.*

[*The laughter again wards off anxiety.*]

D. You mean you really aren't sure whether you have *enough fluid?*
P. Yuh, I guess so. That's very good. Well, egg is good anyway, isn't it, i.e., raw egg, much better than cooked. Actually it has all the protein and everything, so I can take an egg, but while I take it, I always think of it and I say to myself, this is the kind of stuff that is supposed to *make a man potent,* but after all I don't have an egg in my beer every day. Maybe only once a month.

[*He tries to minimize the meaning of his drinking "eggs," and begins to rationalize it. The fear is now clearly revealed.*]

D. You feel you are *not potent* enough?
P. Perhaps, yes I guess I do. No, really consciously I don't think of these things. Maybe I'm not really so damn potent, all right. I'm just like everybody else.
D. Of course, but little Dick doesn't feel that way. He needs the egg in his beer, or some cod liver oil.

P. Aw, no, no, oh, *I don't know.* (Pause) I really *hate that little bastard.* As far as I am concerned, I really feel potent enough. I mean, well, potent enough, what the hell does that mean?

[*He, the adult, who wants to be potent (big), "hates that little bastard" for his megalomanic infantile wishes of being a superman (with inexhaustible fluid).*]

D. Potent enough to marry?

[*"Marry" should mean being on a man's level.*]

P. Well, not on account of *not enough fluid* or anything like that. Maybe this is what they call a sublimation or something like that. It could be that I take an egg in my beer because I feel I am *not man* enough, not *potent* enough; that is, I feel that I haven't got a good job and I haven't *got enough money.*

D. Or enough *fluid in the joints?*

P. Ha, ha, ha, possibly. Maybe it is so. I should have a lot of it left because I certainly don't use up too much, ha, ha, ha, not more than other people. When I was a little kid I didn't do it half as much as the rest. [*Reassuring himself.*] All through latency, you know, I didn't masturbate. In fact, I didn't do it until quite late, i.e., masturbating in the active sense. Of course, I was stopped when I was a kid with that infantile masturbation. Then as I grew up, then of course sex was very bad for me, anything pertaining to it. Then of course, Frank [*his alter ego*], my pal who—by the way—has become a fully ordained priest, of course I grew up with him. He got ordained just a month ago today. I grew up with him all the time, and he thought sex was a dirty thing too. Do you remember how I told you one time about how scared I got and gave up sex completely, so I didn't masturbate.

[*This solution calls for too great a renunciation for him.*]

D. But now you don't want to be a priest?

P. Oh, I *don't know.* If I had the calling, it would be all right, but if I hadn't gone in the Service I probably would have been a priest because after all, Frank and I grew up together, after all.

[*Part of him ostensibly wants to give up genital activities and devote himself to "God" (father) and be taken care of. In this way, he could continue to masturbate secretly and again attempt to have his cake and eat it, too.*]

D. But now little Dick can't accept *religion* wholeheartedly, as you said.

P. Yuh, he's had a taste of it, and he kind of likes it.

D. But he also feels guilty and is frightened?

P. You said it. And he can't completely *relax* and say ah, this is wonderful, like she does. You know what I mean, like her.

[*Now the identification with "the little girl" is out in the open. Not a boy, but only a girl can "relax" and does not have to be guilty and frightened.*]

D. Like her?

P. Yuh, I suppose so. If I got married, perhaps I could, say perhaps if I ever could get married. If I felt big enough, it would be a *different* sort of relationship.

D. You mean you then would feel that you were acting *like a man?*

P. Yuh, I guess that's it. But for that matter, I feel *like a man* right now. You know what my idea of a man is—well, it really isn't any more, but *you know* what it used to be—strictly a Don Juan kind of a character.

[*He feels like a man. But the ideal of a man was a Don Juan. It seems as if his compulsive neurosis with the hypochondriacal fears saved him from becoming a psychopath.*]

D. You mean like a rabbit?

P. Ha, ha, yes, that's it. A real *killer,* a captivator, who can horse around and really do it. That *was my idea of a man.* But now I don't think that's my idea of a man at all. A man doesn't have to be a rabbit all the time. He doesn't have to go out and get a different one every night and do it two or three times, like all those guys who brag they do it three times a night, five nights a week. I don't feel like that any more. I think a fellow who does those things is just trying to prove things to himself. You know I really think that once I get a good job, all my troubles wil be over. I tell myself again and again, I'm as much of a man as the next one. I've got what it takes just as much as they have. (Pause)

[*Time will tell whether what he says is a victory of the adult ego over the immature one, or whether it is only lip service. Here he reveals the infantile "super rabbit" ego ideal.*]

P. So you don't think those pains in the neck are really serious? Do you think I'll get over it?

[*Again, the ominous questions are heard!*]

D. It's up to you.

P. Yes, I guess you're right. It's up to me. I think I can do it.

[*He has identified with the therapist, for the time being.*]

D. Congratulations on getting your degree. Let me know how things go.

P. OK. Thanks a lot, doctor. I'll let you know how things go.

Discussion

The sector was centered around the meaning of bowing the head and snapping the neck. The associations to it led to his ambivalence over his adult sexual role which was essentially a continuation of infantile masturbatory tendencies. This infantile behavior was so guilt-ridden and so threatened by fears of punishment, that he needed defenses expressed in his compulsions and in bodily symptoms, i.e., the snapping of his neck.

In this interview the patient's conflict was clearly revealed in many

CHART 1

ASSOCIATIONS CENTERED AROUND THE COMPULSION TO BOW THE HEAD

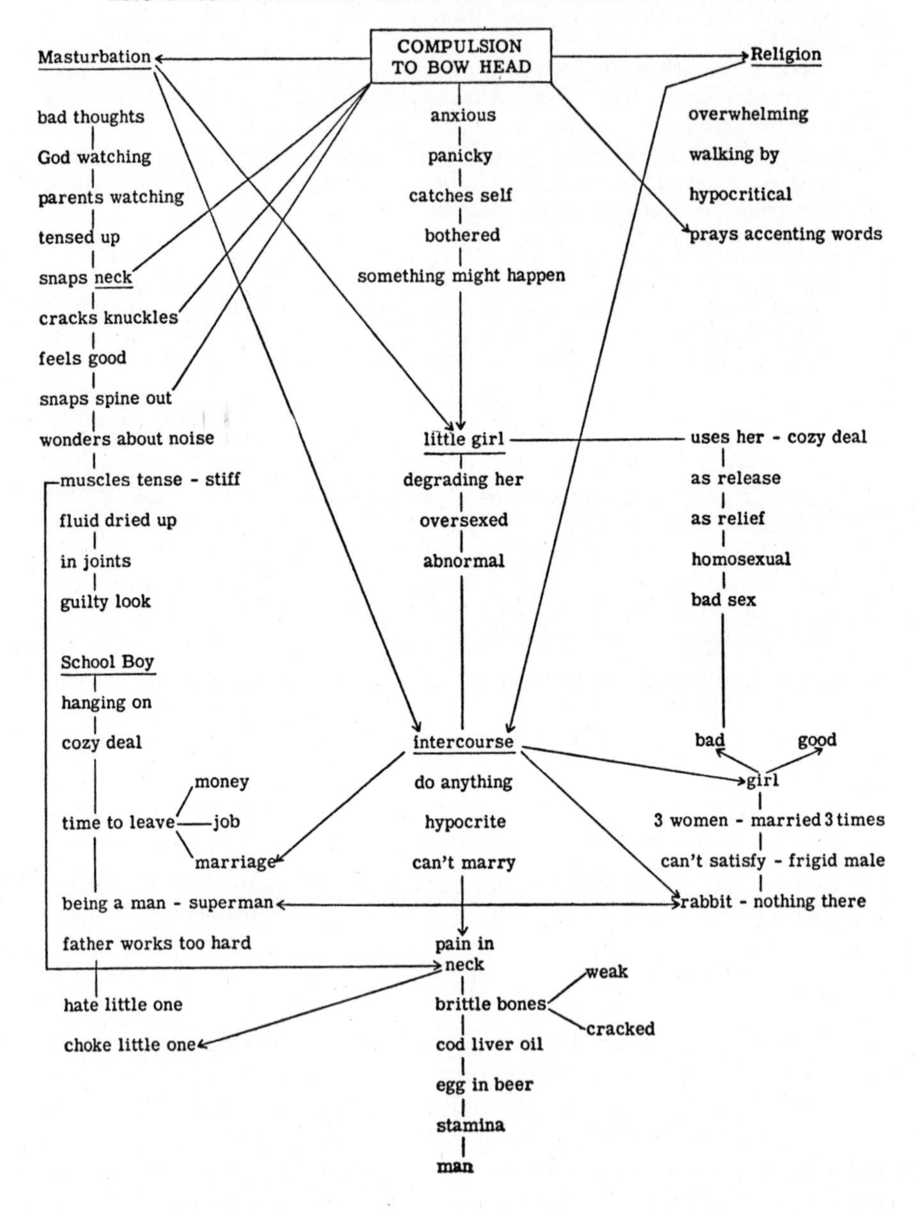

of its aspects, and a constructive solution encouraged in keeping with his own needs and those of his reality world. The interview shows in detail how the technique aids the patient to face, again and again, unconscious material disguised by and anchored in somatic symptoms, and how by means of continual confrontations with the associative material the patient can finally achieve some insight within the chosen sector, and to a certain degree attempt a better adjustment.

A significant detail of this interview seems important enough to be mentioned, because it is an indication of the therapeutic progress made during the interview. In the beginning, attention was called to this patient's use of the phrases "I don't know," and "You know," as typical for patients with a compulsive-obsessional neurosis and expressing the ambivalence conflict. This patient used these phrases forty-two times in the first third of the interview. Twenty-two times in the second third, and only thirteen times in the last third. This reflects the degree of resolution of the conflict.

An interview with the same individual six months later will be discussed in Part 2 of this chapter.

Part 2—The Bad Conscience

Introduction

Maintaining continuity in a sector refers principally to keeping within a limited area of a patient's intrapsychic life, and confining one's efforts to a thorough exploration of one aspect of a recurrent problem within this area. This aspect may refer primarily to an organ or a symptom, and secondarily to a parent figure or a sibling rival. Thus, one interview might deal with the relationship of head pain to maternal figures and passive-aggressive strivings, and another interview with the head and its relation to conflicts involving the father and aggressive competitive wishes. In any case, concentration on the ramifications of one aspect of a complex situation permits a more thorough working through of material over a large segment of time, and the development of the perspective and detachment necessary for the ego to modify its defenses in anxiety-provoking situations. Once the main problem is correctly outlined and understood by the therapist, it is comparatively easy to select key words which will keep the interview centered around this problem in the most efficient and economic manner.

The previous interview was concerned with the problems of a patient who utilized obsessional thinking, compulsive behavior and somatic preoccupations with his body, in an attempt to master large quantities of anxiety based essentially upon the persistence of unresolved infantile passive and aggressive libidinal wishes. He had an overly protective mother who spoiled and petted him but was greatly concerned over any sexual activity. His sibling relationship was unfortunate, i.e., he was the youngest of seven, all others being girls. The father was taciturn and morose and slept with the patient up until he was fourteen. He had covertly encouraged rebellion but had never offered advice or aided him in his quarrels with his mother or sisters. At the same time, the father had occasional frightening outbursts of rage directed at all members of the family. The temptations to play a passive role were tremendous, as in this manner he could:

(1) escape from competition with fantasied supermasculine adult male figures;

(2) escape from incestuous guilt feelings;
(3) avoid aggression against both parents;
(4) be taken care of by his parents;
(5) deny masturbatory impulses and guilt feelings for "playing around" sexually.

The patient's defensive passive wishes and feminine identifications led to outbursts of anxiety. He also had retaliatory fears of his aggressive and defiant impulses toward parent surrogates who forbade phallic activity. The principal area of conflict centered around his infantile masturbatory activity.

Therapy concentrated in the area of his conflicts over his masturbation led to an increase in ego strength which had allowed relatively more adult interpersonal relations, sexual and otherwise, and an ability to work successfully in school and in the business world.

The following interview will demonstrate how continuity can be preserved in interviews, in this case six months apart. In the interim, the patient had graduated from college and remained at home, being supported by his parents while engaged in part-time work. Meanwhile, he had not found it necessary to see his therapist.

INTERVIEW

D. How are you?
P. Still *struggling* along, I guess.
D. What do you mean, *struggle?*
P. Oh, just about what I said—still having these *problems*. Well, school is done, anyway.

[*"Struggling" is an obvious key word for use in the sector, and for linking it up with the "problems" which should be clarified.*]

D. What do you mean, *problems?* What kind of *problems?*
P. Gee, *I don't know*. It seems that I am going into *conversions* or something. *You know* I've always *complained* about being tense, but *Jesus*, I'm still *tense* as all hell, in all situations—social and otherwise, mainly *social*. *You know*, I *tense* up. *Jesus, I don't know*, I just feel all tightened up. *You know*, I can carry on all right, of course, but well, I just feel myself *progressing*—while having luncheon today, well, *you know* of course there is an amount of *anxiety* associated with anything like that. With me, I'm kind of *conscious* of it, and I could just feel myself *tensing* up, and as the luncheon progressed, well, I got really tightened up toward the *end, you know*, I could feel it tighten in the *back* of my *neck* and *my back*.

[*He tries to intellectualize without relief. The struggle (problem) becomes indirectly defined by the antithesis: religion (Jesus) versus social (sexual) relations, and the conflict solution: tension and stiff-*

ness in the back of the neck. He refers everything to the "back" side, which expresses his passive tendencies and needs. The neck symptom is added as a key word.]

D. Your *back* feels tense?
P. Yeah, and then I get anxious, probably before then I convert it into anxiety or tension or something like that.
D. You get anxious first?
P. Yeah, I get very anxious in some *situations.*
D. What *situations* do you mean?

[*The "general" some place, something, must be exemplified in the "specific," interwoven with the past, and only then "regeneralized."*]

P. Well, for instance, oh, I don't know, going *some*place, going out with a *gal* or *something.*
D. Going out with a *gal?*
P. Oh yeah.
D. What girl do you mean?
P. (Giggles) Any *girl*—not any particular one, with any gal. (Pause) Or even with *guys* sometimes too. I mean in some sort of a situation in which I take a direct part, I *tense* up, I get anxious. This is the way I seem to do it, and then I kind of *look around* for these defense mechanisms, trying to *grab,* oh, you know, an *obsession* or a *compulsion,* which I don't do any more, or very little anyway.

[*"Social" is specified as "gal," but also as "guys." This expresses his ambivalent passive-active, masculine- feminine problems. "Taking a direct part" means becoming responsible for "social" activity. That makes him anxious, tense (stiff) and he has to "grab" (bowing the head) to ward off the guilt. This is what he did in the past.*]

D. You try to *grab* something?
P. That's right, something I can lay my anxiety on, in other words some sort of an obsession or a compulsion, or in other words, we'll say, "Did I do this or did I do that"?

[*The patient has a penchant for intellectual shop talk, which must be discouraged by ignoring it. Economically speaking, he must be made conscious of his efforts to evade religious and sexual problems, which are representatives of his superego and id, and then encouraged to find a more practical and adult method to satisfy both sides.*]

D. How do you mean?

P. Well, for instance, did I do something, did I *lock the car,* or did I *bow my head* when I went by the church, or something like that, as an example. See, in other words, I try to displace my anxiety onto some particular thing, and that would mean falling into the obsessions or compulsions.
D. You mean when you get *anxious,* you wonder if you have left *something* undone?

[*Can his insight be trusted?*]

P. Yeah, *undone,* something I *should have done.* I have put the anxiety on an obsession or a compulsion of some kind. I tense up. It's a vicious circle.

D. You get *anxious*. Then you *grab something?*

[*His own terms are repeated.*]

P. Oh, well, I don't necessarily *grab something*. I'm just trying to displace my anxiety. Well, in general, I'm *preoccupied*. I should have said displaced, rather than grab something. I really just try to reach out for something to allay this anxiety, see what I mean. I try to find a reason for this anxiety. I say to myself, I'm anxious about some *damn thing*, and I try to put it on an object. I'm really *anxious* about the way *I look* or *some damn thing*.

[*He senses that he has disclosed too much, and changes "grab" into "displaced." He "looks" at this "damn thing" as he feels others (God or parents) do, disapprovingly.*]

D. You are like *a damned thing?*

[*The main surface problem.*]

P. I guess so. I'm always *anxious* about the way I *look*—do I look *right*.

[*What part of his "I" does not look right? As a child, he was anxious about the way his genital looked, but to bring this out immediately involves and invites intellectualization.*]

D. You mean do you look *bad* or not?

P. Yeah, I guess so. *I don't know* what it is. I'm just anxious about the way I appear to other people. (Sweats)

[*This means, "I don't want to face what I know."*]

D. And you think you might look like a *damned* thing that isn't *right*, that isn't *good*.

[*The "I" and the phallus are the same at this level.*]

P. I didn't mean *damned thing*, not that *I'm* damned, I don't think I'm as bad as that. That *damn* doesn't mean anything. I don't think.

D. But it did in the past, do you remember?

[*Purposefully ambiguous, to allow him to bring out and develop the problem in his own words.*]

P. Oh yes, I'm always anxious about me, continually so— how *do I look* to other people, do I look *right*.

[*He compares "his looks" with that of "others."*]

D. *Little* Dick used to wonder if he was a *damned thing*, and did he *look right*, when he was an altar boy.

[*The interviewer confronts the little one with the adult one, the bad boy versus the altar boy.*]

P. Yes. (Laughs) He also *grabbed* that *damn thing*, yeah, he did *once*.

D. Once, what do you mean? Only once?

P. Oh, you know, that incident there where I was stopped from that infantile masturbation or *something like that,* you know what I mean. (Pause) You know, when I was afraid to play with it, and thought it might be *chopped off.* I guess it was really a *big thing* to me. I guess I played with it until I got *quite old,* then I said it isn't right to be *playing* with *things* like that. Now I don't have to.

[*His efforts at isolation and intellectualization are plain. His reference to "quite old" indicates that he is still a little boy.*]

D. What do you mean?
P. Well, I have some *girl friends.*
D. Now you *play* with *girls?*
P. Oh yeah.
D. Still *playing* with *girls?*

[*We must be prepared to realize that any insight gained from the last interview was miniscule and quickly denied. However, it has to be restored.*]

P. Another thing, I got a girl, well, that I'm almost *serious* about.

[*He suggests a tentative approach to adult behavior.*]

D. How do you mean, *serious?*
P. Well, I'll tell you something. It's really a very interesting relation from the standpoint of how I *feel* about *"her,"* and how *this thing worked out.* This *was* that "little girl" I spoke to you about, the DP girl I told you about.

[*He says that she "was" a little girl: that means, he too "was" a little boy, but both are no longer "little" ones. His relationship to the little girl was previously "without feeling." He gave her a role which he also played himself, i.e., that of a good girl.*]

D. You mean that real Aryan blonde girl?
P. Yeah, that's the one. You remember I told you the last time that I had never made any amorous passes at her. I didn't feel it was right. I felt that if I did anything with her, I had to marry her if anything happened. Remember I told you I didn't feel adequate. Since the last time I saw you, well, we started in. Well, she gave in as easy as *eating pudding.*
D. As easy as *eating pudding?*

[*It was known from previous interviews that words in connection with eating, obesity and greed were important and highly charged for him.*]

P. Yeah, well, that's just a colloquialism, it's just a phrase. It was really easy. Ha, ha. Well, I've been *seeing* the girl, and as a matter of fact I'm *almost serious* about the girl. She is a very nice girl, and she is very serious about me. As a matter of fact, I feel she is *too sexual* for me. I really think she is, she is a *nympho,* too.

[*He fears that she, like the other girls and himself, is "abnormal." This means that sex and love are combined.*]

D. She is?

P. Yeah, she is absolutely not me. You can go and go and go, and there is just *no satisfying her*. I remember, well, one instance, I took her to well, you know, I just felt I wasn't *going to be man enough*. Here's this girl, a very *lovey-dovey* sort of girl, and once a night is enough for me, but in order to keep her happy, I sometimes go twice. The second time it's almost a *strain* on me, sometimes even three times, like this time I mean. I just have to force myself. It's not spontaneous.

[*He is afraid of giving too much away. In a previous interview, he expressed the fear of losing too much fluid and of drying out his joints. "Strain" is like cracking.*]

D. You were *afraid* you might *strain* yourself?

P. Yeah, it's a *strain*. It's hard for me to get an erection. What I mean by a strain is, it's—well—it's just not spontaneous. I keep kissing her and nothing happens, so she starts playing around and the *worst* of it is she told me that she had never been in *love* before and she told me everything. She really has fallen for me, and it's for the first time, and you know how I react to any girl that lets me. I say to myself, "Oh, you old whore." Only I really know she isn't that kind of a girl at all. She is really a nice girl, Doc. *You know* what I mean.

[*His personal relationship anxieties were displaced to his phallus and radiated to his entire body, which took over attributes once belonging to the phallus, and provokes anxiety.—Like the girl, he too has never been in love.—Problem of the little one reconciling his image of the pure, ideal mother with that of the "old whore" (bad mother).*]

D. How do *you* mean?

P. I know she is a *nice girl,* and yet I tell myself that I don't want *that kind of a girl,* that really I just want someone to *play around with,* and I keep calling her these names, and yet she hasn't done anything that I haven't done.

[*He phrases it rightly, that "she" hasn't done anything (with him) that "he" hasn't done (with himself). He would like to remain at the playful, childlike level.*]

D. So, if, as you say, she is just like you, you mean that you are a "damned old whore" too?

[*Repeating his own conclusion. It was he who called mother by this name in his mind.*]

P. Oh no, no, I don't mean it that way. (Pause) I guess I still got that double standard business, you know. But *you know* I have a tough time, to get the desire to do it more than once. I don't feel right, but you know she is really nympho, it's a strain on me if I have to do it like that, and then when I can't get an *erection* on, I feel anxious. I feel I've lost my *manliness,* or when she is telling me all of her background. She has never told anybody those things before. She just says she doesn't want to keep anything from me.

She told me everything about herself, and boy, I still feel she is a *little whore.* I really can't love her. *She* is a *little whore.* She had an affair with a *married man* before she met me. If it were another girl, I wouldn't care, but this girl I *really feel something* for, but I ask myself, "Am I justified?"

[*When he "displaced" his problem onto his genital, he did it reluctantly. He must become conscious of this before any settlement can be made.—"Tense, stiff" is now substituted for by "erection" that makes him "anxious," i.e., afraid of "losing" the "manhood."—There is a "little whore" and an "old whore." "She" plays a double role, especially that of his passive feminine self. At another level, "she" is a mother figure. Here the therapeutic progress becomes clear: he can allow himself "to feel something."*]

D. You ask yourself are you justified, in view of the fact that you have done the *same things yourself,* is that what you mean?

P. Well, I feel sorry for her, but how could you *marry* a girl like that?

[*"Marry" means "exposing" what he is doing. He is beyond the pale—too "little" and too "bad."*]

D. You mean you wonder if you could *satisfy* her?

[*Relating to being too little: how can he do what an adult man does?*]

P. Yeah, she's practically *nympho.*

D. So, you mean that a girl like that, who has had experience with another man and who might measure you up against this other fellow, a *married man,* how could you handle her, huh?

P. That's it exactly. How do *I know* she won't find me *inadequate* and *leave me* for *another man.*

[*He acts like a man, but feels it is only an act.*]

D. You don't feel sure you can *satisfy* her?

[*"Satisfy her" refers to his fears of dissatisfying, depriving "him."*]

P. No, I don't. And yet, I feel she wants to talk about everything. She tells me everything so frankly and I put on the *big father act* and say to her, "That's all right, honey." Then I *hate myself* for *acting* that way.

D. You mean you coax her to tell you all these things, and then you despise her for it?

P. Yeah, that's it. Yeah, I keep saying it's done, it could happen to anybody, forget it, it's all over, but I don't believe it myself.

D. But perhaps you call yourself names because, as you say, and have told me, there's a part of you that wants to be like Frank, the priest, and there's another part of you that doesn't like that and has done these things.

[*This reduces the conflict to a level he can feel.*]

P. That's right. I am a *promiscuous* sort of a guy. I still feel as if I'm doing wrong. I keep telling myself there's nothing *wrong* with *sex,* but I keep thinking of *God.*

[*Both sex and God are conceived of only in their infantile meanings.*]

D. You mean God knows?
P. Yeah.
D. So you treat her the same way that you treat yourself, but you really feel very anxious, huh?

[*He attempts to externalize the problem, and we reverse the process in order to encourage a different solution.*]

P. Yes, exactly. I say, "There's nothing wrong with this at all," but I really don't feel it.
D. And then you wonder if people are *looking at you* and know that you are *bad* and that you aren't doing the *right things,* and that maybe you are damned.
P. Well, perhaps. This girl I really like so much that I wonder, I keep *wondering* whether I'm *justified* in *condemning* her.

[*If he were sure, he'd have no problem, as she is he himself.*]

D. Because you *wonder* about *condemning* yourself?
P. Well, I have all sorts of doubts. I say to myself, now, if I ever should get *serious* about this girl, serious enough to *marry* her perhaps, that is, of course, I am *afraid.* What is there to stop her from going around with someone else if I got *married,* and if I can't *satisfy* her?

[*The resurrected infantile problem.*]

D. You doubt you can satisfy her, because she has had experience with others?

[*We cannot reduce this too carefully to a narcissistic problem.*]

P. Yeah, that's it in a nutshell. (Pause) That's it, the fact she has had these extracurricular activities with other guys (pause)—but she has told me, she has come out and told me, something another girl would not do. She is repentant. She is very *serious* with me. I didn't even ask her about it, so then I pull this *big father* act.

[*He "pulls the big father act" to inflate his ego against a narcissistic injury, when being compared with other men.*]

D. You act like a father?
P. Well *you know,* the big father act, "That's all right honey, we all do things that are *sinful* and *wrong.*"

[*This is another aspect of his superego.*]

D. *Sinful?*
P. Yeah, *sinful* and *wrong.* I tell her it was a mistake, that she is forgiven. I tell her she is a *nice kid,* it could happen to *anybody.*

[*He plays a lenient father figure in relation to her, in the manner he wished father had done to him.*]

D. But you do all these things to yourself, you call yourself names, too, and speaking of playing the role of *father.* You, yourself, said you once wanted to be a priest like Frank, your pal. Back in the past, you used to feel that you too were *damned.*

[*This gives him a chance to isolate the situation for a while in the past.*]

P. It's true. I do these things and I try to rationalize, but I still say to myself, "God will remember."

D. You mean that *"God knows"* or heaven knows?

[*Terms he frequently used.*]

P. Right.

D. And so you treat her like you treat yourself. You make believe everything is all right, and that everything is on the up and up, but inside you call yourself names, as well as her, and you feel you are condemned?

P. Well, it's hard for me to see it with myself because I got so many good arguments for the opposite. I tell myself, "Oh, don't be silly, others are getting it, it's good stuff, you can't miss it." (Chuckles)

[*He is truthful, and is able to reveal his infantile objections to his adult insight. A one-sided attempt at rational behavior.*]

P. And yet, *I don't know* how I feel. I really say to myself, "I *love her.*" She is the *first girl* I've ever really felt that way about, that I have ever loved, and yet she had an affair with a *married man,* her boss, and it makes me *furious.*

[*This is a new feeling, tending to rekindle all the past anxieties. Before, he said* she *was in love for the first time.*]

D. You are mad at the "married man"?

[*"Married man" refers to a father figure.*]

P. Oh, Jesus, yes. I say to myself, people who live in glass houses shouldn't throw stones, but, oh, God, do I get P.O.'d.

[*As a child, he wet the bed.*]

D. Because you two are alike?

P. Oh, you mean the girl? No, I don't, it's different. I really believe in the old double standard. For a girl who knows a guy is married, it's just morally wrong; it isn't right. Now for a guy to go messing around with a married girl, that's wrong too. I'm not saying it's right, but it isn't as bad as for a *little girl* to go around with a married guy who is almost old enough to be her *father,* so you see, I'm all mixed up about this girl. I like her.

[*He has double standards. "Married" refers to parental figures, and they are equally incestuous objects. His passive feminine feelings toward father are worse than a little boy's feelings toward a mother.*]

D. But you said that you were *mad* and afraid?

[*The two key words referring to the infantile compliance and disobedience.*]

P. I am afraid, sure I'm afraid. I say to myself, if I marry her she might go around with somebody else. She did it before, why won't she do it then, which I don't like. I say to myself, "All right, let the past be buried with the past," that's all right, but if she has got such low scruples, if she is going to do that, yes, and then again, she just about *seduced* him, and not he, her, so you see how *mixed up* I am. Yes, she has confessed to me, she has come clean, she has wanted to tell me everything, without me asking. I'm torn between the emotions of *love* and *hate*. I don't want to wreck the girl. She really loves me, and I say to myself, "If this girl was really a virgin, I wouldn't hesitate in wanting to marry her," but I just don't know whether it's *enough*.

[*He is all mixed up: who is guilty, the seducer or the seduced? He is torn between several things: father-mother, good-bad, normal-abnormal, girl-boy, love-hate, etc., all part of the ambivalence conflict in an obsessional individual. He is not sure whether he is enough of a man for a little girl, who knows what a married man (father) has.*]

D. You mean you would like to *marry*, but you don't know whether you *have enough?*

P. And then also the fact of her past.

[*He cannot trust himself.*]

D. You feel you haven't *got enough* of what *she wants?*

P. And then she might go somewhere else. (Pause) Yeah. (Pause) How is my *reasoning*—does it sound *normal*—it's conventional, isn't it—somewhat, what do you think, now that I have told you my story, and wrapped it all up in a *nutshell?*

[*He now strives to avoid the painful reality by cathecting his "reasoning."*]

D. It's as you said, "you want to marry her, if you could 'satisfy' her"?

[*"Satisfy" in the sense of permitting himself to give enough.*]

P. Yeah, but *that doubt is always there,* and it won't leave. The fact that I can't trust her—.

[*This is* his *past.*]

D. You mean the fact that *you can't trust yourself?*

P. No, no. It's not that I can't satisfy her so much, but the fact that she has done what she has done, that she was the *active* partner, that she seduced him. She is a very attractive girl. She is very good-looking. She could have anyone she wanted—a lot better than me.

[*In his retreat into masturbatory activity, he took a glorified image of himself as the love object. For this reason his demands on himself are those of the superman and of the most beautiful woman.*]

D. What do you mean?

P. (Chuckles deprecatingly) That's just what I mean, she could have a lot better than me. (Pause) I feel really that I am not so *good.*

[*If he builds up one part of himself, the other one remains "not so good" (inadequate) in comparison.*]

D. *Not good?*

P. Yes, not at all *good.*

[*He feels safer talking in terms which relate to the aspect: good and bad.*]

D. In what respect??

P. In every respect, that I, well, I'm getting *bald,* oh you know, I'm always concerned about *this guy,* me, oh, I look in the *mirror* and I see these circles under my *eyes*—then there's all these tensions.

[*The result of not being good in the past. He is concerned about the bad "guy" who has lost too much (fluid, hair).*]

D. So you wonder about your *hair;* you wonder about your *potency;* you wonder about your ability to get a *job* and support a girl; you wonder about your morals, your own morals. It looks like you can't trust yourself on account of your past performances.

[*Summing up and pointing toward the problems of guilt for which he fears punishment.*]

P. Yeah, I suppose, yeah, I'm really dissatisfied. I don't like myself at all. Do *you know* I'll bet, for instance, right now, that if someone came up and offered to swap with me, as is, I would be willing. (Sweats and mops brow)

[*He cannot "satisfy" either part of himself. His "narcissism" is almost insatiable.*]

D. Who do you have in mind right now?

P. Father Frank.

[*His infantile wish to be the father has many sources, the two main ones being: (1) the* father *with whom he competes, and who has more; (2) the* priest—*his alter ego—who takes over the power and glory and bigness of God, the Father, but has to give up sex.*]

D. Father Frank?

P. Yeah, maybe I'm *competing* with him. After all, we grew up together in the formative stages, you know.

D. He has *got more* than you?

P. Well, no, no, well, of course, he has got more than me in certain respects, *you know.* He's *better looking, more hair*—you know my *mother* was always *comparing* me with him.

D. Then you feel he has more looks, more hair, and more everything?

P. I wouldn't remember.

D. You don't remember?

P. Well, I've seen him when we've gone swimming, but I never paid any close attention.

D. You looked?

P. Yeah, sure I looked. He was on the average of, well, a small guy, about like me. You know, nothing extraordinary.

[*He is referring to the genital.*]

D. But you would rather be like him?

P. Well, I say that, you know, he was *always* put up to me by my *mother.*

He is her *ego ideal;* yet you know, he looks effeminate in one sense. He was down at the house the other day. Here he is, the *Padre,* the *big shot,* and *mother* says to me, why couldn't you have been like him. Then I *snapped right back at her,* because I don't want to.

[*He is talking about the part of himself which he ambivalently admires and hates. He feels mother prefers the man who does not act like a man; this puts her on an equal level as an inadequate man. He reacts by "snapping back at her" just as he used to do to himself, i.e., "snapping the back of his neck."*]

D. So you mean one part of you wants to be very potent, and be married to this girl and be such a man that she wouldn't go out looking anywhere else; then another part of you would just as soon swap and be like Father Frank.

[*The basic dilemma.*]

P. Perhaps.
D. Father Frank who has *more hair,* who is much *nicer looking,* who is much *purer,* who doesn't act *immorally?*

[*Hair has two determinants: (1) losing things; (2) "more hair" is more like a woman.*]

P. Yeah. (Long pause) Do *you know* the feeling I've got lots of times. I wonder if it's a *normal* feeling. I say to myself, "I would like to *go away* and *make something* of myself." I really want to, I want to *show people up.* Sometimes I have a genuinely *warm* feeling for *other people.* I say to myself, I want to make something out of myself, and then we can all *share* it. I really want to make something of myself though.

[*"People" are the family, especially mother and father, and also the different parts of the ego.*]

D. And show Frank up?
P. And show *everybody* up.

[*"People" are "everybody" to him.*]

D. In what way?
P. Oh, to make something *successful* out of myself. I don't say, for instance, I want to make a *million* dollars, just so I can have some *fun.* I would like to make a million dollars, just so I could say to these guys, "Ah, you fuckers, you"—all to these other people.

[*As could be foreseen, he has to build up the masculine part of him, since the feminine became too much inflated. This expresses: (1) the wish to be the biggest; (2) the scorn at the bad part of himself.*]

D. You mean, you want to show them that you're a bigger one than they?
P. Yes.
D. That you've got more of what it takes, more hair, more money, more potency?
P. Yeah.
D. More of everything?

P. Yeah.

[*He appears depressed.*]

D. And yet, there's a part of you who believes that Frank really has more in some ways?

P. Yeah, but I don't really want to be like Frank any more, not now. (Pause) But to her I am, you know, I really always wanted to have *religion,* yet I can't believe in it like I used to. Maybe I should be more like Frank, and not a guy who comes home at three o'clock in the morning, and stays out half the night.

[*He has reached the limits of his aggrandizement, and relives the struggle of doing wrong and feeling watched by "God" and/or a parent.*]

D. Doing what?

P. Oh, you know. I'm out with these *good deals,* and it's tough, you know, because my *mother* asks me, she asks me, "What do you do?" And she says, "What do you do until three o'clock?" and I say *talk.* (Laughs) Then she says, "I can't imagine what you talk about to that time." She probably has ideas, *I don't know.* Personally, I don't give a *shit.*

D. Really?

P. No, I don't. Of course, I don't really want to *hurt* my *mother,* but I am *independent* enough so I can do what I want to do. In other words, she hasn't any idea, of course, that I am *promiscuous* at night. Oh, of course not, oh no, I *know* that, and yet I will go ahead and do it.

[*His attitude of reckless rebellion in this derogatory term against mother meets fears of "hurting" mother. "Independent" to him means "promiscuous."*]

D. And part of you wishes to be like Father Frank, like *mother* wants you to be?

P. I *don't know.*

D. Then you feel that really *mother* is *not satisfied* with you as you are?

P. (Loudly) *I, myself,* am not satisfied.

D. Like *mother?*

P. I am *not satisfied* with the way I *look,* the way I *walk,* the way I *act.*

[*He admits his failure of ever being satisfied with either image of himself.*]

D. *Mother* also wasn't satisfied with you. You, yourself, have said that she wanted you to be a *girl* when you were a little boy. Mother didn't want you to be a *man?*

[*Using material from previous interviews where he repeatedly claimed his mother had said he should have been a girl, as girls were "less trouble."*]

P. No, she held me *back.* I guess she didn't want me to be one; even now, there's a kid that lives up around my way, she says, "Why can't you be like him. He's a nice kid," but he's strictly a *mama's boy*. He's an only child. He is a *nice guy*. He doesn't *go out* at night at all. He stays at *home* and *plays* with her, I guess, stays home and plays with his "fiddle."

[*In college he had written a paper for a psychology course, based on the theme of maternal overprotection; so there is a danger of this becoming a simple intellectual discussion. He blames mother's overprotectiveness for his masturbatory activity.*]

D. She wants you to be like him—stay home and play with your *"fiddle"?*

P. She must be that way. Anyway, I've never seen him go out with girls. He goes to night school. He *works conscientiously* during the day. He is always with his *mother*. My mother wants me to be like him, I guess.

[*Mother wants him to remain a boy who works like a man, but stays at home with her.*]

D. She wants you to stay home?

P. Believe me, I don't know.

[*He doesn't know what he wants to do, or which sex to be.*]

D. And as you say, there's a part of you that thinks maybe you really should be like Frank or be like this boy?

[*He accepts this confrontation half-heartedly.*]

P. Maybe there is, a subconscious part, not conscious though, because I don't like to be like *this guy*. Undoubtedly, there must be something. I like to be with these *girls*.

D. But when you do, you feel inadequate. You feel you aren't a big *enough* man?

[*He is more inclined to accept the confrontation with his superman wish.*]

P. Yeah, I keep wondering whether I'm as *good* as these other men that these girls have been with. Yes, what does it all mean? I'm so full of doubts. I'm always *comparing myself* with others.

D. But this was so, even when you were a *little boy, comparing* yourself with others. You were wondering whether you were going to be a *man* or whether you were going to lose it and become a *woman*. And you wondered if you were in between, like that "circus poster of the hermaphrodite."

[*Weaving in past material that refers to previous memories covering his childhood fears.*]

P. Yeah, I remember, and one of my breasts was a little larger than the other, the left one.

[*The feminine side he had removed while in the Service.*]

D. You really thought you might become a woman? You used to look at that poster and wonder. You felt so inadequate as a man, as you said.

P. That's true. Yes, yes, that's true, it's true, but now I'm not worried about becoming a woman.

[*He continually wishes to isolate the past.*]

D. Now you worry whether you are a real man, and at the same time you feel that you can't be a man and that you should be more like Father Frank, not more like that sissy, who stays home with "Mama." You still aren't sure?

P. Of course, I feel I'm a man now, and I'm not afraid of being a woman any more; yeah, I'm a man, kind of *soft* and pudgy, comme-ci, comme-ca, but not a rugged man. I'm not like some of these *robust guys,* and yet it doesn't seem to affect this kid at all. She's in love with me, I tell you.

[*This rational part is only a thin veneer and must be encouraged by clarifying the dilemma and making conscious the feelings that his ego avoids and denies. The interviewer does not make a choice for him except indirectly by encouraging constructive tendencies.*]

D. You mean *she accepts* you as a *man,* but you don't?

P. Yes, that's right.

D. You don't *love* yourself?

[*The confrontations are repeated to give the ego time for integration.*]

P. No.

D. You don't *accept* yourself as a man?

P. No, and I wonder what she *sees* in me.

D. If you can't *accept* yourself as a man, you wonder how she can?

P. Something like that. I'm not really *manly* at all. I just hand out a line of bull. I wonder how she can *believe* it.

D. Because you can't *believe* yourself?

P. God, no. Ah, the way I act, I'm *tender* and everything. I put on such *an act,* you know, I'm kind of *afraid.* It's too good an act.

[*He acts the way he would like to be—calm, rational and strong. But he dreads the emotional involvement with the old heartache over mother in the past, and the possibility of his exposure as a hostile child trying to act out his boyish daydreams.*]

D. You mean, how is she going to react when she finds out that you feel too *little* and too *inadequate* as a man, to be like she would want you to be?

P. Yeah, maybe she'll be *heartbroken,* and *you know,* I just feel *different* about this girl. I've never felt that way about any other girl before, and that's no kidding. I really do feel *tender* toward her. Sometimes I get so *mad* at her too, that I feel like "beating the shit" out of her.

[*This is for him a new experience in sincerity (real feelings), before which his defenses against emotional participation have crumbled. The oedipal child-mother relationship has been revived, i.e., love and hate.*]

D. Like you did toward mother?

P. She is the exact *opposite* of my mother. They say guys always marry a girl who is exactly like their mother, but God, she is not like my mother at all.

[*In the unconscious exact opposites are closely related.*]

D. What do you mean?
P. She is different, I mean. Oh, I don't know. She is *religious,* but she can get along without it.
D. Whereas mother is—?
P. Very *religious.* Of course, she looks something like my mother—dark hair and dark eyes, in reverse, because she is a blonde with blue eyes and not like my mother.

[*He explains the difference of religion, using "hair" and "eyes": dark (dirty) versus light blue (clean). There is more than one mother image at different developmental levels: (1) the ideal mother; (2) the bad mother; (3) the child's mother image; (4) the present mother; (5) the physical mother; (6) the feeling-evoking mother; etc.*]

D. But you said that you wanted a pure girl who was like mother before she married.

[*"Married woman" means dark; "pure" means light.*]

P. Well, all guys want a girl like that, don't they? *You know* yourself they do. When it comes to a showdown, lots of guys want a girl like that.
D. Like what?
P. Oh, I suppose like dear old *mother.* (Pause) Yeah, really, it knocks your ego down.

[*He does not realize also that the mother image has been considerably modified by his own narcissistic identification with her.*]

D. What do you mean?
P. Well, here is a girl who has been had by someone. Why can't I have a girl who is a *nice, pure one,* who hasn't been had by anyone?

[*"Pure" means also "clean," and "I should still be this way and mother, too."*]

D. Who wouldn't compare you with anybody?
P. Yeah, yeah, then of course I turn around and I say, "Dick, you're an imperfect bastard yourself. You've been screwing around and having your share of stuff, different affairs and what not, so who the hell are you to expect someone so pure." (Laughs) *I don't know.*

[*The dilemma of the child trying to reconcile his image of mother as a "pure" one and a "bad" one; i.e., adults have to be "hypocrites" like himself.*]

D. You mean, little Dick thinks differently. He still feels you shouldn't be that way, and that she shouldn't be that way— you should be *pure,* and should stay home and do what *mother* wants you to do?
P. But there's an awful lot of that "little Dick" in me right now, that little old *religious* Dick. He's still there; that religious Dick says to

me, "Dick, you're doing wrong—you shouldn't be screwing around," but (chuckles) in the crucial stages, the other guy takes over.

[*He is still a child, unable to effect a compromise; i.e., his ego is too weak and can only go to extremes, giving in first on one side, and then on the other. The psychopathic acting-out tendency becomes transparent.*]

D. But you pay for it. You don't have any rest from that other side of "little Dick."

P. Yeah, it's true. You know, lately, I've been having trouble getting an *erection,* which I think is possibly some difficulty. Maybe I think I'm not doing right.

[*His harsh superego stirs up a rebellion, and in this sense works in partnership with his instinctual demands. However, as each is insatiable, there is a difficulty in obtaining satisfaction. The compromise solution is an infantile, magic one—a symptom instead of a rational one, in keeping with all aspects of his reality situation.*]

D. Little Dick says no, you shouldn't be doing this?

P. And then at other times I feel, "Boy, but here's a *nice deal.*"

D. Another *cozy deal?*

P. (Chuckles) Another *cozy deal,* God! Yeah, I say to myself "Don't let this slip by, have a good time."

D. But also, you said before that the adult Dick, too, is getting tired of *cozy deals.*

P. There's nothing to it, in a way.

D. This fellow who has one cozy deal after another?

P. Uh, huh, but they don't mean much actually.

D. How do you mean?

P. I mean these *cozy deals.* (Pause)

[*One part of him wishes to make this situation into the old, infantile, cozy deal.*]

D. And you have a *cozy deal* with this Aryan girl who is also a *nympho,* as you said?

P. Oh, with this girl it's *different.* (Pause)

D. But you look perplexed. I don't think you're sure; after all, when you were here before, you were telling me about this *cozy deal* you had, and how you had this real 100% Aryan, *pure* girl. But then you find out that she is not, and you call her a *whore* and you are dissatisfied, and you would like to *look around.* Maybe you think you will find this pure girl somewhere else?

[*His increase in maturity is on a shaky foundation and must be integrated with past material.*]

P. Yeah, it's true, it's true, but this is *different.* In a way I feel *different* about it with this girl. She told me these things. She came right out, she *confessed,* she tried to be *good.* She lets me in on it, and she seems like she's really *in love with me.* She can't even explain it to herself, how she feels the way she does to me. It was right that way from the start. Finally when I got up my *courage* and I decided I would try it, there was nothing to it. It was easy.

[*This girl appeals not only to the weak, adult part, but helps to heal the narcissistic wound inflicted by the parent.*]

D. And then you begin to feel *tense* and *anxious* with her?

[*Returning to the original key words to get into the past and to consolidate the sector. That is a technical rule, when one channel of associations within the sector is almost exhausted. At the same time it is a test of the ego strength: whether it still needs the same defenses when confronted with the "problems."*]

P. I've *always* felt *tense* and *anxious.*

D. How do you mean, *always?* You remember?

P. Yeah, a long time ago, ten years, more so since I've been in the hospital, since I've been here, because I think what I've done. You see, I don't have those *compulsions* and *obsessions* the way I used to have them, and I'm able to *work* and I'm able to *study,* and I'm able to *get along;* I'm able to be on the *outside* anyway, but I'm still *anxious* and I haven't gotten over it. This stuff is really *deep-rooted,* isn't it?

[*The results of therapy in capsule form, i.e., a more efficient distribution of ego defenses.*]

D. And you said you've had this feeling since you were sixteen—ten years ago?

[*His former choice of this number must have some significance. It is therefore introduced again.*]

P. Oh, *I don't know* how long I've had it. I really think I've had it since I've been in the hospital. Oh, at times I have the feelings like I used to have though, *you know,* that obsessive compulsive stuff, but now it doesn't *mean* so much to me. I don't feel *anxious* about doing them any more, so much as *other things.* Occasionally I'll do something like—I'll be anxious about whether or not I put out a cigarette butt, and I'll look at it again, make sure; I still do it occasionally, but very rarely. Now I have more *physical* and *somatic* discomforts, and I'm tense. I tighten up. I wish you could give me a magic formula.

[*His obsessive-compulsive defenses against anxiety are no longer adequate. The obsessions and compulsions stood for "other things." There has been a change in pattern.*]

D. To stop getting anxious?

P. Yeah, that's it.

D. But you said that your anxiety makes you tense, and you have to grab hold of something. Is that your formula?

[*Returning to the masturbatory symptom sector keystone.*]

P. Well, no, now wait a minute, am I right in what I said, because this is what I think of with the insight that I have. Well, it's like this.

I am too anxious. That's number one, and after all, when you become anxious it has physical symptoms—your heart beats fast—your capillaries dilate, etc., and you have psychosomatic discomfort. Well, all right, anxiety is a *terrible thing* though; so you want to *pick something* up or to *grab something,* to displace it. (Chuckles and laughs shamefacedly and continues.) You know, *grab something,* displace it onto a *lamp* or *something.* (Voice now rises.) This is an obsession or a compulsion. Now that in itself uses up the energy there, plus the anxiety makes you tense inside now, that's a conversion. (Pause) Right?

[*There is a great amount of intellectualization. Vaguely he becomes aware of what he means as he says it, then tries to hide from the insight. This must be worked through repeatedly.*]

D. Perhaps the little one in the past, when he was *anxious, grabbed something.*

P. Well, no, now listen is that *right,* what I *said* now. Is it that way?

[*The interviewer does not answer loaded questions. This is obviously an escape by displacement.*]

D. But as you said, when you were *anxious*—it was then that you *grabbed something.*

P. What I want to know from you is, am I *right?*

D. You mean, are you *right* in respect to your *thoughts?*

[*The patient wants a yes or no, i.e., the interviewer should take sides. That would leave his conflict untouched. The only thing to do is to pose the basic problem again. A basic problem with an obsessional compulsive individual. Shall he be: (1) good or bad; (2) sissy or tough; (3) feminine or masculine; (4) clean or dirty; (5) adult or child; etc.*]

P. Yes.

D. So you mean a part of you wants *to know* whether you are *right* or *wrong* in your *thinking, but you know* and *I know* that what you are concerned with is, "Are you right or are you wrong in what you are *doing.*" One part of you says, "I'm doing *wrong,*" and the other part of you says, "I'm doing just what the *others* do. I got a *cozy deal.* I'm doing okay. I'm *right.*" Part of you says, "I should be *home* with *mother,* and should do what she wants me to do." Another part of you says, "No, I don't want to be *home* with *mother;* I want to use my little girl." Then there is the grown-up part which says, "You have had enough *cozy deals,* and it's about time you became a man." And the little one says, "No, if you trust this girl, she will go for a 'bigger' man."

P. Maybe, it was that way with the other girl, it's true.

D. And before?

P. And before I had another girl, and before that another girl, and before that another girl.

D. And before that you had your *compulsions.*

[*This confrontation seems now safe.*]

P. (Pause) Yeah.

[*He doesn't want to face it, even though he has been over it again and again.*]

D. (Pause) And you *grabbed* hold of cigarettes and made sure they were out. (Pause) And then you *grabbed* hold of "something."
P. Yeah, that's right.
D. And you still *don't know* whether you are *right* or *wrong,* and you feel *anxious?*
P. Yeah. (Pause) Oh yeah, I guess *I know* I'm right. (Long pause) But I'm not absolutely set on the fact that I am a hundred per cent right.

[*A weak ego needs to be one hundred per cent right.*]

D. Because part of you feels you are wrong?
P. Yeah.
D. It's really your way of living, isn't it? You would prefer never to know whether you are *right* or *wrong.* So you want me to tell you that you are *right,* that your thinking is *right.* Then you'll feel better; but you and I know that deep down underneath you cannot go on having *cozy deals* forever, without *feeling* that you are *wrong.*

[*This is the answer to his question.*]

P. Yeah. Well, all right, *which part* shall I listen to?

[*He might appear to accept any decision of the interviewer, but this would only be paying lip service.*]

D. Which part do you *want* to listen to?
P. The *adult part.*
D. That would be good if you could do it, but there is still that little one who says to himself: "Ah, I haven't got what it takes. This girl is going to find that out; although I act like a man, she is going to find out it's all 'bull.' Then she will go with a real man." And then the little one will say, "It isn't worth it."

[*Since he gave the answer and took sides, further confrontation can be tried, using his own words. He immediately looks for an escape route.*]

P. Yes, and there's something else. *You know,* I tripped the kid up in many ways. I tell her why don't you go out with *someone else,* and she really gets *hurt.* She bawls and *everything.* I wonder if I mean it or not. I think sometimes I do. It's just as if I really say, "Go ahead, go out with *someone else.*"
D. You're really afraid you're in too deeply?

[*He had repeatedly talked of fears about getting into these things.*]

P. Yes siree. I'm really afraid because I feel different about her. I feel more tender. I really feel what you might call, *you know,* what the poets call *love;* yet I wonder: "Am I the kind of a guy she really wants? Does she really know me, the *real me,* you know?

[*He sees himself only as a child with an adult woman.*]

D. You wonder if you've got enough, enough hair, enough looks, enough fluid around your joints, enough for a man—you couldn't bear for her to find out?

P. (In a low voice) Yeah, I guess I couldn't, and it would *hurt her.*

[*As he was hurt in the past.*]

D. So little Dick is always comparing himself to a big man, like little Dick did when he compared himself to *father,* who worked so hard with a pick and shovel. (Pause) Like you said, his job was a man-killer, and he worked for *mother.*

P. That is right. I'm not going to *kill* myself for any woman.

[*This is what love and marriage threaten: killing the little one, and death of the father.*]

D. But little Dick wanted to please mother so badly, almost to the point of wanting to be the little *girl* that you said she wanted you to be, and he felt so *bad* because he couldn't be like father and he couldn't please mother. He didn't like to face it. He tried to make believe that he had a *cozy deal* then, and now. But the adult part says: "Dick, you are now almost twenty-six. You should really be a man like father." As you said, these cozy deals are just like masturbation. You feel not only mother disapproves masturbation, but now you think that God, the Father, is looking at you and says, "No cozy deals." You are afraid you are too little, and you are afraid of either being killed by *work* or being left by the girl. (Long pause) Yet *you and I know* that you don't have to work with a pick and shovel, and that even if you did, after all, it really didn't *kill father;* and *you and I know* that even though this girl has been out with other men, she still seems to prefer you. She, who has been with those other men, still thinks you are the best, as you said.

[*A summary of what has been revealed and a confrontation with reality using quotations of the patient's statements in the former interview. The interviewer takes over the role of the "I don't know" turning it into an "I know." In that way, an agreement is established when the patient identifies himself with the interviewer. The patient has shown most of the elements of the oedipal situation: (1) longing for mother; (2) feelings of infantile inadequacy; (3) longings for the big things fathers have; (4) the wish to get them magically, leading to (a) father's death and (b) his castration; (c) the wish to solve his problem by giving up phallic aggressive activities and being the clean, good little "girl" mother wanted.*]

P. No, no, that's true.

D. But Dick minds, the little Dick who measures everything by "the damn thing," the little Dick whose estimation of himself varies with his estimation of his "thing," who always hasn't got enough fluid, enough hair, enough anything. "Little Dick" is hard to satisfy.

[*Exhaustive confrontation. Now the interviewer says what the patient had said before. The roles of the little one and the adult one are reversed.*]

P. Yeah, it's true. I haven't *got enough* anything yet. I haven't got enough money; I haven't got enough jobs; I haven't got any goddamn "thing" (Pause) to a degree of course.

D. What do you mean by "not enough of a goddamn thing?"

P. Oh, I know what you mean. Yes, it's that too. I haven't got enough "cock."

D. It is as if little Dick feels so pitifully excluded from everything. Yet you and I know he really has many things.

P. I guess what I really need is a good *job*.

[*This is an escape in the manner of "I will now be practical."*]

D. You mean the one you have isn't *big enough?*

P. Right. (Pause) Yeah, it's all the same, isn't it? (Long pause) So that makes me tense, huh. Now I mean what I said before to you, was I *right?* Is this an anxiety displacement, this tension, is that right?

[*Again this insight is only temporary. His compulsive need for questioning is still apparent.*]

D. You mean do you think right?

P. Yeah, am I right?

D. Whether you are right or wrong?

P. Yeah, yeah, tell me, so I'll know how *good* I am as an *amateur thinker.*

[*"Amateur" is a child who plays. Can an amateur be as good as a professional?*]

D. You mean now you want to solve your problems by "playing" with your *thoughts,* the way you used to play with your *penis* and the way you play with *cozy deals.* You ask, "Do I think right, can I think like the *big thinkers,* are my thoughts big ones?"

[*A confrontation, using his own words.*]

P. Yeah, yeah, it's true, it's true.

D. Little Dick is always concerned with his "thing," isn't he?

P. No kidding, it's true. I am just not satisfied with myself as I am, but now I realize that my cock isn't going to *grow smaller,* that I won't *lose it,* and that it *works* most of the time anyway.

[*Referring to fantasies he had as a youth, that he might turn into a girl, representing: (1) the wish; (2) the fear; (3) the punishment.*]

D. You mean, the *adult part* of you realizes it's so, but little Dick doesn't. Little Dick is insatiable. He's never big enough.

P. I guess so, but how am I going to handle it—that's what I would like to know.

D. You want me to *show* you how to *handle it?*

[*Confronting him with his "magic" fantasy.*]

P. (Laughs) No, no, I want to know whether I'm *right* or whether I'm *wrong.*

[*It almost sounds as if the ambivalence has not been softened up at all.*]

D. But if I said one part of you was right, the other part would say it was wrong, and vice versa.

[*This is the dilemma.*]

P. Oh, I'm more mature than that. I really understand when you talk about little Dick. I can see it.

D. But what are you going to do when little Dick overcomes the adult? Then we see, no matter what the adult says, he becomes tense and anxious. Is little Dick in command most of the time?

[*The interviewer alternately stirs up first one part of him, then the other.*]

P. *You know,* I even hate to go downtown in the daytime. You know, I feel I don't quite *measure up,* even when I go shopping—things like that. They are not real phobias because I *can go* and I *do go,* but I'm tense. I really feel they are *looking at me.* I'm always wondering "what do they *think of me.*"

D. You mean whether you are a big, adult man, or an inadequate, little boy?

P. Yeah.

D. A little boy who has cozy deals and is playing around all the time?

P. But I don't want to be a little *boy.* I want to be a *man.* Why can't I do something about it? You know, and I know that little Dick never can *forget* these things. I've accepted the fact, you know there's one thing. I'm not as much *afraid* as I used to be. I'll say that much. I'm a lot *braver* than I used to be. (Pause) Ha, a year or two ago, ha, I wouldn't have even *dared* to think about this girl the way I think now. I wouldn't have even dared to get as close as I've got with her. I must be *braver.* I must be *stronger,* and yet I have these feelings now and then in this *body.*

[*He reassures himself by measuring his gains in therapy.*]

D. You mean now you think of your whole body like you used to think of your "damn thing?" You haven't got enough *hair,* you haven't got enough *"good color," you haven't got enough "muscle,"* you've got too much *fat* like a *girl,* you haven't got enough *money*—

P. (Interrupts) Yeah, that's it. I really and truly realize that I'm just *different* from other people. No two people are alike, are they? Am I *right?*

[*He wants reassurance, but it cannot be given.*]

D. (Continuing) —and even though you know that you have done a whole lot, that you have gone to college and have done very well—been on the Dean's List; you have graduated—the first person in your family to do so—even though you know all these things, at times little Dick takes over, and you feel you haven't got enough.

P. Yeah, you know (here he begins to grin and lisp), you know, that little Dick, he was never satisfied in the past, but I am getting more and more satisfied. It does take a long time to overcome it, doesn't it, but then again, what the hell, I can't get *rid* of that guy. He'll always be with me, don't you think? Am I *right?*

[*In the interview, he is a little boy with the omnipotent father who has given him another dose of magic medicine. Again one has to discount some of his insight.*]

P. Here I am, almost twenty-six, and I haven't done too bad. I realize that eventually I'll work through all my problems, but *I like to hear it from you.* I *can't help feeling* that way. Am I right?

[*This assertion can be confirmed.*]

D. That's right.

P. So I ask myself, what shall I do? I don't want any of this *tension.* I want to get *rid* of it when I get it. I don't feel *good.* I *bend* my neck and I can hear the bones go *crack,* crack, crack, and I say to myself, why? By the way, why is that?

[*As the end of the interview approaches, he turns again to his anxieties, to his compulsions, and somatic symptom defenses. The "pretense" of ignorance as a defense is again expressed in the compulsive question: why? But the impermeable persistence and the detached patience of the interviewer is inexhaustible.*]

D. You mean you haven't enough *fluid?*

P. (Laughs) Well, hasn't it got something to do with the *muscles* around the *bone?*

[*An infantile fantasy?*]

D. Maybe you need more *eggs* in your beer, is that what you mean, or *cod liver oil.* Little Dick always will feel inadequate, although *you and I know* that now you are beginning to see how large a part of you little Dick is.

[*"Eggs in beer" and "cod liver oil" as support of masculine stamina had been referred to by the patient in the last interview.*]

P. Yeah, I know, it's this perfectionism in me. I'm continually comparing myself with someone, and trying to be something that's *impossible* to be.

D. You mean that's what little Dick feels?

P. The hell with little Dick; that's what I'm trying to overcome.

D. You mean that *goddamn* thing?

[*Another confrontation.*]

P. Well, I'm trying to look at this from an adult, rational point of view. You know, I realize that's me, and that I'll always have a job *mastering* myself, but there's my family and my whole background; you know how that has been. I got to overcome it. It's a *tremendous job,* a *tremendous* load.

[*It seems as if the adult ego is finally ready to master the infantile needs.*]

D. You mean little Dick has to overcome his *masturbation* problem, which he transformed into *compulsions,* and then transferred onto the *women?* Now he still can't decide whether it's *right* or *wrong.*

P. Yeah, it's so, it's so. When you talk about it, I can see it, but when I get outside, I don't think of it all the time.

[*An understatement, yet his ego boundaries have been enlarged: (1) the unconscious has become conscious; (2) his work and love life are relatively more adult; (3) he can master his anxieties better.*]

D. And now when little Dick gets anxious, he still wants to *grab hold* of something?

P. Yeah, it's true, or he tries to use this *methodical* type of *thinking.* I always feel I should be like Father Frank and then I rebel because I don't want to—it's difficult.

D. You mean it's difficult to satisfy two such irreconcilable parts—one of which wants to be so *pure,* and the other wants to be such a *big man.* The adult part of you, *you and I know,* that there must really be a *compromise.* The adult part knows that you won't have to *work* yourself to *death,* that you don't need a *superpure* girl or a *nympho*—that this other girl is just like *you,* too, a human being. The adult part of you knows this.

[*Final confrontation: it cannot be repeated too often.*]

P. It's true, *you know.* Instead of really seeing it, I just look at the words and recite it like a parrot to myself, all of this stuff.

[*More insight to be worked through. He tends to turn insight into magic words by a kind of incantation.*]

D. You mean, like you did with your prayers when you said Our—Father—Who—art—in—Heaven. You thought of the words. Even your prayers for forgiveness of your sins were turned into *games.* You pay attention to the *words,* but not the *deed.* You are always putting on an *act,* as you said. Is that what you mean?

P. Yes, I want to turn it all into theories. I want to read books about it, but I really can't do it unless I really face it. Is that right?

[*He himself states the solution of his problem with far more truthfulness than before.*]

D. And work it out.

P. That's right, but then when I go into, let us say, a *social situation,* when I go and apply for a job—what do I do about that *tension* and *anxiety?*

[*At the end of the interview the key words of the very onset of the session appear again: social situations—tension—anxiety. This makes the interview an entity.*]

D. Who is asking that question now—*little Dick* or the *adult?*

P. Little Dick I know, here I go again, look for that *magic* formula. The only thing I can do is realize that I'm just as *good* as anybody else, but answer me this—what type of *work* do you think would be suitable for my *personality?*

D. Which part? *Little Dick* or the *adult,* the part that wants to be like Father Frank, or the part that wants to be mother's boy? Or the part that wants to be a superman?

P. No, no, no. I mean the adult part, the real *nice part.* (Then sees what he has said and bursts out laughing.)

D. You realize what kind of question you have asked me. Looks like you are going to have to make a *compromise,* huh?

P. Well, don't give up hope for me, Doc.

[*The dilemma and ambivalence of a compulsive is expressed in all word concepts.*]

D. Certainly, good luck to you.

P. Okay, good-bye.

D. Good-bye.

Final Discussion

The entire interview was kept in the area of his main problem, i.e., the meaning of his infantile masturbation in its various aspects. His problems embraced:

(1) His use of his body in thoughts as a phallus to express, in the present, an infantile problem from the past, showing that his infantile masturbation appears to have been symptomatic of a conflict over his need for love and expression of his instinctual drives;

(2) A disturbed child-parent relationship leading to a faulty ego and superego development with a symptomatic expression manifested in defective interpersonal relationships and defective intra-ego relationships.

This interview shows the necessity of confrontations, again and again, with the problems and the methodological need of returning to the key words. Although separated by a six-month interval, continuity of interviews was maintained, and the synthesizing abilities of the patient's ego were apparently augmented.

Follow-Up

Approximately one year later, the patient phoned that he was working as a salesman and had become engaged. The latter situation had made him moderately anxious, and he felt he might need another session. In a phone call a week later, he stated his work would not permit him to come and he would get along on his own for the time being.

Two years later he telephoned to announce proudly that he was a successful salesman, was married, and had become the father of a child.

Four years later a Christmas card informed the therapist that he was well and happy, and had two children.

CHART 2

ASSOCIATIVE STRUCTURE CENTERED AROUND A COMPULSION TO BOW THE HEAD

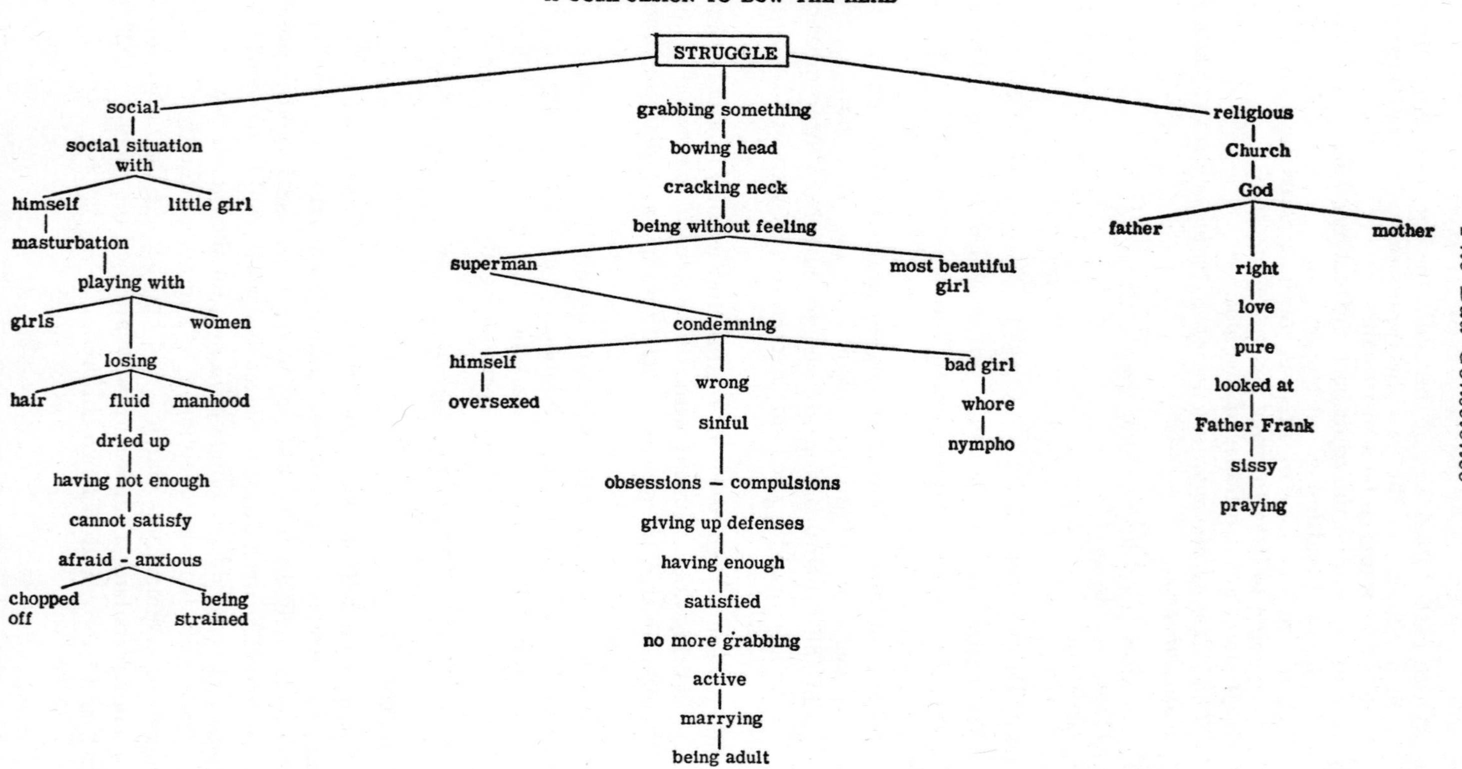

CHAPTER V

Reticence in the Interview

Part 1—The Struggle Within

Introduction

The associative anamnesis and sector therapy techniques can be applied also to aggressively reticent patients. With these cases, a greater degree of verbal activity on the part of the therapist may be necessary at first, until a positive transference has developed. By and large, patients who come for therapy are pent-up individuals who, if given the chance, will readily become communicative. However, in certain cases, the act of talking or opening the mouth is so highly charged with aggressive or passive-receptive fantasies, that the ensuing anxiety will severely limit the speech function. In any case, activity on the part of the therapist should be of the noncommittal variety and reduced as the patient opens up. Of great importance is the ability to tolerate silent periods without uneasiness and impatience. Such periods are not a waste of time, and may even occasionally be very necessary for settling a favorable transference relationship. When a good understanding of the patient's defense mechanisms has been obtained, it may be possible to by-pass or undermine this type of resistance. However, it is seldom necessary to allow a silent period to last more than five minutes, which in itself may seem a very long time.

The following interview illustrates a method of dealing with an impulsive patient whose physical size and proneness to violent rages tended to make his therapists to be on guard. He had been considered a difficult patient because of his reticence.

Case Presentation

A twenty-three-year-old veteran complained of severe headaches for the past five years, during which he would act "out of his head" and do "crazy things."

While in the Air Force, he first developed headaches which he described as starting in the back of his neck and head and gradually spreading to involve the entire head with a throbbing pain. During a severe attack he would do "crazy things" because of the pain, but was unable to remember anything that occurred. He had been told that he was assaultive, destructive and threatening. Since his discharge from the Service, he had continued to have periodic headaches. On the evening before admission, he developed a severe headache, remembering nothing until he found himself being restrained by several neighbors after doing considerable damage to his parents' home.

The patient was the older of two siblings. A sister, two years younger, developed seizures at fourteen years of age and was treated for epilepsy. She married at sixteen, was divorced approximately two years later, had one child, and remarried recently. The mother was married at the age of seventeen to a man of thirty. She was described as "emotional and overprotective," and at times "like an older sister" to the patient. He felt much closer to his mother, and in many ways identified with her. The father was described as a passive individual who had always been somewhat distant in his relationships with the siblings. He had been employed as a greens keeper at a local country club for the past thirty years, a source of domestic difficulty from both the financial and social aspects for the patient's mother.

The patient's earlier years were marked by family discord, mainly over the father's drinking. There were frequent moves and a separation of the parents, the patient going with his mother. He attended four regular grades at school and stayed two years in a special class because of behavior and learning difficulties. As a child, he had frequent temper tantrums, did poorly in school, was in frequent difficulty and finally was expelled for disciplinary reasons. Prior to his enlistment in the Air Force he attended trade school for a short time. He remained in the Service approximately fifteen months, but his headaches became so severe that he was hospitalized and later discharged. The onset of his headaches coincided with the date of his sister's marriage.

Since his discharge from the Service, the patient had worked at several factory-type jobs, none of which he had maintained for any length of time. Prior to his admission, he had been forced to leave his job and had been doing the cooking and housekeeping for his father, since his mother had recently gone on an extended vacation. There was a long history of minor accidents.

Most of the factual information was obtained from neighbors. Physical workup was negative, and indicated laboratory and X-ray studies were normal. Sector material concerning the *head* led to outbursts of aggressive material, frequently acted out upon himself and hospital personnel. This is the sixth interview with a new therapist. By now he had ceased complaining about headaches, and the chief problem was the meaning of the violent, self-punitive acting out.

INTERVIEW

D. How do you happen to be in the hospital?
P. (Long pause) *Temper,* I guess, I don't know.

[*He sits bowed over in a dejected manner, head in hands protectively.*]

D. A guy doesn't get a *temper* without having reason for it. How come you got yours?

[*"Temper" is a key word previously related to loss of head.*]

P. Well, I just don't like to be *bothered.* (Looks meaningfully at doctor)
D. Bothered by what—life in general—is that what you mean?

[*To avoid pinning him down too early.*]

P. Yuh, that might be it.
D. But at least *part of you* feels you would like some *help,* or you wouldn't remain at the hospital, huh?

[*Aiding the later ego-splitting and suggesting a less aggressive course.*]

P. I don't want to be *helped,* or some *God damn thing.*

[*"Help" is a dangerous word because of anxiety and his passivity. He also feels like "a thing damned" or abandoned by father ("God"), as will be seen later.*]

D. I think you want to be *helped* but you are *afraid* maybe it's too late, or that you can't be. Isn't that it?
P. I don't know what it is. (Long pause)
D. But you've got some ideas?
P. Yuh, I guess I have, but I don't want any *sympathy.*

[*He cannot accept sympathy: it would be an admission that he needed help.*]

D. We're not here to give you sympathy. You can get that on the outside. We just want to help you to *help* yourself, so we've got to know something about you.
P. Aw, *I'm screwed up,* I guess, uh, oh, I don't know what the hell it is. I guess it's the life I lead. Anyway, I'm screwed up.

[*"Screwed up" basically refers to his concept of himself as a passive infantile person who feels attacked. He continually acted out this role by accident proneness and injuring his fists punching walls. At this point, it was decided to try keeping him in the sector of his ambivalent need for, and rivalry with, a father figure.*]

D. Well, you can always get unscrewed What got you *screwed up* in particular?
P. Oh, work, education—and uh, *everything,* I guess. (Pause) Aw, ah, I'm disgusted. I don't want to talk about it.

D. You mean you felt you were not getting anywhere by yourself?
P. Not getting anywhere? (Looks disgusted, gazing off into the corner of the room, grim-lipped)

[*The look implied that it was much worse.*]

D. What do you think?
P. What do you mean, right now?
D. After all, you've thought these matters over yourself plenty.
P. Yuh, but it always comes right back to the same thing.
D. And what's that?
P. (Long pause—three minutes. Blurts out:) Oh, I don't know. For one thing, I guess I don't have any *faith* in myself. Another thing, everything I do seems to be *wrong*—and another thing, I give myself a *pain* in the *ars* and I get pissed off at myself.

[*Symbolically meaningful statements showing that he is the one who attacks himself. They also betray the way he fears being attacked by others and how he attacks others.*]

D. What gets you pissed off?
P. (Loudly) Because I can't do anything *right.*
D. What did you do that was *wrong*?
P. *I blew up* last night. I couldn't *help myself* and I blew up.

[*He had attacked the doctor the previous night. This behavior has very complex motivations. In fighting with a paternal surrogate on the outside, he attempts to gratify: (1) a need or wish for a passive relationship with the attacked person; (2) a rebellion against his passive yielding to this need.*]

D. Why do you hate yourself so much? What did you do to deserve that?
P. Oh, I fooled around in school a lot, and I never got any place. I'm *sorry* now that I did fool around. The folks told me but I didn't believe them or *anything.*
D. How old were you then?
P. (Long pause. No answer)
D. How old are you now?

[*More easily answered.*]

P. Twenty-two. (Pause)
D. What do you mean by saying you *fooled around* in school?
P. Well, I'd get my work done, and then I'd *fool around* a lot, *fighting* all the time. (Voice trails off disgustedly)

[*Fooling means fighting.*]

D. *Fighting* with whom?
P. With the *kids.* (Long pause) Then I'd sit and tap my *pencil* on the desk all day long and drive the teacher *nuts.*

[*This is overdetermined. He fools (fights) provocatively with the teacher through his "pencil."*]

P. Ah, I don't know. I got *kicked out* once. Then I went back again and I was going to be *expelled,* but they put me in a *special class.* I stayed there for about a year. I felt I *didn't belong* there, felt that I *belonged* in high school or *something.*

[*The most important word now appears, i.e., "special class." This is what he continually fights. Its meaning is closely allied to being defective, queer and inadequate, as he felt as a child.*]

D. Not such a good feeling to be in a *special class*?
P. Yuh, and then I got out and got a job.
D. After the special class?
P. Nope. I only went to the fourth grade and then I got a job in a machine shop, and I worked there for about ten months. Then I quit and joined the Service. I was in about a year; no, more: I was in twenty-two months and twenty-two days. While I was in there, I got *a bitch of a headache.* I was in New Mexico. It was the first headache I ever had. It was while I was working there as a *cook.* It was while I was *cooking* one night. All of a sudden the *headaches* come. It was like a vise *pushing* on your head. I couldn't get rid of it. One night I got up and I threw the foot locker through the window and really went off my rocker, did *everything.*

[*The figure twenty-two is obviously overdetermined. His real age was twenty-three, and his Service record showed approximately twenty-five months. The pain in the anal area is now displaced to the head. He gave himself the pain in the "head." The "head" doesn't function, and he sees himself in the feminine activity of cooking. He rages against his surrender to the female role, for which he has to sacrifice his "head."*]

D. What do you mean?
P. Aw, I don't know. The *pain* just got so *painful* I couldn't stand it. I just went off my rocker. That's the way I size it up. I don't know whether it's true or not. I kept on having them even when I got *home.*
D. What do you mean by home? Who is at home?

[*He has the same trouble at home. The standard way of obtaining information, and it leads back to the head.*]

P. My father and mother. (Long pause—holds head with his hands)
D. How did they *feel* about the *headaches?*
P. Oh, I guess like any other father or mother. I *wouldn't know;* I *suppose* they were interested.

[*The sarcasm is obvious. From now on, there will be an endeavor to direct his thoughts and feelings to the figures in the past in order to attenuate the aggressive emotional reaction in the interview situation.*]

D. You mean they didn't give much evidence they were interested? Is that what you mean?
P. Oh no. They wanted me to get well, I *guess.*
D. You guess? You mean you're not too sure?
P. Yuh, I'm sure.

D. Really? (Long pause) How many in your family besides you and your parents?

[*This approach is at present not feasible economically, so we allow him a short rest.*]

P. I have one sister. There's four of us altogether.

[*There are two units of two in the family: "father and mother" and "he and the younger sister."*]

D. Four altogether? And how old is your sister?

P. Oh, she's younger—a year and four months.

[*(22!)*]

D. What does she do?

P. Oh, she's married. Her husband is in the Army. She's got one kid.

[*But the sister married somebody else. He "let" the husband be in the Army. From whom has she the "kid"? However, it would have been premature to take up the meaning of the "kid."*]

D. And you were in the Army too?

P. Yuh, I was in the Air Corps—the Army Air Corps. I went in 1946 and got out in '47. I never flew.

D. And it was in the Army that the *headaches* began?

[*Back to a key word.*]

P. Oh yuh. (Long pause) I've been trying for *some time* to find something that I could *blame* my *disposition* on. When I went in the Service, I was *five feet two or five four*—I don't know. When I came out, I was *six feet two*. When I went in, I could sing *soprano;* when I come out, I'm a *bass*.

[*He is constantly looking for something, (somebody) he can blame instead of himself. He has an alibi: he wanted to be a man.*]

D. You were a completely changed guy!

P. (Laughs and nods. Long pause—four minutes)

D. What did they think of you at home? Did they like the change?

[*To get his own reaction indirectly, he is asked what the family thought of him as a man.*]

P. I don't know. I *guess* so. Jesus, I was tall when I came home—tall and lanky.

D. Do you mean they weren't particularly interested?

P. Yuh, I *guess* they were as interested as any other parents would be, I *guess*.

D. So you went away a little boy singing soprano, and came back a big man with a bass voice. How did the family feel about that?

[*This is the heart of the problem. He still feels like an inadequate little boy displaced by a girl. With this assumption, we can expect to hear: (1) the rejected wish to be a girl baby; (2) the rage at the little girl and mother, and also at his own aggressive self; (3) identification with mother and baby, to replace the lost relationship; (4) turning to the father with whom he has been unable to identify for a solution (see Final Discussion).*]

P. Nah, they didn't recognize *nothing.*
D. You were still a *little* boy?
P. Yuh, I guess so. (Long pause) I *always* will be, I guess.
D. What do you mean? Do they tell you that?
P. Uh huh.
D. Like a little boy?
P. (Pause) Mother is all right. Whenever I'd get in trouble as a kid, she'd always *stick up* for me. (Angrily) *My father never would.* (Pause) My *mother* would *always* go to court. I had to go to court a lot when I was a kid and all that *crap.* (Long pause)
D. I suppose you wish your father had *stuck up* for you?
P. (Nods head glumly. Long pause—eyes redden)
D. A guy needs a father when he is little, don't you think so?

[*We are now trying first to develop the father sector. "Stick up" has protective anal implications as well as aggressive ones.*]

P. Aw, listen, stop it, I'm going to *bawl* in a minute.
D. So what's wrong with that?
P. (Angrily) I don't want to *bawl.*
D. Why not? Are you a sissy to *cry?* Here anything goes. Is it a disgrace to want a good father who'll "stick up" for his boy and show him how to grow up the way he really wants to?

[*The positive transference has to be bolstered up.*]

P. I don't think I've ever had that. I don't know what it is like.
D. That's what I thought.
P. (Bitterly) You ask him to go fishing, bull shit! I ask him to go to ball games—bull shit! A couple of times he did go. He went to a football game and, boy, I'll remember that for the rest of my life!

[*His need for love was met by what he felt was an anal, aggressive act. This relationship is compulsively repeated.*]

D. When was that?
P. Oh, a high school game, in 1944 I guess.
D. Just before you went in the Service?
P. Yuh.
D. And you were still a kid with a soprano voice, only five feet four?
P. Yuh, that's right. I was standing at a railing talking to a friend of mine, and he says I wish my son could be out there playing football. (Long pause) I always wanted to play football and everything like that, but I was in a *special class* at the time. (Pause) So he says, for Christ's sake, I wish my son could play on the football team and (voice drops off) not be *stupid* like I am.

[*The positive transference begins to develop, with the father image appearing in a new light.*]

D. Did he say that?
P. Sure he said that.

[*These were as much his thoughts as father's. "Stupid" means inadequate "head."*]

D. You mean he insinuated it?

[*This tests the reality aspects, softens the accusation, and encourages explanation. "Special class" now begins to take on more meaning.*]

P. Yuh, that's right, he insinuated it. He didn't say *stupid*.
D. He didn't say it right out loud, but he might as well have said it?
P. Yuh. When I went back home, I told *her* all about it, and she said, oh yes, we were speaking of it one day. Your father always wanted a son who would go to high school and *play football* and *be a star*, or even be a *lineman* or *something like that*—anyway play high school football.

[*He reveals the boy's daydreams of a father ideal, with whom he could identify himself.*]

D. He always wanted you to be a star? (Pause) For him?
P. Well, it ain't all that. He'd like to see me like any of these *ordinary guys* around here, hold *good jobs*, you know, all of *those things*. I guess he's got a right to.

[*"Ordinary guys" are "stars."*]

D. It would be nice for a kid to be loved by a father not because he's a star football player, but just because he's his kid, wouldn't it?

[*The interviewer equates himself with the father image and verbalizes the boy's wishful thoughts.*]

P. Boy, oh boy, I never knew that feeling. (Tears come to his eyes)

[*Here he became "grounded." Now we can get more meaningful material around the father relationship.*]

D. When were you transferred to a *special class?*
P. In the fourth.
D. Was that when your *troubles* began?
P. Oh, I guess it was when I was about twelve years old, but I've had *troubles* before. I've *always* had *troubles*.
D. *Always?* Do you *remember?*

[*The "boy" is ready to talk.*]

P. Aw, I seemed to get along all right in most things up until the fourth grade—and then I don't know what the hell happened. Well, we *moved* so "God damn" much. I was in one town in the fourth, and in another town while in the third, and the fourth at another town, and back to the third again in another town. It always seemed I could get no further than the fourth.

[*Parents are more than "persons," they are "the home." Moving from the home means a loss reinforcing the basic feelings of deprivation. He could not get further in school because he wanted to remain the "little boy" before he left home, i.e., the "special boy" belongs to a "special class."*]

D. You moved around a lot?
P. Oh, for Christ's sake, I lived in exactly sixteen—no, *eighteen homes.*
D. Eighteen homes? How come? Where were they—in this State?
P. Right in the city of P——, and right around there in the suburbs.
D. Why so many homes? What was the trouble?
P. I don't know what the hell the trouble was. I guess *my father wasn't making much,* or *something* like that.

[*"Trouble" means that the image of an ideal father collapsed. "Something like that" means, "Father was inadequate" and the boy's dream of becoming a "star" could not be realized.*]

D. What kind of work did he do?
P. Oh, he's been a laborer for twenty-two years.

[Twenty-two *is a magic number. He is twenty-two; he was twenty-two months and twenty-two days in the Service. Another "22" were the two units of two in the family. But, in the course of time, the "two" were not always the same. The ideal father image and he were "two."*]

D. And he didn't make much?
P. Oh, he does *now,* but not then. I guess we had to move. Then again, I don't know whether it was on account of *that* or not. My folks *separated* when I was a little kid. Boy, I can remember back when I was about *three years* old!

[*This separation was a loss which he wants to undo. He now reveals an important screen memory of another separation which preceded the later loss.*]

D. Really? You have a very good memory. What do you remember?
P. Oh, well, I was in a closed room, uh, something like a porch. I was leaning against the screen and the screen fell through. I fell out. I fell two stories, and I landed on my hands and knees without a scratch, and that's a fact. My *mother* will verify that. (Pause) So my *father* took me and the screen, the screen and I, upstairs. He put the screen on the floor and went out of the room to get some tools to fix it, so I went in there, and just—to show you the way I display my temper, I went and stamped all over that screen. That's the kind of a temperament I've got.

[*This sounds like a birth fantasy, another kind of separation. He calls* mother *as a witness. It also reveals the meaning of his accident proneness. He is longing continually for his infantile, magic, omnipotent and invulnerable state. He turned to father, who had the "tools" (a man's "tool"). He got mad with mother's screen and smashed it.*]

D. You mean you got mad at the *screen?*
P. Yuh, I got mad at the *screen.*
D. For *letting you down?*

[*The infantile sources of his spells of assaultiveness and destructiveness become transparent. Madness with mother for the separation from her.*]

P. Yuh.

D. Maybe you were mad at *father,* too, at the time. He too *let you down.* [*Confrontation with the later madness at the father.*]

P. Well, not *that time.* He *picked* me *up.* I guess he was *scared.* (Pause) But my *father* had a *temper,* too. Jesus, I took some *wicked beatings.*

[*If he scares father, he will be picked up instead of let down. He now shows his identification with the beating father, and again a meaning of the accident proneness is suggested.*]

D. When you were a kid?

P. Sure, I got *belted* and *kicked* and *punched.*

D. What for?

[*To obtain more screen memories.*]

P. (Chuckles) Oh, he caught me in the *bathroom* once, uh, *smoking,* and he came in and he told me, don't smoke, if I ever catch you *smoking* again, I'll beat your ears off. So I says okay; so I goes out. A week went by, and I bought a couple of nickel stogies and I took them up in the bathroom and I was *smoking* them. So he came home from work and there was a space up there about three inches from the top of the door, kind of transom, and he saw the smoke pouring out of there, so he opened the door and there I was—caught *red-handed,* and he *beat* the hell out of me. I went upstairs and, Christ Almighty, I couldn't smoke for a week.

[*Children do different things in the bathroom. Smoking, like masturbating, is a forbidden activity. "Red-handed" displaces the "redness" from another part of the body. Which end did father beat him on—the "head"? Or which end did he smoke with?*]

D. But you did it again? You wanted to be a man quickly?

P. Gee, I wanted to smoke, I liked it.

D. And so you said to hell with him?

P. Well, I took a chance. You can put it that way.

D. You hoped?

P. That he wouldn't catch me at it.

D. Or that he would be a decent guy about it and let you do the things that all boys try to do.

P. Well, it's funny, you know. About a month later I got caught smoking again, another *cigar*—I mean a *cigarette.*

[*A little cigar; a cigarette. Father is the cigar smoker, and he wants the big one but can't handle it.*]

D. How old were you then?

P. Oh, thirteen, I guess. So he says, if you want to smoke, go ahead. That's all there was to it. He brought home *cigars* one night, and I smoked one lying on the couch, and I got sick as a *dog.*

[*This is an attempted passive relationship with father, and will be seen more clearly when he talks about his relationship with his dog.*]

D. You could never tell what he was going to do?

P. (Long pause. Finally, musingly) I did a lot of crazy things when I was small.

D. You did? (Long pause) You can say anything here. (Offers patient a cigarette; he accepts it, and doctor lights it for him, taking one himself)

[*He is accepted as an equal.*]

D. What do you mean by crazy things?

P. Oh, I put paper bags on my head and made believe I was *Captain Marvel,* and I'd climb telephone poles, and then there was a girl on the school steps who refused to give me a *kiss* when I was a young kid, and I ripped the coat right off her.

[*He refers to himself as a superman, with the big poles between his legs, who is admired by the girl. When the girl let him down, he treated her as he did the screen, and as father treated him. The girl is a mother figure.*]

D. You lost your *temper*? You were in a hurry to do grown-up things.

P. Aw, I used to have a *wicked temper* just like my father. He had a *wicked temper* too. Of course, now it's all *toned down* a little.

D. Maybe he's getting a little older and can control it better?

[*Indirect suggestion.*]

P. Yuh, but he can *still* get quite *mad.*

D. So you're like *father*?

P. I guess just in that line of *temper.* (Long pause)

D. So you were mad at him because, as you said, he didn't show you much affection?

[*Taking up the fantasy in relation to father.*]

P. Oh, I don't know. Everything I did was screwing up. Well, it's like now, uh, say, he'd take me, well, I remember once he took me ice skating and I *cut* my *lip.* I was about eight years old then. Right here, I guess I cut it on the skate. So I *cut myself* and he had to take me home. Everywhere he took me, I did *something.* It was mostly my fault, I guess. I was always screwing it up, doing the wrong thing.

[*Whatever he does now, he gets "hurt." When he gets hurt, father is scared and shows affection. Therefore he hurts himself (cuts himself). These token sacrifices have both positive and negative oedipal aspects, i.e.: the wish to be treated like a girl, and a wish to receive what he needs, magically.*]

D. You felt you couldn't do anything right for him; so you said, what's the use?

P. That's right. I still feel it. What's the use?

D. Do you mean—if father didn't have any faith in you, how could you have any faith in yourself?

[*But the sacrifice doesn't pay off: father left him.*]

P. That's right.

D. How old were you when your folks broke up?

P. About ten—nine or ten, I guess. I lived with my *mother*, and my *sister* lived with my aunt, and *my father went off by himself*. I think that's the way it was.

[*He fabricates a sad story: he smashed the screen (mother) and fell through it. He cuts himself off to get father's love. Father leaves him and he returns with his self-damaging pattern to mother.*]

D. When you were nine or ten?

[*This was when he went in a special class.*]

P. Yuh.

D. When a guy needs a *father*?

[*Separation meant father rejected him as well as mother.*]

P. There's only one *good thing* I ever did in my life.

D. And what was that?

P. Well, it was when I was about five. My *sister fell* into a well, and I ran home, a thousand yards uphill. My *mother* ran down and pulled her out. She called the firemen and they came up and gave her artificial respiration, and brought her to.

[*One wonders—did he push her? This, too, is a screen memory around complex birth fantasies. Father saves the boy, and mother the girl.*]

D. That was a lot.

P. A loss?

[*A slip of hearing. The death wish against the sister is evident. We aid him with the denial. His accident proneness is probably also motivated by guilt and atonement feelings.*]

D. A lot. If you hadn't, she would have been *dead* now.

P. That's right. They worked on her quite a while. My *mother* really saved her. The God damn *firemen* didn't know what to do. My mother said don't handle the child that way—so she took over. (Long pause)

[*More rage at the inept father. Firemen are men with hoses.* Mother *knows what to do.*]

D. So it was after your folks broke up that you were having trouble in school?

[*Returning to "special class."*]

P. Oh, I don't know. It seems, well, it's funny, I was *always* getting *hit by cars, everything* was happening to me. I can remember when I was going to one school. I started when I was about six years old. All of the *troubles* I got into. Of course, they only *separated* for a *few months*. They came right back together again, but all those places we lived in—Jesus!

[*He phrases his self-destructive pattern: "I was always hit by cars." In the decisive years of childhood, the uncertainty of the parental relationship made any role he took unstable.*]

D. What was the *trouble?*

[*The meaning of trouble was revealed before: the superman father image collapsed.*]

P. Oh, my father was *drinking* all the time.

[*Father appears as the drinking figure.*]

D. Perhaps he was *disgusted* with himself, too, for not making *enough?*

P. I guess so, I don't know. I guess that's right. I guess he was *disgusted.* I'm like *he* was then. He's got *reason,* too. He had an opportunity to become a *captain* in the Navy and to belong to good *ball clubs.* He screwed them all up. His *grandfather* was a *captain.* He's a captain in history, Captain B. There's a lot of B's on the Cape, and a lot of them in history. They were *famous* people. My *grandmother* used to tell me all about them. Then when she did, I'd *hate* myself all the more.

[*Now he reveals his ideals and shortcomings as taken over from father. Both remained "babies" (drinkers) who never became the real famous stars or Captain Marvels they should be. Both of them disappointed mother. Another blow put him in a special class. His infantile ideal of father collapsed, and he got mad with father as well as with himself.*]

D. How old were you then?

P. Oh, nine or ten, I guess.

D. You hated yourself for not being a Captain Marvel?

P. Yuh, I guess so. I guess I was *mad* at my *father* too. It seemed to me he ought to be a *better guy.* Then, if *he* couldn't do anything about it—how could *I?*

D. You needed a better father?

P. Anyway, I never knew what I wanted to do. I had no idea at all. I tried machine work, but that drove me nuts. Yuh, I was pretty good at it, but I don't know, I was winding armatures and the *smoke,* uh, or *something* drove me nuts.

[*"Smoke" reminds him of his failure as a man, i.e., he can't handle "stogies." This symbolizes the painful father-son relationship.*]

D. What do you mean?

P. Oh, it used to make my *eyes water* all the time. Every night I'd come out of there with a *headache,* and I was having a tough time outside. I bought a Ford and the *God damn thing* was a *60 hp.* and all the time I'd thought it was an *80 hp.* Then I screwed up the bearings and the thing *wouldn't go,* and I had to get *rid of it.* Then I taught my *girl friend* how to drive, and she smashed *that one* up. Aw, I'm screwing up all the time. Everything I do seems to be wrong. I'm a good example of a *sad sack.*

[*The permanent threat of his need for self-inflicting injury turns to his head as "headache."—He is crushed on both sides: always inadequate and always losing things.*]

D. You mean you were angry at yourself for not being a Captain Marvel?

P. (Long pause) And then there's these doctors around here. Jesus, I don't understand these people.

[*Father (doctor) is responsible that he is a "sad sack."*]

D. What do you mean?

P. Oh, you sit down, and they stare at you.

[*"Staring" is an assault. Doctors stare at him.*]

P. They won't talk to you—they drive you nuts. A guy wants some *advice* from an *older person.* Now take, for instance, Dr. X; he's my doctor—our doctor, I should say. He won't answer any of *my questions like you do.* I blew up, and I hit him the other day. I really didn't hit him. I just pushed him; and the way I talk in there to him. I just can't control my temper. I talk that way, and then I feel like a heel, and *he never does anything to my back,* and *I feel worse.* Heaven knows, I try. I put *my fists through walls* and do every other *God damn fool thing.* After I do it, I feel *relieved.* I don't know why.

[*He provokes a beating and feels worse when he doesn't get it, because he must then hurt himself.*]

D. You mean your doctor is just like your father; he doesn't give you any advice or help. Only you now beat the hell out of him or yourself.

P. Aw, I guess he thinks he's helped me out in a way, but I don't see how. I feel the same *God damn way* as I did when I first came in here.

D. As you say, this has been going on for a long time.

P. Don't get me wrong. I liked my Doc. He was a God damn good doctor. I just didn't understand him. He never used to say anything. I guess it just takes time.

[*Here he shows his ambivalence plainly.*]

D. That's right. It takes time to get to know anyone, and for guys to get to know each other.

P. Ah, it's me, too; I'm always trying to find a *shortcut* to getting things. You're right. I want it *quick.*

[*This can almost be taken literally, i.e., castration as a magic solution.*]

D. It would be nice if *shortcuts* like that existed.

P. Yuh, I'd like to have someone tell me what's *wrong* with me—*quick* like that, so that I could do something *quick.* That's what I get *pissed off* at. I feel the Doc *knows* and *won't tell me,* but you're right; it takes time.

D. As you say, you really never had a father to show you how, and this has gone on for a long time. It's not easy to grow up all over again overnight. You would like to get rid of this "sad sack." You hate "this little one" who needs a father so much. It seems to me that you're treating that poor little fellow just like your father treated you. Of course, it's easier to punch the wall when you hate yourself than it is to really wrestle with these things—to find out gradually what they are, and then control them. For instance, you tried to take it out on the screen when you were a *little fellow.* Now you are big and laugh at that, because you realize it can't be done; the screen has no feelings. But even now you're trying to take it out on the wall. It's not the fault of the screen, or the wall. Nor is it your fault. Perhaps you wouldn't blame your father either, if you knew more about him.

[*The confrontation with the material he has produced so far, begins with, "As you say." It aims at ego splitting through playing the role of good father who tells him what is wrong with him, by confronting the adult (conscious) part of him with the child (unconscious) in him.*]

P. Yuh, I guess he's had his *troubles,* too, or he wouldn't have gone out and drank so much. And he used to have *nightmares* too, just like *mine.* By the way—what do you do for those?

[*"Nightmare" means "doing something wrong when sleeping with men." Does he in the dream do to himself, or let the father do to him, or does he do to father what he wishes, but is afraid might happen, when he is awakened? It must be the assault of a man on another male.*]

D. What do you mean by *nightmares?*

P. Oh, that I'm *running away* and doing something *wrong.* I *yell,* and *scream,* and I wake up, and my *heart* feels like it's going to *stop.* You feel *scared.* You don't know what to do. I sweat when I wake up, and—God Almighty—I don't know. I've had them ever since I come in here.

D. And not at *home?*

P. Oh, at home I had a *few,* not as bad.

D. How long did you have them at home?

P. I don't know—I don't know. (Pause) I've *always* had *trouble sleeping,* I guess. Every time I'd wake up I'd find the *sheets* would be this way, the sheets would be that way. Sometimes my *mattress* would be out in the middle of the floor even. Yuh, whenever I'd wake up in the morning, the sheets would be all over the place. Aw, "shit," I wake up now and the guys tell me I'm screaming, and I keep them awake, and I feel self-conscious, and I want to get the hell out of this place. I just want to be *left alone.*

[*He is running away from his own wishes, which frighten him.*]

D. You are so *disgusted* with yourself.

P. Yuh, and when they say something to me, I jump down their throats.

[*He confirms the meaning of the nightmare: an attack on men by him, or the reverse.*]

D. You give them hell before they say anything to you?

P. What I mean is, I think *too God damn much.* That's what my trouble is.

D. I think you're right. You mean about this sad sack?

P. I'm *fed up* with it, everything. I say I don't believe in *God;* yet I go home, and now take for instance, I used to have a *beautiful dog* when I was *twelve* years old. Jesus, he was *beautiful.* He died. It was a sheep dog. He *couldn't see* with his hair all over the front of his eyes. You wondered how he could see. They say if you *cut the hair off,* they can see better, but I *don't believe that.* I used to take him for walks up in the hills in the summertime. Beautiful up there, and we'd sit down, up near the *water tower.* We'd be *snuggled* up close to one another.

[*This, too, is a screen memory. The dog and he portray the fantasy of an ideal father-son relation without danger. In this relationship, nothing had to be cut off.*]

D. You mean like *real pals?*
P. Yuh, just *daydreaming,* you know.
D. Like a *father and son.*
P. Yuh, in a way.

[*It is obvious now.*]

D. What were you daydreaming about?
P. Oh, I'm getting sick. Don't, Doc. I'm liable to cry. (Patient gets up and strides around, pounding his fist against his palm)

[*Here again is the fantasy, "I'm getting* sick *or* hurt *by my fist (father)." He can't accept help, because he needs to be hurt. An attempt is made to let him see that he, the little one, can have father's love without injuring himself, and that it is not wrong to be loved by father.*]

D. This is tough stuff to express. You have a lot to get off your chest.
P. Aw, a couple of times I was going to commit *suicide.* (Starts to cry) But I guess I turned chicken. Once I took a *knife* out of the kitchen, one night I was feeling *depressed.* I came back in the hospital. The nurses *pissed me* off. I swore and I cussed and I ran out the door, and I wound up somewhere near the Turnpike. Then I started walking back. I remember walking between the new homes up there. I came back all screwed up with muck all over me. I just blew my top and lost my *temper.*

[*He equates himself with the dog who died. He takes a knife and wants to cut something off himself or to stick it into himself; i.e., suicide. He expresses his feelings of wanting to kill and to die.*]

D. You really *hate* this poor *sad sack.*

[*He acts out on himself the old rage of the kid.*]

P. I'm still a kid, that's it.
D. Not entirely. Only a *part of you* is a *sad sack,* but there's another part that is able to *control* him, as you've shown here.

[*Since he calls himself a kid, the adult part can be confronted with the ideas of the kid.*]

P. But I'm still screwing around.

D. Well, we see this little sad sack cutting himself with a knife, or pounding himself or kicking himself. But you also have to see whether you can be a good father to him and show him how to grow up.

P. Yuh, I suppose so, but I hate that bastard.

[*He calls the "kid" a bastard. That means he wants to separate himself from the "kid."*]

D. That's all right. Why do you hate this sad sack?

P. Oh, I know what I'm doing is wrong, but I just can't stop doing it. I don't *want* to stop. Look at last night. I got *pissed off* while I was in there shaving, when I *cut myself*. Now listen. I like Dr. X. Now when I call a guy a *prick,* I don't have to *mean it.* I realize I'm really *calling myself* a *prick.* Well, anyway, he came into that latrine last night where I was shaving, so I don't know what happened. I felt *depressed.* There was a big dance up here last night, so I was going to shave, but all I did was walk up and down that God damn corridor and walk around in circles. I felt lousy, so I just blew my top. I ran up against a wall. I don't exactly know what happened, but the doctor came in and I said get out of here, I don't want to see you. I was looking out the window. Then I came back to the ward, and Dr. X was there. He looked at me and I walked by. My whole arm was smeared with blood.

[*His madness against himself acts against the "prick." His self-destructive tendencies are efforts to appease his cruel superego and thus ward off intolerable depressive and anxious feelings. In another sense, he relieves the depression by establishing the old father-son relationship by cutting his right arm, the masculine side ("prick").*]

D. Which arm was that?

P. The *right arm.* So I come back into the ward, went into the latrine and started shaving. So he opened the door. He says, let me have a look at that. I says what. I knew God damn right well what he was talking about, so I was only leading him on. I was just being a wiseguy, just screwing around. So he says to me, "You know God damn right well what I mean," and he says, "Now listen—unless you don't want to co-operate with us and go halfway, we won't go halfway with you. What I mean is you'll get the hell out of here."

D. This seems to be the kind of help you want from father all the time—a "damn good" beating. Did father believe that beatings were necessary? You and I know that beatings didn't do any good in the past, and they won't do any good now. You cut off your nose to spite your face, don't you? You hate yourself, just like your father hated that little sad sack—or as you thought he did. You wouldn't treat your dog that way. You said you were good to him and the two of you cuddled up together.

[*The interviewer uses for the confrontation in the sector "you and I"; the "you" being the little one; the "I" being the interviewer representing the adult, observing part of the patient. He can accept at present what the interviewer phrases for him, but it will be a long time before it will have enough meaning to be utilized. Such a con-*

frontation is close to an interpretation, and must be worked through. If he can accept it now, it can be used repeatedly in future sessions.]

P. Well, now I'll tell you another thing. The first week I was here when I went home for the week end, as I've said, I've always hung around with little kids, although I could fight anybody and I don't give a God damn for anybody, no matter how big they are. I could lick anybody or take a beating, yet in school and everywhere I always hung around with younger kids, all of the time when I was ten years old.

[*He played the "good father" role with the kids without "beating" or being "licked."*]

D. Why was that?
P. I know why. It was because my father never brought me up the way I should have been.
D. You were the good father to them that your father wasn't to you, huh?
P. You're God damn right. I *stuck up* for them.

[*A good father is a kind of mother, who "sticks up" for the child.*]

D. Why do you not treat yourself a little bit that way?
P. That's right, because that's just the way I used to act to those kids. Whenever they got into trouble, I *stood up* and *fought* for them. I would go down and *stick right up* and tell them off if they tried to *hurt* those kids. For instance, I was talking to a kid who wanted to *quit* school, and I told him, don't ever quit school, don't be the way I was. *Stick around,* kid. I don't know whether I convinced him or not. Yuh, I really wish I had never *quit.*

[*He "stuck up" for the kids but also advised them to "stick around." His speech has phallic, aggressive characteristics.*]

D. Have you ever thought of taking any of these vocational tests here, and taking any of the schooling they offer?

[*The interviewer links up the present schooling with the past, for the confrontation.*]

P. Yuh, I've thought of it. I want to go down there but I'm *afraid* I'll screw it up. If I only knew how to do *mathematics* I'd be all set.
D. Well, what would you have said to one of those *kids* if he'd said that to you?
P. Oh, I'd tell him he could *try* it, anyway. Maybe it takes more *guts* to try it.
D. I think you're right.
P. Aw, but there's more to it than that, Doc. I was such a *louse* in many ways.
D. What do you mean?
P. Aw, I used to act crazy. I used to choke cats and throw them in the water. I was a *cruel bastard.* I remember a kitten I threw out into the pond. It would come back in and I'd throw him out again. I kept doing it until he drowned. My mother says I told *her lies.* In

fact, I even lied about the kitten. I said that uh, uh, another kid, *Dick,* did it.

[*The confrontations by making him an adult observer (together with the interviewer) of the little one, bear fruit. It becomes clear that he was the protector of the "kids" against the attacker, because the "attacker" was only a projection of his own destructive tendencies, just as he himself is also the kid, the "sad sack."*]

D. So there were two sides to you—a little sad sack who was always punishing himself and getting hurt, and killing kittens, who needed a father and who did it to get father's love; then there's the other one who wants to help the little sad sacks out, as he wished father should have done to him. Maybe your father was that way? Maybe he did love you?

P. Why aren't the doctors like you, for Christ's sake. That X is a good psychiatrist, too, but why aren't they like you? They won't converse and talk like *you and I* do together. They won't say anything to me.

[*He rediscovers the loving father. The "you" and "I" appear in changed roles.*]

D. You mean like your father? From what you said, that little "sad sack" needs a lot of help, and the "you and I" have to work together helping him. I don't think pounding him and kicking him will do him any good, do you?

P. Yah, I guess so. You make it sound silly, and here I go again. Now I want to blame myself and say I'm a silly bastard for doing it. Then I'll hit myself for hitting myself. You know, I'm afraid I don't think like you. I'm the only person in the world, *I'm afraid,* that thinks like I do, and I don't know why, and I'm scared in a way. I'm afraid I'm different from others. I'm afraid of being, uh, a little *queer* that way.

[*We have strengthened the reasonable ego, and now he comes a little closer to his fears.*]

D. But as *you've said,* you've always felt as if you were in a *special class,* too much of a *little boy* who needed a loving father and wanted to be independent too. But *you and I know* that only a part of you is that way—that's the poor little *sad sack.*

P. Yuh, I need to know those things though, but Jesus, I just don't know what to do. You know, I've always been afraid to admit that I didn't, and then again I've always felt like a *dope.* I always felt I was such a *stupid bastard.* Well, I hope you're right. I guess you know. You've done an awful lot of studying and reading and have had a lot of experience. Jesus Christ, I wish I'd had a chance to do things like that. I can tell you one thing, my toughest job is going to learn how to control that *temper.*

[*"Dope" and "stupid" are ways of being "queer" and in a "special class."*]

D. That's right. When you were a little boy you kicked the "screen," and now you're still kicking things. Maybe you'll treat yourself like this father who said he *didn't mind* what you did.

[*We attempt to build on the remnants of the good father introject, i.e., a more motherly father who will stick up for him.*]

P. Well, last night the nurse spoke to me about *bending over backwards* to be *good,* and I'm going to try. When I came back, I had a cyst *operation* and *split* the wound open, hitting myself. She said, want to go for a walk? I says a walk, okay. So we went out. We walked up the street, and she said, one thing that's wrong with you; you're like a tree that stands *straight up* against the storm and doesn't bend. Why don't you bend with the wind? That's something I don't do. I take it all; I absorb it. I'm always taking it *up the ars.*

[*He now expresses the difficulty more plainly. Being good is such a threat to his weak, phallic masculinity. His accident proneness is an attempt to castrate himself and renounce phallic aggressive masculinity. It is as if behind the operation there is an anal pregnancy fantasy.*]

D. Or getting the doctors to do it to you, like with Dr. X in the latrine the other night.

P. Yuh, that's right.

D. You mean when you're not "sticking it up your own ars" you're getting others to do it for you? Did you mean your father?

P. You got something there. I guess I did. Boy, I could tell you.

[*This sounds remarkably out in the open, but his understanding is superficial, piecemeal, transient and unreliable. It is largely breast beating which he has learned to enjoy masochistically. The deeper wish to be castrated is, of course, unconscious.*]

D. Maybe this was the little boy's idea of how to *grow up,* or how to get a father to *show him* what to do, to care for him. But I think your idea of going with the younger boys and being kind and considerate and defending them was a lot better. Don't you?

P. Well, it sounds better *here,* anyway. Jesus Christ, the things that I do. I've gone down and dashed right into the woods there and come back with my face all scraped up—bleeding, clothes torn, God.

D. Okay. "You and I" will work together. (Stands up and they shake hands. Patient leaves)

Final Discussion

This example of sector therapy illustrates several important components of the method:

(1) It shows how reticence based on transference resistance can be at first by-passed and then gradually overcome. In the interview situation, the interviewer was able to appear as a father figure who fulfilled the patient's unconscious wishes in a way which made his destructive sacrifices superfluous.

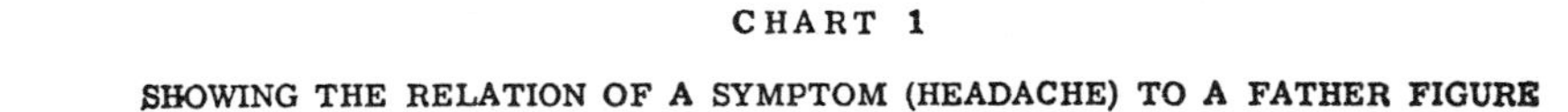
CHART 1
SHOWING THE RELATION OF A SYMPTOM (HEADACHE) TO A FATHER FIGURE

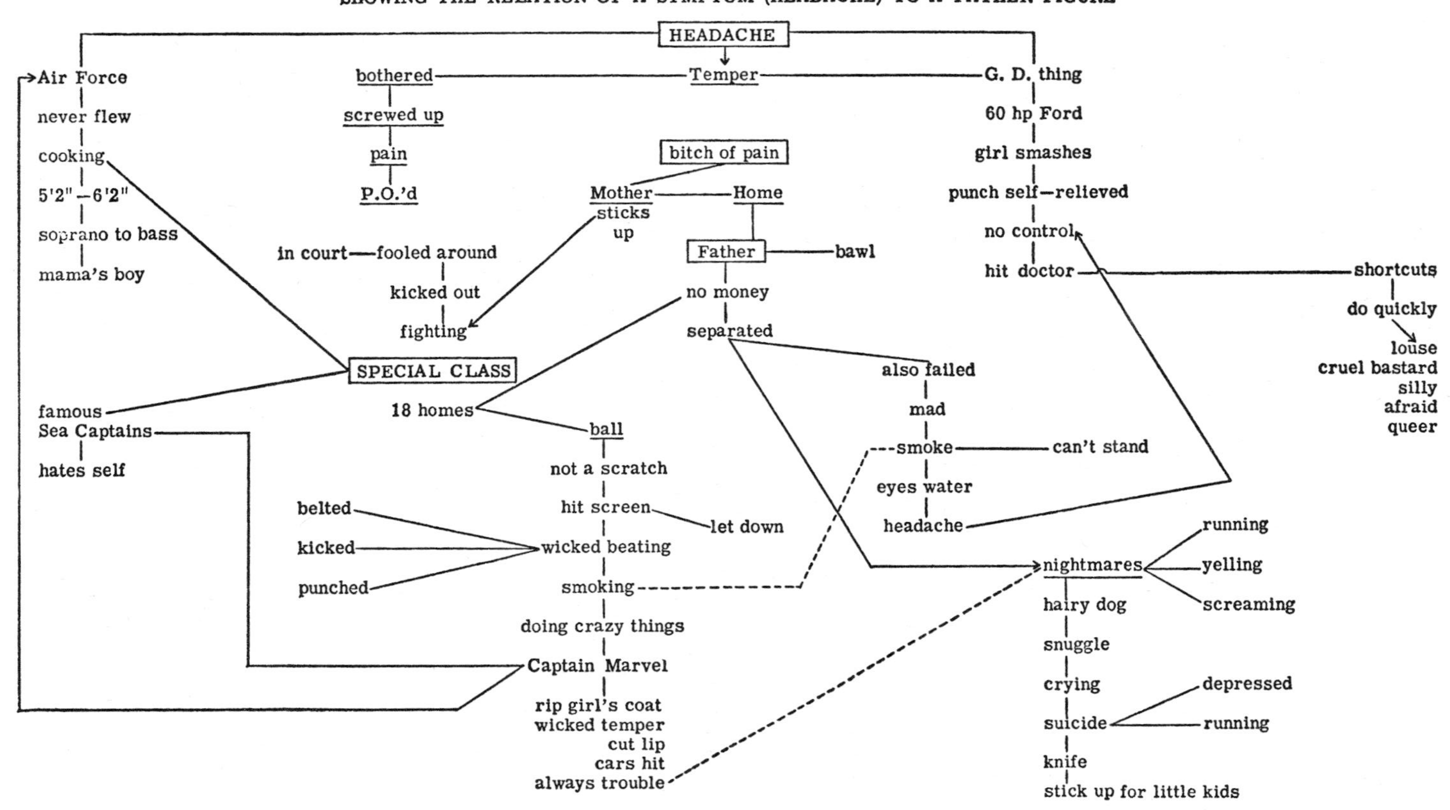
HEADACHE
Air Force
never flew
cooking
5'2"—6'2"
soprano to bass
mama's boy
bothered
screwed up
pain
P.O.'d
Temper
G. D. thing
60 hp Ford
girl smashes
punch self—relieved
no control
hit doctor
shortcuts
do quickly
louse
cruel bastard
silly
afraid
queer
bitch of pain
Mother
sticks
up
Home
Father
bawl
no money
separated
in court—fooled around
kicked out
fighting
SPECIAL CLASS
famous
Sea Captains
hates self
18 homes
ball
not a scratch
hit screen
let down
belted
kicked
punched
wicked beating
smoking
doing crazy things
Captain Marvel
rip girl's coat
wicked temper
cut lip
cars hit
always trouble
also failed
mad
smoke
can't stand
eyes water
headache
nightmares
running
yelling
screaming
hairy dog
snuggle
crying
depressed
suicide
running
knife
stick up for little kids

(2) The splitting of the ego into the conscious, observing part, and the infantile, immature one, was successfully applied, and understood by the patient. By his identification with the interviewer in the acceptable father role, he could recognize his destructive attitudes as being the needs of the "kid" to get father's love, and to face it. It also became clear that mere recognition in this specific interviewing situation would not suffice to give his ego enough substance to master his infantile needs for good, or even for a longer time.

(3) The interview fulfills also another requirement of this method: Structurally it forms a unit, and the content of the key words appears in all its meaningfulness in the finale.

(4) It is a good example of how a seemingly insignificant key word can be used as an anchor for ramified associations, which elucidate the structure of the personality pattern. Here it was the figure "22" by which the patient's separation suffering and unification need was screened. By and large, whenever the same number appears repeatedly in an interview, it is most surely the abstract concept of later objectifications, which play an important role in the patient's unconscious.

(5) This therapeutic interview finally demonstrated that the interviewer used for the confrontations only unconscious material which was within the grasp of the patient. In this manner, deeper interpretations became unnecessary, as in the case where dreams were used in the interview. Dreams can rarely be interpreted in a goal-limited psychotherapy because the material provided in the interview is for the most part insufficient. They need a basis for "interpretation," which only a thorough analysis can supply. Otherwise, the therapist does no more than translate symbols.

(6) The course of this interview proves that through the interviewer's guidance, the associative material was kept within the sector decided upon at the beginning of the session.

Follow-Up

Initially, the patient appeared to be a rather condescending, overly polite individual who expressed a great deal of remorse over the damage that he had done to his parents' home. His headaches were fairly frequent, two or three times a week, and appeared to be associated with periods of frustration and anger. During a headache, he was frequently assaultive to objects on the ward, threatening to other patients, and demanding that something be done for him. On one occasion, during his early hospitalization, it was necessary for him to be transferred to a closed ward for a twenty-four-hour period. Later in his hospitalization the same behavior was associated with frustration and displayed without the presence or complaint of headache. He maintained a threatening, dominating, aggressive behavior as a thin façade for dependent cravings and numerous feminine identifications.

Following the cessation of headaches, he exhibited a marked tendency to accident proneness throughout his hospitalization. Later, his periods of self-injury manifested by frequent pounding of his fists decreased considerably, and it was felt that he had developed an increased tolerance for frustration. He was then granted a thirty-day leave of absence for trial of adjustment on the outside, but failed to return from this leave and was discharged as AWOL. Three years later it was ascertained that the patient had rejoined the Service and was in Korea. It is probable that he was ambivalently motivated and that he was looking for the "good father" relationship through suffering, and possibly with dying (suicide) in mind.

Part 2—The Sacrifice

Introduction

The following interview represents a similar situation of reticence in a veteran who uses his head to express fantasies revolving about the father and about becoming a man. This interview was remarkable for the length of the pauses. The patient had been seen before in one brief interview.

Case Presentation

The patient was a twenty-seven-year-old, World War II veteran, complaining of severe headaches which began following his discharge from the Service two years previously. He had returned home and worked for his father, who was a carpenter. The father was described as domineering, violent and strict, and frequently beat him, at one time sending him to the hospital with a broken nose.

The patient had three older sisters, an older brother and two younger brothers. The four older siblings had become married while he was in the Service, and on his return he found himself placed in the role of the oldest son. He became engaged shortly after his return home, and approximately six months prior to his admission to the hospital encouraged his next younger brother to leave home and join the Navy. The father disapproved violently of both happenings, and shortly after the younger son left, went to the hospital with stomach and bladder trouble. Two months previously, his fiancee's father, who was kind and considerate to the patient, died from a C.V.A. The patient's headaches then began to be accompanied by nausea and stomach pains, and were so severe as to incapacitate him. The interview demonstrates how reticence due to pent-up anxiety can be at least temporarily overcome.

Interview

D. How are things going?
P. (Sits in chair, head in hands, and makes grunting noises)
[*Any type of communication can be utilized indirectly*.]

D. Pardon me—what did you say?
P. (Lets out long sigh)
D. Why do you *sigh?*

P. I don't know. (Pause) My *head* is *killing me.*

[*Thus his head represents a dangerous object or person, as well as an endangered part of his body, i.e., the attacker and the attacked part.*]

D. Your *head* is what?
P. My head is *killing* me. (Pause) Feels like it's *breaking* all of the time.

[*If something "breaks," he dies. This can be either at the object level, signifying an injury of a part of the body, or at the personal level, signifying a break with someone or something, or a loss. (He was under pressure to break with his family.)*]

D. What do you mean?
P. Well, it's under *pressure* all of the time. It's *always* that way.
D. What do you mean by *all the time?* How long has this been going on?
P. Oh, for a few years. It seems to be getting *worse* all the time.
D. What do you mean?
P. (Sighs and shakes head in a hopeless gesture)
D. Under *pressure?* In what way?
P. (Pause) Oh, nothing; I just feel *lost.*
D. What way do you feel lost?
P. Sometimes *stupid.* I can hardly keep my *eyes open.* (He drops his head in his hands and mumbles)

[*If he breaks he will be lost. He defends himself against separation anxiety by inhibitions of thinking, and behaves like one who defends himself from his problem by falling asleep.*]

D. What did you say? It is hard to keep your *eyes open?*

[*What does he not want to see?*]

P. (Nods head. Long pause) Seems to be getting *worse* for the past four months.
D. Worse? What do you mean?
P. The *whole business.*

[*"Whole business" refers to himself as a whole.*]

D. Could you tell me more about the *whole business?*
P. (Long pause) It's hard to explain.
D. Of course. But you must have some ideas?
P. Well, it just seems to be getting *worse,* and every time I *talk* about it, it *doesn't help* any. It's been two weeks now, and I don't know. It just seems to be worse than ever.
D. You mean the *whole business?* Why does it seem worse to you than ever? How was it *before?*

[*To get to the past.*]

P. (Pause) Everything seems *odd* and *strange* to me.

[*He is talking at a number of levels: we know one, i.e., about his feelings of unreality, and his attempt to escape from the head killing him.*]

D. *Odd in what way?*

P. (Pause—then faintly) I don't know. It's just as if I were in a *dream.* It's like a *dream* all the time.

[*What happens in the dream?*]

D. Some *dream!*
P. (Grins slightly)
D. Well, at least you're able to laugh at it.
P. I get *sick* of it. I know that.
D. Sick?
P. *Sick* of the *whole business.*

[*"Sick" and "whole business" are brought together.*]

D. Can you tell me more about the *whole business?*
P. Well, *everything* seems to be *wrong* as far as I know.

[*"Everything" is wrong with "the whole thing" which he cannot use.*]

D. Do you mean everything you thought you *knew* seems to be *wrong?* In which way wrong?
P. Well, the *whole thing* is *that way.* It just makes me feel *I can't do anything.*
D. Such as what—for instance?
P. Oh, nothing. (Long pause)
D. You haven't been able to do anything at all? What have you done before that you can't do now?

[*Using the impasse to get into the past.*]

P. Oh, I've been like this for *two months.* (Pause)

[*Two months ago the good father died, i.e., father of his girl. It was evident that he reduplicated his own situation in that of his girl's, hoping to obtain a good father through marriage. But this information cannot be used, since the patient does not refer to it verbally.*]

D. Two months doing nothing? I thought you first said it's been worse for two weeks?
P. Oh, well—it's been tightening up all the time, ever since I came in.
D. Ever since you came in for what?
P. Well, my doctor sent me in.
D. He sent you in?
P. Yuh, he figured I'd find the answer here. I went to him. I had *headaches* all the time. He was a psychiatrist. He's supposed to know the answer to all those things. (Long sigh) He told me I should have electric *shocks,* so he told me to go to the hospital. So I came, but it never did me any *good.* I never felt any *better.* Then I'd go to see him. I'd sit down, and he'd say, "How do you feel?" Then I'd say, "No better." So it would go on like that.

[*He looks for a magic cure for his headache by being told what is wrong; that saves him from exposing his thoughts. "Shocks" to the head didn't help him.*]

D. You mean like in here?
P. No. Here at least they *tried.*
D. But, as you say, they just *talked?*

P. Yes, anyway, *you guys* at least tried— but not *him*.
D. He didn't seem to be *trying*, huh?
P. It looked to me like I was paying him for nothing. I'm sorry I ever went to him.
D. How did you happen to go to him?
P. I went to my *family doctor* first, and he said I was *nervous*.
D. *Nervous?* What did he mean?
P. He just said I was *nervous*. It's just like I'm now. I can't *stay still*.
D. Did you feel that way then—*at home?*

[*Returning him to his problem.*]

P. (Long pause. Then faintly) Yuh.
D. What went on at home? Who was there?

[*Establishing relationships in the home is of primary importance.*]

P. (Pause) My *mother* and *father* and *brothers*.
D. Your brothers? How many of them?
P. I have two brothers. One is older. He's married.

[*Why does he mention "marriage?"*]

D. How old is he?
P. Thirty.
D. And the younger ones?
P. Oh, one's sixteen and the other's twenty-three.
D. Four years younger than yourself?
P. (Long pause. Then faintly) Yuh.
D. What is he doing?
P. He's in the Service. He just went over in July.

[*Six months ago.*]

D. So he just went over. Then you're really the only one left of the older boys?
P. (Long pause. Patient is silent; rubs head)
D. Why do you rub your head?
P. Oh, I just feel *filled up* all the time.

[*Does rubbing empty the "filled up" head?*]

D. All of the time? What do you mean? How long have you felt that way?
P. Oh, for about a year and a half or so.
D. A year and a half?
P. (Nods head in reply. Long pause)
D. And they said it was *nervousness?* What does that mean to you?

[*"Head," "sick," "whole business" and "nervousness" belong together.*]

P. (Long pause) Well, he didn't give me any X-ray for it. He just gave me some medicine.

[*Obviously he suspected something inside him was causing it, and he distrusted the doctor.*]

D. What made him think it was *nervousness?*

P. Well, they finally said the head was all right.

[*Nothing in the head. Where is it?*]

D. But no X-rays, huh? Do you mean to say he didn't do a *good job?*

P. I suppose so. I guess that's the way I feel now. Of course, at the time I thought he was *supposed* to know what he was doing.

D. But now, (pause) you don't think he did?

P. Yuh, he could at least have taken X-rays. (Begins to perk up a little) Incidentally—(Again buries head in his hands)

D. Do you mean he may have known from the way you *acted* that it was *nervousness?*

P. (Nods head without looking up)

D. So he sent you to a *psychiatrist?*

[*A psychiatrist is a doctor who treats people with something abnormal in the head.*]

P. (Nods head again)

D. And he couldn't do much for you?

P. (Nods head. Long pause)

D. And then your headaches began?

P. No, I had them on and off.

D. Off and on since when?

P. Oh, for the past six months, I guess.

[*Again "six."*]

D. Since the first of the year, it seems.

P. (After a pause) I get this *numb feeling* all over. I was going to be *married.*

[*"Numb" means no bodily feeling. Where and why should he be afraid to have "feelings," when he was going to be married?*]

D. What do you mean?

P. Well, it's just like there was no feeling all over. It's a sort of *block.* I seem to be going around in *circles* all the time. (Long pause)

D. And you say you have an *older brother* who is *married?*

[*To get further into the marriage problem.*]

P. Yuh.

D. You're not *married* though, huh?

P. (Looks up) I will be *married* when I get ahead.

D. What do you mean by that? A *head* that doesn't *ache,* or get *ahead* in what respect?

[*A doubly determined word: to get "ahead." Does one risk the "head" when "marrying?"*]

P. Well, I'm just about engaged. (Pause)

D. What do you mean by "just about?"

P. Well, she's *waiting* for me.

[*Why did he let the girl wait to be married?*]

D. Waiting for you to marry, or what?

P. Well, (pause) I've known her for *two years.*
D. *Two years?* Does that mean you've known her practically since you got out of the *Service?*
P. (Nods head) That's *right.*
D. And so you feel she's the *right* one?

[*Linking his words, and encouraging the faltering ego.*]

P. (Nods head, now buried in his hands)
D. Are you all set to get *married?*
P. If I ever get *ahead.*
D. How do you mean?
P. (Explosively) I'll never get *ahead* working for *father.*

[*He said before, "I will get married when I get ahead." Now he says, "I will never get ahead" as long as he works for father. Father is the head (boss!) who kills what he needs for a marriage.*]

D. Oh, why?
P. Yuh. He is the boss.
D. And you don't like that?
P. (Smiling wryly) Well, we have our *troubles* every once in a while.
D. How do you mean?
P. Oh, we're always having *disagreements* over the *work.*
D. Over his work, or your work?
P. Oh, it's just *one of those things,* you know.
D. You mean the way you do *things,* or the way he does *things?*
P. (Long pause. He then starts beating his head with his hands; finally buries head in his hands) Ask him!

[*He enacts the role of a father beating his head down to the inefficiency of a little one. Father is "the big head."*]

D. You mean he is the one who decides?
P. (Long pause. Nods his head slowly)
D. I take it you don't like working for him?
P. (Raises head slowly and gives the doctor a disgusted and expressive look)
D. Words can't express it, huh?
P. (Sits up in chair and grins back, with a disgusted shaking motion of the head)

[*Sign of a positive transference.*]

D. How come?
P. (Now visibly more relaxed) Oh, it's a *hard thing* to explain. It's a *funny thing* though; it's, uh, it's just that *things between us* just don't seem to *click.*

[*Before: Every "thing" is wrong with his "whole thing." Now: Father's "thing" doesn't click with his "thing." This is more than an isolated figure of speech. Like all others, it has deep fantasy roots in the unconscious, in this case revolving about a phallic relationship.*]

D. It's difficult working for a *father.* Is that why you were *nervous?*

P. My brother didn't have to do it. He is an *estimator*. He has a Civil Service job. If I went with him, I wouldn't have to take it.

[*The older brother left with his "thing" and "got ahead," i.e., married. Brother would let him have his "thing."*]

D. You mean the married brother?
P. Yuh.
D. What do you mean?
P. Well, with him, I could do what I want out there.
D. You mean—get away from *father* and *marry?*
P. If I had *anything saved up,* I might, but I can't now.

[*Even in such a setup, marriage is too much.*]

D. And what does your girl friend think of it?
P. Oh, she's *all for it.*
D. And what does *father* think?
P. Oh—he doesn't like it. He wants me to *stick around.*

[*It is not he, it is father, who wants him to "stick" around him.*]

D. And how about mother?
P. She thinks it would be a *good idea.*
D. So she thinks it's a good idea; the girl friend thinks it's a good idea; and you think it's a good idea; but father doesn't. So you stay?

[*We confront him with his need indirectly, i.e., we don't say father.*]

P. (Pause) Oh, I don't know. Well, I make up my mind to *quit him,* but I *always go back.* They have *always* been around here.

[*He is unable to separate himself from father, and always comes back to sacrifice his head.*]

D. Do you mean by "always" that you hate to leave home?
P. You might put it that way. You see, he wants to go back to the old country.
D. He comes from there?
P. He was born there. He goes back every summer.
D. He, too, wants to go home?
P. Yuh, he's one of those guys that *never liked to be away from home,* I guess.

[*Does he imitate father's pattern? It is now out in the open: he is conscious of the overwhelming need to "stick" to father. But that arouses his masculine pride.*]

D. How come?
P. Oh, well, all his brothers, sisters, family are there, and I guess he just wants *to be around them.* (Long pause) But *not me.* I've made up my mind to *leave.*

[*Father "sticks" around* his *family.*]

D. When did you make up your mind to go?
P. (Long pause) About a year ago. My brother is in D——, and I think I can get a job there working in a hospital.

[*Why a hospital? In case he gets "sick," he will be taken care of. He turns to another father figure, the older brother to whom he will stick without the risk of losing his head. He prefers it to "marriage." Is there a risk in marrying?*]

D. And you plan on getting married?
P. (Long pause) When I get over this *headache.* (Patient is silent for three minutes, rubbing head violently)
D. Not an easy *problem* to solve?
P. It gets *worse* and *worse.* She's not going to wait forever.

[*Any way he turns, he may lose something.*]

D. You mean your girl?
P. Yuh. Sometimes I wish I'd stayed in the Army.

[*It is safer to be with men.*]

D. There at least they told you *where to go, what to do:* there wasn't this problem of getting *married,* or not getting married, *leaving home* or staying with *father.*
P. But honest to God—I really don't know what to do. I can't *use my head.* I'm *dumb.* I'm *stupid.*

[*Is there a way out for the panic-stricken little one, other than to stop thinking? He feels the fight is hopeless.*]

D. Who says so, father?
P. We *fight* all the time. He don't like the way *I do things,* and I don't like the way *he does things.* (Long pause) Oh, I don't know *what to do.*

[*How does father do "things" compared with his doing "things?"*]

D. What did you *want to do* before?
P. *I don't know.* I guess I *never* did *think* much about it. I guess I *never thought* I could be *anything.*

[*He had already given up as a child. As the child in the middle, between two brothers, he was in a bad position. The younger children had mother, and the older ones were bigger, especially the older brother. He never knew which way to turn. The younger brother going away and father getting sick, evidently aroused too much guilt and anxiety, but he has not mentioned father's sickness as yet.*]

D. You mean getting married, go away from home like your brother?
P. (Just nods head)
D. How come?
P. (Long pause) Well, I *had* to stay home. You see, my *father* was in the *hospital.*
D. In the hospital? When?
P. Last Christmas.

[*In going away one ends in a hospital like father. At Christmas: birth of the Christ Child and when children expect magic and presents.*]

D. What was the trouble?

P. Oh, his *stomach* and *bladder*.

[*What sickness does father have inside his stomach and bladder? What or who made him sick? This material is closely connected with pregnancy fantasies which could not be explored, as the hour was drawing to a close. The pauses had been long.*]

D. Stomach and bladder. (Long pause) And you had to stay home in his place?
P. (Nods head buried in his hands)
D. A big job?
P. (Nods head)

[*What made him silent again? Was the confrontation with the sickness of father, whose fate will also be his own, too much for him to face? He holds his head in his own hands protectively.*]

D. And you mean that's why you can't get married?
P. (Keeps head buried, nods it again vigorously. Long pause)
D. Because they need you?
P. (Nods head, then suddenly) Yuh, and it's been a *long time,* too.
D. Since when?
P. From November until April.

[*"Six" months ago is when brother left, and father went to the hospital. He could have linked these occurrences in many ways. Six is also the number of his siblings.*]

D. And now father wants to *go away again* as if he doesn't need you?
P. Oh, I suppose he does.
D. You mean he says he does, but you're not so sure? (Pause) You figure they might get along without you?
P. Well, they just went away for a vacation, for a month.
D. What? They went for a month's vacation?
P. (Rubs head vigorously and appears more and more furious. Long pause)

[*The fight between his passive wishes and his masculine protest is apparent.*]

D. You mean, they can get along without you?
P. (Nods head, assenting vigorously. Long pause)
D. But father says he still needs you?
P. (Keeps nodding head. Long pause)
D. Which means you can't get married?
P. (Blurting out angrily) But I'm going to!

[*The deadlock is broken, at least temporarily*]

D. You mean, whether he says so, or not?
P. (Nods head. Pause)
D. You mean, if he can go to the old country and take a month's vacation, they can take care of themselves. They don't need you.

[*For ease of acceptance, the roles are reversed.*]

P. Of course, there's my youngest brother. But he's only sixteen.

[*He now tries to drag in the youngest brother, but in a resentful fashion. The interviewer heads him away from this new battle, because his ego appears weary of fighting, and the older brother represents a more masculine ideal. His turning to the younger brother may well have signified his yielding to more passive wishes to remain home with father.*]

D. But your oldest brother, he's married and he has been able to leave the family and is making out fine in D——?

P. Yuh. I *really* would like to go out there. He keeps asking me. He tells me he'll help me find a job, and *this time,* by God, I'm going to.

D. You mean you've said so in the past, but it didn't work?

P. (Pause. Loudly) That's right. You see, I was always the kind of a guy who thought about my family. I didn't want to go so far away and leave *them* all *alone.* I figured *they needed me.* My *father always* said he did, and if he didn't say it, anyway he *acted* that way. *Sometimes I wonder why I did it.* My older brother didn't. He was able to get out, but then I guess I was *always that way.*

[*"Sometimes I wonder why I did it," is a good occasion to end the interview. He at last seems to be prepared to face his problems.*]

D. What do you mean?

P. Oh, nothing. It's just the same old stuff. Whenever there was anything to be done around the home, my brother would be away and I had to do it. He was big enough to go out. They never said anything to him. The other one was too little. Trying to be a *good guy*—and what did I get for it?

D. You were "unlucky Pierre"—always in the middle.

P. You said it.

D. Okay. I'll see you Wednesday.

Discussion

It took the entire hour to get into the past where information could be obtained which would link up the head with relevant material. In the pauses, the patient expressed his problem on a preverbal level, through his posture, i.e., sticking his head into his hands. The interview, although incomplete, succeeded in bringing out within the sector one of his basic conflicts, namely, his anxiety over leaving father to whom he sticks and for whom he wants to sacrifice his head, the symbol of his masculinity. That prevents him from acting on a heterosexual level in marriage. His "head is killing him," as he says. This is a disguised expression of a homosexual panic. He gave the impression of being in a prepsychotic condition.

Follow-Up

After twelve weeks of sector therapy, the patient declared that his head no longer ached, and he demanded discharge, planning to marry and

CHART 2

SHOWING THE RELATIONSHIP OF HEAD PAINS TO A FATHER FIGURE

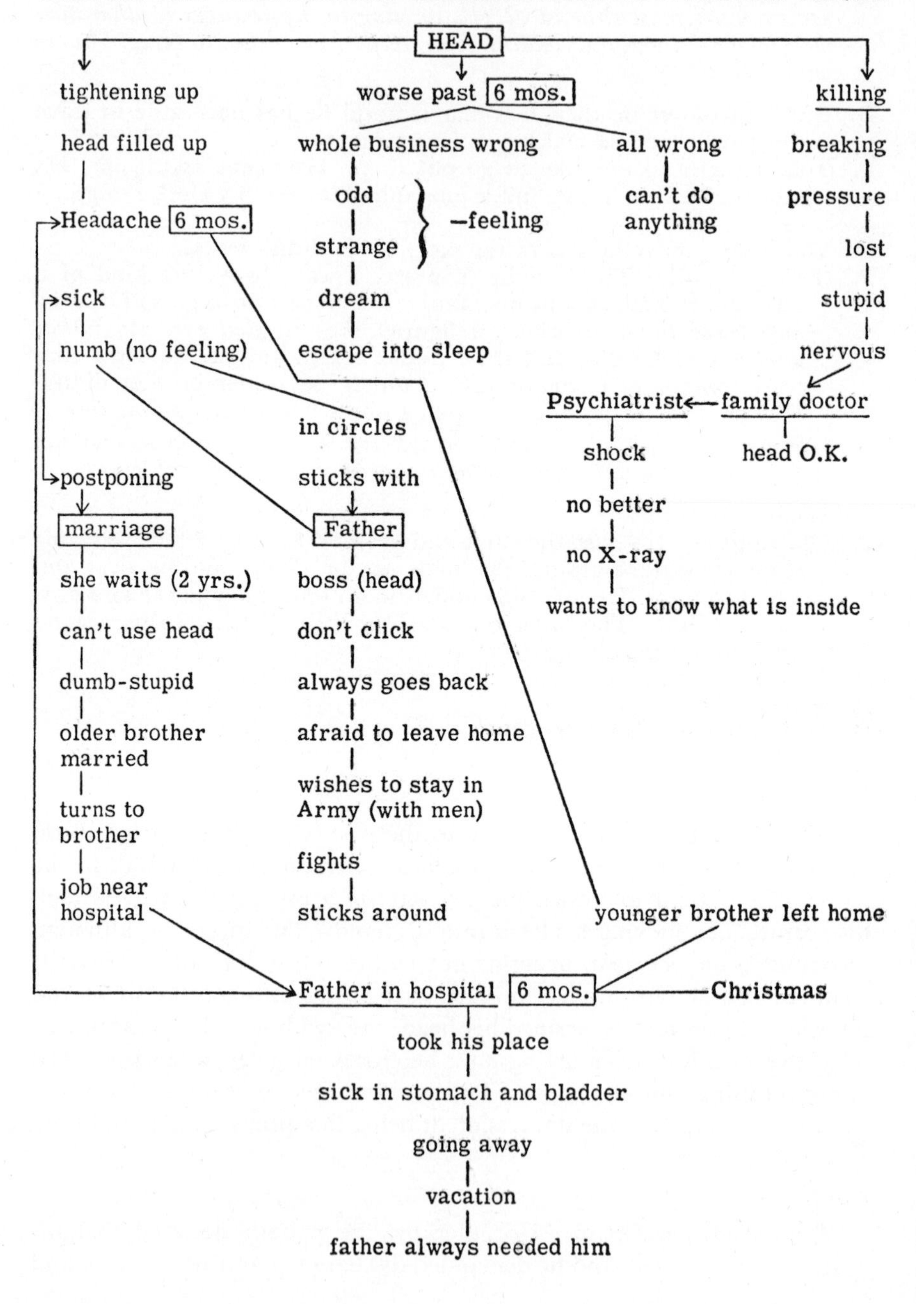

leave home. He was released on a thirty-day leave, during which his girl made active plans to marry. He then returned to the hospital with feelings of depression and of estrangement from reality, along with violent hatred of all authority figures, and was admitted to the Closed Ward Service. At this time, he had no headache, but verbalized paranoid delusional material and preoccupation with his *stomach*. Ten months later, after a course of insulin coma therapy and later electroshock therapy, and following psychotherapy, he was able to go home on a trial visit and for six months remained symptom-free. Three years later he was living with his parents, was unmarried, and received therapy at a mental hygiene clinic.

CHAPTER VI

The Repetition of the Material and the Ending of Therapy

Part 1—The Overburdened Mouth

INTRODUCTION

When dealing with severely regressed or ego-defective patients who are incapacitated by a large number of symptoms, sector therapy may become a long-term proposition. With these cases, seemingly endless, important subsectors may be discovered. Since sector therapy is based on psychoanalytic principles, long-term therapy of this type has to enter several sectors. However, psychoanalysis not being feasible for those cases, sector therapy can be considered the only choice, if psychotherapy is at all economically indicated.

Patients vary considerably in the amount and solidity of insight they attain and which is necessary for practical application to everyday problems. In a concept of working through by continual confrontation with the verbalized material, it is implied that a patient's ego, by means of recall, abreaction and identification with the therapist, can gradually become strengthened to the point where past behavior can be integrated with present behavior, and future aspirations and gaps in the affective, mnemonic and cognitive components bridged. An enemy of this process is the anxiety developed as unconscious material becomes conscious and the boundaries of the ego are enlarged. The length of this process will, among other things, depend largely upon the ability of the patient's ego to tolerate this anxiety. When a patient in the interview situation shows that he can tolerate anxieties aroused in everyday living, and can make a good adjustment at home, at work and at play, with his family and friends, therapy can be considered as finished, and the process of weaning him may begin. One need not be unduly concerned by residual symptoms of a transient nature. The sector material will plainly indicate when this stage is reached. With severe cases, a long and gradual process of weaning from the therapist is necessary. In some cases, the patient himself will be a judge of its length and the frequency of interviews. In a strict sense, there is no such thing as a "complete" working through in therapy of this type, due particularly to the transference relationship to the therapist.

In this chapter, we shall illustrate the weaning process in action, how important material is worked through, and how a difficult transference situation is handled. With the majority of patients in this kind of therapy, it is important to cultivate a sense of the timelessness of the therapeutic relationship, and instill in them the feeling that the therapist will always be available when needed.

Case Presentation

A thirty-year-old statistician was admitted to the hospital because of feelings of depression, inability to work and painful feelings centered around his mouth. His symptoms had begun following his discharge from the Service, and had become progressively worse over a period of six years. Following a promotion at work where he was appointed as head of a department, he became increasingly agitated and depressed, incapacitated for work, and received both electroshock and insulin-shock therapy in a private hospital. After a period of six months and no change in status, he was admitted to this hospital.

For as long as he could remember he had felt inadequate in all spheres of life and had easily become depressed and anxious over numerous fantasied failures. His father was depicted as too passive, never making much money. The patient was never proud of him. Yet he always set a "terrific pace," never understood him, would not tell him what he wanted, and never gave him enough—a perfectionist. The mother died when the patient was fourteen. All her family had Ph.D.'s and where Phi Beta Kappas. She was brilliant but a "cold fish" type, unhappy with her husband. Just prior to her death she developed a severe agitated depression. He had "no feeling one way or another" at the time of her death, but felt very "guilty" over the death of a girl friend two years previously. When he was one and a half years old, a brother was born who died a few months later of an obscure intestinal ailment. At that time, his mother became ill and was away with her first depression for an unknown length of time. At three he had another brother who was his exact opposite, i.e., easygoing and lazy, who laughed at him and nicknamed him "sucker" for doing so much work for father. He hated and competed with a sister who was four years older, and loved and identified with a sister five years younger.

Enuresis persisted up to eleven and intermittently thereafter until eighteen. Chronic spastic colitis had been present for an indefinite period with an increase in frequency and severity since age fourteen. Masturbation was a problem from age three, when he wore "aluminum mittens," until marriage at twenty when he suffered from ejaculatio praecox. The patient had been involved in five major automobile accidents and numerous minor ones. He was subject to a variety of obsessions and compulsions for as long as he could remember. In spite of them, he had completed college, maintaining a B+ average, and had received an M.A. degree in mathematics. During the war he enlisted as a private and was commissioned on the battlefield. He was extremely capable and well regarded in his field of work. His wife was described as a duplicate of his mother, compulsive, rigid and "cold." They had one child, a boy aged three.

Physical examination and laboratory procedures were negative. He showed no retardation in thinking, his speech was clear and rational and his thought processes were logical except in one sphere referring to a group of symptoms centered about his mouth. His body image in this area felt distorted, and at times he feared he would die any moment. He was "too weak" and suffered "too much pain" to sit in the interview situation for the first six months, and lay on his right side in order to be able to talk. His mouth felt torn apart, and there was a compulsive need to suck the fingers of his right hand and spit and blow through his mouth. He walked in a manner like a case of advanced Parkinsonism.

The patient was seen three times a week over a period of seven months. At the end of this time, his symptoms were minimal, and he went on a month's leave, following which he was discharged. He was seen in follow-up interviews approximately once a month over a period of a year, during which time his symptoms and difficulties were minimal. It was felt that he was a compulsive-obsessional character whose defenses had crumbled, revealing a latent schizophrenic psychosis. This was confirmed by a Rorschach Test.

In therapy the over-all sector, *Mouth,* thinned out directly into numerous subsectors revolving around such actions as sucking, talking, spitting out, blowing, tasting, biting, smelling, chewing, and indirectly into numerous lesser sectors. Anal and oral elements were inextricably confused; at one time, he wiped his mouth with toilet paper while at stool. Chart 1 (page 190) shows the main ramifications of the material. At the end of therapy the mouth symptomatology appeared to have represented above all an autistic, magic act which endeavored to restore his mother as the bringer of good juices and good feelings. Hostile feelings against the brother born when he was one and a half years old, and against mother for leaving him, had been denied and repressed, so that at three, when his second brother was born, he was already fearful, timid and anxious and unable to show hostility in any form, to the point of masochism. During the war, however, his hostile feelings toward his brothers found adequate expression. He was an artillery observer and once said, "I fought the war with my mouth." This was the one time in his life when he felt happy and not guilt-ridden. After discharge from the Service, he had to use so many devices to defend himself against his aroused aggressive impulses that he felt continually exhausted. Finally, his overburdened ego-defensive mechanisms gave way, leading to a deep oral regression.

At the time of his discharge from the hospital, his ego had been considerably strengthened and his symptoms were minimal. By unraveling the material connected associatively with his mouth, his attitude toward the former delusional material had changed remarkably. The majority of interviews revolved around his great need for an oral relation to his "mummy" and his wife, their coldness, and how he had taken over the role of "mummy" himself. Also prominent was his ambivalence concerning himself and them, his working for them and being overworked by them and not getting enough love in return, being tired and not knowing what to do. Anxiety-laden tendencies to turn to father and the men were always in the background. As the appended Chart 1 shows, the principal sector dealt with the mouth. The various subsectors and their connections and ramifications are also demonstrated.

The first interview to be considered in entirety will illustrate a portion of the working through of material connected with the MOUTH. It took place six months after his discharge from the hospital, and followed the birth of his second child. The patient had been seen on an outpatient basis once a month.

INTERVIEW 1

P. Well. . . . (Hands doctor a cigar)

[*He had phoned in requesting an appointment following the delivery of his wife. He was neatly dressed and walked and talked in an animated manner.*]

D. Well, congratulations. So she had the baby?

P. Well, she was due originally, the doctor said, the *11th.* Then last week he said today, and Saturday morning she began to *run* and *drip,* and *drip* and *dribble,* so on Saturday noon I took her in, and Saturday night or Sunday morning she delivered and it was complete. It was a girl.

[*His wife and child now are taking over his own feminine fantasies. His enuresis stopped, he said, at eleven, and he had talked continually of running and dribbling in connection with his enuresis.*]

D. Now you have a little boy and a little girl?

[*Now both sides of himself can be expressed.*]

P. Yes, a boy and a girl. Just right. (Chuckles) What with your *influence,* and with the influence you have exerted on me in the past year or thereabouts (laughs), it helped.

D. What do you mean? It has helped you to have a girl?

[*To accept the feminine side of himself.*]

P. (Laughs loudly and says, half humorously and half sarcastically) Oh, yuh, sure.

D. How do you mean?

CHART 1

SHOWING KEY WORDS AND SUBSECTORS DURING THE ENTIRE COURSE OF THERAPY

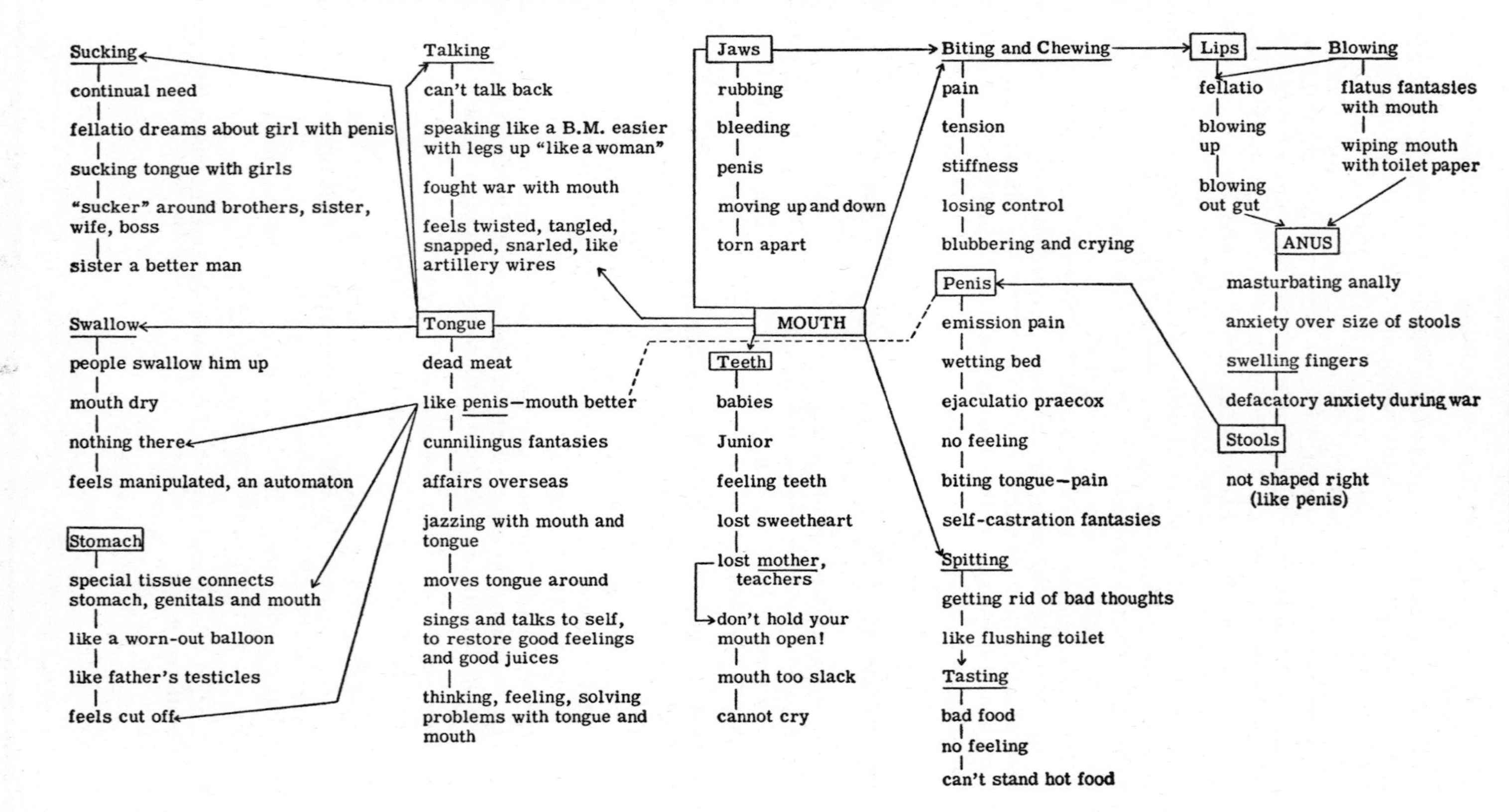

P. Oh, I was just kidding. After all, maybe it has had some impact on my sex determining genes. (Chuckles again)

[*This is the unconscious fantasy, now acceptable as a "joke."*]

P. At least we got what we wanted. That's the main thing. And I've been on pins and needles ever since. The fact is I'm going over to see her right after we finish here. She's at the hospital and doing very well. Yesterday was kind of a *low day* for *her,* I guess. Talk about a compulsive-obsessional personality, boy, she was right out hanging clothes on the washline right up to the point where she dripped. That's how compulsive she is. She had to work all the time.

[*The anxiety is attached to outside events in a normal fashion and no longer acted out so much on his body, i.e., mouth. The baby is a mixed blessing. When he talks about his wife he is talking about part of himself.*]

D. You mean like mother used to be?

[*The reference to mother should guide him back into the past.*]

P. Uh huh, that's right. I even had to take the wash in for her. Then on Friday afternoon I had given a pint of blood downtown, so I got my job done just in the nick of time. Although she didn't need any, still they make those arrangements though, to insure yourself against any cost. (Pause) My only *trouble* is, I haven't been able to *settle down* or *sleep* very well since. (Pause) I had *too many things to do.*

[*This must be the reason for the requested session. "Settling down" and "sleeping" in the child are connected with being fed, and we have to await the opportunity of introducing the "mouth."*]

D. How do you mean?

P. Well, I started out with the idea that I would *take care* of our boy, at least nights, and until after breakfast; and boy, it was a mad rush, and what's more my car broke down; and that was kind of upsetting; and then *my* grandmother has thought that it would be best if she took care of him all the time, and it got down to where it was almost a battle between *me* and *her* as who would have the *boy,* which she has done. That would be all right, only it has left me kind of *lonely.* Anyway, I've been pretty busy. So I guess that will be all right.

[*His reference to "my" grandmother is a slip, as he meant the boy's grandmother, thus showing his identification with the lonely boy of the past. The battle between "me" and "her" reduplicates a battle he had with mother in the past when he was identified with her. She lost her little boy, and he always feared a retaliatory loss of his genital (little one). At another level, it is a battle between two mothers for the baby. "Lonely" is a key word which gives the interviewer an opportunity to return to the past and his attempts to busy himself.*]

D. Now you are in the position you were in when your brother came along; only, of course, then you already had your sister?

P. Oh, you mean I'm the one that is shoved *out in the cold,* huh? Well, I'm *lonely* anyway. Of course, I act a lot *like she did,* that is, keep busy all the time. It keeps me from being *lonely.*

[*Mother had been described as one who kept busy all the time. By keeping busy, he restores the mother, in one sense.*]

D. You were *lonely* then? Do you remember?

P. Yuh, you know, I see it plainly now. With the *mother gone,* I, I try to fill up all the *gaps* that are left by her absence, at least now. I do all her work, as well as my own.

[*This is exactly right but must be amplified and reiterated.*]

D. Become *mother?*

P. Yuh, become *mother.* It's hard to do everything; yet I try. I act like the *mother* and the *child* both. (Laughs)

[*He means only in the present which is not too helpful unless it is connected with past feelings, and especially with the mouth.*]

D. But this is what you said you did when your little brother was born—tried to fill all the *gaps,* especially that big *gap* there, the *mouth,* huh, when you tried to *restore the good juices?*

[*These words had been used repeatedly by him in describing his mouth symptoms.*]

P. Well, it's a funny thing, I found myself *flailing around* with my *tongue* in my *mouth* since she's been *gone.* It's sort of trying to get the *satisfactions* that you normally get by having people around.

[*These symptoms are still present and must be drained of their affective charge.*]

D. With your *mouth,* huh?

P. Yuh, that's right. And I've done a lot of *talking.* I've made all the phone calls I could reasonably make. I even called my brother up, and around Monday or Tuesday I called up my sister. I was just doing everything and doing my *work,* too, and going in to see my wife, so I was pretty active. (He keeps patting his left side and occasionally he sticks his finger in his left ear) In fact, the *pressures* have been such that I could hardly sit still very long. It's as if I was overstimulated by these *pressures.*

[*His patting himself seems to represent the active, masculine ego reassuring the passive, feminine, baby side. Sticking his finger in his ear looks like filling in a gap and may symbolize feeding at an oral level, at another a sexual relationship. He has to bring more material. His symbolic movements involving activity help to break up passive sensations arousing anxiety. These occur when he sits still.*]

D. You mean in your *mouth?*

P. Well, some of them *reflect* there, yes.

[*A far cry from his complaints when he was admitted to the hospital.*]

D. But no longer all in the *mouth?*
P. No longer, it's—now it's *all over.*
D. Better distributed, huh?

[*The mouth has been relieved from carrying the entire burden of expressing his anxiety-laden drives.*]

P. (Laughs) Yes, it's a lot easier to bear when it's all over than when it's concentrated in one spot. But if I'm not careful they tend to go right back into my *mouth.* I just make myself.
D. How do you keep them distributed. How do you do it?

[*This question tries to test how he arrived at this concept.*]

P. Oh, I don't know. I sort of *relax* and let them distribute as they will rather than allowing them to *concentrate* out on my *mouth.*
D. How do you do it? I notice you *hunch up* when you say that.

[*He had momentarily returned to the old posture (see history).*]

P. Well, let me put it this way. (Long pause) When *good things* are happening, I tend to feel *good,* especially in through *my face,* like when you are around *someone* you *like* [*This refers to the good mother.*] or doing something you want to do, or listening to good music, or driving fast in a car. You get a *good, flushed feeling,* and then if all of a sudden conditions are such that you are *disappointed* or that *feeling stops,* then I tend to make an effort to *restore* that good feeling by various means.

[*In reality by the magic of imitation.*]

D. You mean you try to get those *good feelings* to come back to your *face?*
P. Well, I try to *keep* them there all the time.
D. So that if they are there in your *face,* they will spread *all over?* How do you mean?
P. Well, just as long as they are there, I feel all right; otherwise, I feel sort of *empty.*

[*"Face" is apparently used instead of "mouth." When he feels his mouth empty, he begins to be depressed.*]

D. Do those *feelings* in your *face* reassure you?
P. Yuh, they *reassure* me, and if I'm not getting them I feel very, uh, *anxious* and, uh, *depressed,* but it is more *anxious.*

[*Thus the illusory mouth feelings ward off the depression.*]

D. You mean as if it were a warning that you were going to *lose everything?*

[*Losing things refers to all facets of his personality and to all levels of development. When he plays a passive role, he has to give up activity, and this arouses anxiety. Using the mouth actively to receive passively is the compromise solution.*]

P. That's right, that's right, and as that condition develops, I'll go to all sorts of devious means to keep them going.
D. Such as?

P. Well, I might use the telephone to call up people I know and *talk* to them, or *smoke,* or *chew* candy, or *work my mouth* around, or have a *glass* of beer, or (Pause) well I might try to think about *good things,* or try to *settle problems,* anything to keep it up, to keep the *good feelings going.*

[*At the height of his illness, he had declared that he thought with his mouth; i.e., everything took place there, like a newborn baby.*]

D. *Solving problems* helps that feeling?

[*He had discussed this in connection with solving crossword problems.*]

P. Well, yes.

D. So that's what you meant when you said you *thought* with your *mouth*?

P. Well, that's partly true.

D. You mean you feel your mouth when you are thinking and *solving problems, as* if you were *talking out loud*?

[*Closer to a more normal ego attitude. In reality, he dwelt on the feelings in his mouth to escape from his problems; i.e., he concentrated on sensory details to avoid larger and more overwhelming feelings and thoughts.*]

P. Uh huh. I sort of *talk to myself.* It's the same thing that happens when I meet *someone* that I like to *talk* to and feel *pretty good* when I *see.* When you have to *break it off,* well, you just, well you just try to keep on going. It's a sort of *talking* to *yourself.*

[*This was his solution to a painful and inadequate relationship with mother for whom he worked so hard.*]

D. To keep up the good *feelings*?

P. Yuh, I noticed it Tuesday afternoon. I was at a meeting, sitting there *listening,* and I had to keep quiet and *listen* to somebody else. I had to do it for about two hours, and by the time it was up I was so anxious that I could hardly sit still.

[*The passivity of the situation was too anxiety-provoking, as passivity has been connected with: (1) feminine birth and loss fantasies as a child; (2) his anxiety-laden childhood; (3) being in relationship to a man who uses his mouth or fills his ears with sounds.*]

D. You wanted to use your *mouth*?

P. That's right. I find myself doing the same thing around the apartment. I'd tell people about *the baby* and various things that would make me feel *good.* Then when the wife came home I just couldn't do it any more, and I kind of couldn't settle down to any kind of calm work.

[*The activity must serve also as a denial of some wish connected with a baby.*]

D. But are you *ashamed* of using your *mouth*?

[*Here he had begun to cover his mouth with his hand.*]

P. Well, that's true too. How do you know?

D. Because, although you don't *suck* on your *fingers* any more, you take your *hand* and cover your *mouth* over when you talk, and then you put it down like you did just then.

[*Utilizing his postural movements which announce the emerge of a painful thought that he would like to hide. The preliminary remark is a boost to his ego to help him reveal his thoughts.*]

P. Well, back when I was in the hospital doing that, to some extent those *mouth* reactions that I got were somewhat *painful,* partly I guess because my *teeth* weren't in very *good shape,* I guess, and I had been inactive for so long. I just couldn't *restore* the *good feelings,* but now, well, it's my interpretation of it, I may be all wrong. So much of the time I'm getting the *good feelings* that when they stop, well, I, I endeavor to get some of it back by sort of *rubbing* my *mouth* or *using* my *tongue,* and I find also that I *overwork* my *mouth,* so that I, well, I, like today, I, I attempt, well when I get up, and you're about the first person I have been able to *talk* to for any length today because I've been all *alone* up until now. Why, for the past two or three hours this morning already I've had these *pressures* building up in my *face,* and I have to sort of *satisfy* them. It's like a person who is used to *talking* a couple of hours every morning and then doesn't, and the desire is still there and the result is he will *beat* his *gums* and *chew cigars* and do all sorts of things, and then his *mouth* feels after a while sort of *mashed in* as though he had *overworked* it, sort of *weary* and *worn.* So then you sort of make those *movements.*

[*Teeth represent an active, aggressive part of the mouth and in previous sessions had led to sexual frustrations, i.e., frustrated phallic aggressive activity. "Rubbing" or "overworking" his mouth refer, at one level, to masturbatory impulses. In the previous interview, he had complained of being overworked sexually by his wife, and in the past by mother in connection with chores.—"Pressures building up": All his life he had shifted from one type of masturbatory activity to another to avoid anxieties connected with the loss of mother and the little one being cut off from good feelings. "Mashed in," "weary," etc. were words he previously used, describing his childhood impressions of father's genitals.*]

D. So it is as if you do two things: (1) you sort of try to restore the good feelings, the good juices, and (2) you try to soothe and sort of bind up your wounds?

[*A narcissistic solution acted out upon his own body.*]

P. That's right, one of my big troubles all along here is that I've been kind of like a *child* in many ways, you know, all full of enthusiasm or desires to do something. He's unable to *articulate* and *express* it properly, and he *stutters* or *stammers,* or *all sort of things.* It's as if he's got more *pressures* than he really can *control.* Also there may be certain fears and frustrating elements that get him all *tangled* up.

[*Although his insight is very limited, it enables him to remain satisfactorily in the reality world. The feelings of the child had been completely denied and repressed and are gradually becoming conscious, allowing for a new solution and integration with the more mature portions of his personality.*]

D. Did the pressures ever make you *stutter*?

[*It might have been better to take up the fears and frustrating elements.*]

P. No, I've never stuttered, but I often will not be able to talk too *coherently* and I tend to *overshoot* what I have to say and *back track,* well, in such a way that it isn't an *even flow,* and it isn't as satisfactory as it should be if things went a little more smoothly; and, of course, for the past week I've been *stimulated* up to a pretty high level, and as a result I haven't been able to talk *calmly* or *softly* or *quietly* or *easily.*

[*His speech suggests the presence of urethral libidinal elements and fantasies.*]

D. But don't you do very well?

P. Oh, I'm doing pretty well right now, but sometimes at work I don't, and I *overshoot* the mark in my *talking.* I get too *anxious.* Then I don't get the *satisfaction* that you get from making yourself clear. I'm like a fellow who is telling a joke and is so anxious to get to the point that he doesn't introduce everything. Well, even right now, for instance, when I came driving in here and was in a hurry to talk to you, when I came here I found you were *busy* with *someone else,* and then I went down to the *nurse's* office and they were *busy,* gee! (Laughs)

[*As a child, he had engaged in urinary competitive games and had always felt inadequate. So many things revive the painful infantile loss of the mother to the sibling rivalry.*]

D. You mean that was *painful*?

P. Well, it can be very *painful.* It can be *painful* and *disappointing,* and the reaction I get is in my *mouth* and my *face.* It seems to be *painful,* it's somehow there in its own right.

D. And so *then* you do what you did just *now, rub* your face and use your tongue and sort of *restore* those *good feelings*?

[*Bringing his postural movements to consciousness.*]

P. That's right. Well, I'll tell you, you keep doing these things and you feel that you are *overworking* them and *yet it really isn't enough.*

[*The narcissistic defense is no longer sufficient.*]

D. You mean you have to have *people*?

P. That's right.

D. You mean you can't do it just by yourself?

P. That's right. It's, in a way, it's something I do when I don't have enough *people.* It takes their place.

[*A real piece of insight.*]

D. It was the same way with the little fellow when his brother was born and he had to turn to *himself* to take the place of *mother* who was gone?

[*Connecting it up to the past trauma, referring to the second brother, born when he was three. At that time, the loss he had experienced at one and a half years, when his first brother was born, was re-enacted. At seven, his younger sister was born.*]

P. That's right. I noticed last night I had a *builder* coming over to see me at *7:00* o'clock. After *he* had gone, I was left all *alone* and I wasn't satisfied for the day. I hadn't had enough of that *good feelings.* So I made a couple of *phone calls.* Then I had a glass of *beer* and I was still wishing I could talk to *someone.* Then I sort of got a reaction from that. Now this morning I was pretty anxious. I couldn't *lie still.* I was hoping I could *relax* some and *sleep,* but I couldn't. So I got up and had a glass of *milk.* I used the beer glass and there was a little taste of *beer* in the glass when I drank the milk, and then I felt *terrible.*

[*After the loss of mother, he turns to father (the builder!) with the mouth open. The mouth relationship to mother provides milk; in relation to father he calls it "beer." He wants from father what he got from mother. He also tries to get it from himself. It is known from his history that he turned to masturbation in order to escape from his oral needs.*]

D. Really? How was that?

P. Well, I, I really had a feeling that it was really *wicked* to even take a *drop* of that *stuff* before *meals* and getting up in the *morning.* (Chuckles) I've had that as long as I can remember, that feeling, that's as bad as the height of *depravity.* I had *terrible guilt feelings.* I can even remember back to seventeen when I felt anyone who would do such a thing was beyond the pale. It's *just like* sort of feeling as if I *masturbated.* When I was around that age, I used to set a certain *quota* for myself. If I violated it, I felt *terrible.* I have to keep things in that quota system even, even like *beer.* (Long sigh. Long pause)

[*At seventeen his anxieties over his masturbatory activities were at a peak.The patient's elaborations in regard to the "quota system" make theoretical speculation unnecessary.*]

P. Of course, that's the *bad part* of it. The good part about it is, I'm still going forward, enjoying some things quite a bit. I got a *new tooth* in now which I haven't gotten used to yet, and of course with all the other *tension* feelings in my mouth, uh, sort of tends to be, well to make my head kind of *rock* when I talk.

[*Tooth now represents the narcissistic body representative of the baby which as yet has not been integrated with the body image.*]

D. With all the other *tensions*?

P. Well, all the other *tension* stuff seems to reflect there, so. (Pause) See! (He extracts the single tooth bridge work and shows it)

D. It looks very *substantial.*

[*The interviewer approves the object inserted into the mouth.*]

P. I haven't *slept* with it yet. It's a funny thing. When I put this thing on, the tension seems to increase all throughout my face, and I sort of feel additional *tension,* uh, well, like across the uh, *transverse colon.* How would that be?

[*The addition to the family causes tension. Now he brings up a birth fantasy. Is that the result of having the "tooth" in the mouth?*]

D. How do you mean *transverse colon?*

P. Well, for example, I'll put the thing on sometimes at night, or I had it on this morning for instance, and uh, the *normal relief* I get, uh sort of from *overworking my mouth,* uh that kind of *stops* because when I have this in there *I can't do that so much,* and the *tension* seems to transfer down into here.

[*A reduplication of what happened in the past when his brother was born.*]

D. When you put that in your *mouth?*

P. That's right.

D. And then you feel it *down here?* (Pointing to the abdomen)

P. Well, I not only *feel* it when I put it in there, but I even feel a *pressure* down here when it usually is up *here.*

[*Pressure is displaced downwards. He had described such feelings in his wife, using "pressure" and "tension."*]

D. The same place your wife felt her tension?

P. That's right.

D. You mean with her baby?

P. Ha, ha, it would seem so.

D. In other words, she is *overworked* and feels it down here, and you are *overworked* in your *mouth,* and feel it down there too. Is that only when it is in your mouth?

P. Well, when my tooth isn't in there, I tend to kind of, uh, you know, working my lips and *gnashing my teeth,* that sort of thing. When the tooth is in there, I sort of stop that because it is more painful to do that when the tooth is in there.

[*The emptiness of the mouth gives him a double loss feeling: nothing in the mouth and nothing in the abdomen.*]

D. You mean you have difficulty restoring those *good juices* you were telling me about?

P. Well, partly that I should say, well yes, and partly when I *close* my mouth tight, that is, when I have to *keep my mouth shut* (bursts out laughing here), then the *tension* builds up and I feel it down here.

[*In some situations it is dangerous to open the mouth.*]

D. When the tension builds up, you feel it there, that is when you can't use your mouth?

P. That's right. Of course, that has *always* been the case but it has been more so since I put that bridge in there.

D. You *remember* that even in the past?

[*A good time to get into the past.*]

P. Oh, sure.

D. What do you *remember* about it?

P. What do you mean in the *past*?

D. Well, you said *always,* and I wondered.

P. Well, even before I had this bridge-work done, the same general idea was true. (Pause) Does all this sound *silly* to you?

[*He is getting a little anxious.*]

D. Why? What do you mean? (Smiles)

P. (Laughs) Well, it seems silly to me. (Laughs harder) Yet it really isn't, that is, it hasn't *always* been that way.

D. You mean you wonder why you should have these feelings down here. After all, you haven't a baby.

[*A remark concerning his oral impregnation fantasies.*]

P. Well, that's partly it, yes, I should say so. I guess the *baby* has something to do with it.

D. What makes you think so?

'. Oh, I don't know. I have heard that sometimes men feel the same pains as women do when they are not the *pregnant* ones. Whether that's true in my case, I haven't the slightest idea, because I had the *same type* reactions even when my wife wasn't pregnant.

D. Do you mean that it is a different kind of a baby? Once before you spoke of the little Eddy inside you who has always felt that way, that is, sort of *whiny* and *overworked,* and not getting enough of those *good juices,* who feels *discontented*?

[*Now the interviewer deals with the wife and the little boy, instead of the mother and the patient as a little boy, and mouth and tooth.*]

P. Yes, and having to strive too hard to get those *good feelings.* Of course, my *little boy* complains too some.

[*Past and present become fused.*]

D. You mean your little Eddy at home? How is that?

P. Well, when he gets tired he seems to complain about a pain in the *stomach.*

[*He lets his little boy talk for him.*]

D. You've heard him?

[*The interviewer encourages him, because in that way anxiety-charged material is indirectly released.*]

P. Oh, yeh.

D. *Tired* and *overworked* or not getting enough *attention?*

P. Oh, not getting enough *attention* usually.

D. From mother?

P. Yes, from *mother,* or even from *me* or his little *girl friends.* His main girl friend is a girl about five and he's three, and she's just enough more *independent,* so that when they are out playing and she wants to do something she'll go ahead and do it, and sometimes she's able to move *faster* than he does; so she'll start off in some direction and he won't like that. He can't *keep up* with her.

[*There seems to be in his eyes only "one world": the child's world.*]

D. Can't blame him, but how come? You say she is *older.* Did she get more *love* or more *good juices,* or what? How come she is able to be more independent?

P. Oh, she just seems to act that way, that is, when the situation gets where she doesn't like it, she'll just *take off;* and when Eddy gets *whiny,* she may start to *take off,* and he'll start *whining* all the harder at her like a baby. And he'll *come home* sometimes kind of down in the *mouth,* and I can tell that's what the story has been, and I can also tell because I had had *enough of the same myself.* I can see it, you might say *twice.*

[*Now he is beginning to develop insight. He uncovers again the child-like ideas as his own.*]

D. Down in the *mouth?* You mean he feels it in his *mouth* too?

P. Yeh, yes, and here's another example of it too. It's the *same thing* as happens to *me.* Now he'll wake up in the morning, for instance, oh, *singing* and *cooing* and calling for his *Mommie.* Instead of her going out and maybe seeing him and *cajoling* him out of bed a little bit, she'll berate him for being *lazy* and not getting up, and that gets things off to a *bad start.* Then by the time he comes down to breakfast and he is not *eating* it as fast as she wants him to, she gives it to him again; and after breakfast is over and he goes over and stands next to her, then she is by that time *busy* and eating hers and she doesn't want him *hanging around* her; and by that time she wonders why he is *whining.*

[*He used to sing and talk to himself, and constantly accuses himself of laziness.*]

D. It reminds me of what you used to say about *your sister* and *your mother?*

[*Trying to weave all the material together.*]

P. You mean the big sister? Well, my big sister was never the kind you'd want to *cuddle up* to anyway.

D. She was more independent too?

P. Well, yes, that's right. I guess so was everybody but me. (Laughs) It probably isn't true, but that's the way you feel, and that makes it—that's the way it is.

D. Then you'd get down in the *mouth* and have the same feelings little Eddy has at home?

P. Uh huh. The same thing even happens at work, or happened at work somewhat. The *secretary* is very nice as I told you. One of the guys there who is ahead of me, you could call him the *boss* as much as anybody, has a boss around there, he has appropriated her for a *special job* which takes maybe about a third of her time. It's a very important thing, sort of *special.* Of course, I realize it has got to happen, but my reaction was not to like that, because in addition to her *working* for me she was also doing a *little work* for the whole office and she had to neglect them somewhat; so that makes the other side of me take over for a while. *I feel hurt.*

[*His feelings of oral deprivation break through in reality relationships. He is jealous of the secretary and also of the boss, and competes with both of them.*]

D. You mean the little Eddy in you reacts like your little Eddy at home and feels down at the *mouth*?

P. (Laughs) Yeh, that's it. She's being *taken away* from me (in a mock, whiny voice), but of course she really is, but it's only for a while, so I get the *feeling,* maybe I should make something that's *important* so I'd have her for me, but I haven't got anything *important* to do, as *important* as that.

D. This is somewhat the same fix as little Eddy was in back in the past at home with Mummy.

[*Repetitive confrontation with the loss of the mother, which is the focal point of the treatment.*]

P. Yeh, that's right.

D. He tried to find things to keep Mummy's *attention* on himself.

P. Yeh, and when she's the kind of person who is hard to please, you start to *play* all around and *play* all around, and you *knock yourself* out.

[*Playing around and knocking yourself out refers to the infantile masturbatory activity. He played at being Mummy and Daddy, thus giving himself good feelings.*]

D. Like you did with *Mummy*?

P. That's right, and with everybody else I get an attachment to, because you need them, and sometimes the attachment is so strong that it is hard to break and you can't make up your mind. You're so afraid of *losing anything* in any direction, that you're pushed this way and that way in every direction, depending which way the wind is blowing. So you can't steer a steady course of your own. So with all those things *pulling* at me it tends to leave me *exhausted,* and on top of that I am planning out the first stages of some *new work* at the office. It seems to divide itself into an easy part, which is just finished, and now I'm going into a harder part, and, well, your enthusiasm tends to be a little diminished, and it becomes more of a burden. At least that's the way I react to it. Occasionally, a few times now, I've gotten anxious and fearful that the load might get too heavy again, but really I feel *things* are going pretty *good.*

[*He now turns to the future and "new work," but there is anxiety too, as in the past. The expectancy of loss is always there, and he is constantly prepared for overwhelming blows. He tries to reassure himself.*]

D. Scared of getting *down at the mouth* again?

P. Yuh, that's a good way to put it. There's a certain road you have to travel and if you have a *wreck* in the middle of the road that is halfway down, the next ten times you go down there after that you think of it and you *worry* and *hold your breath* until you get by.

[*Here we get a hint of the significance of keeping the mouth closed to avoid taking in unpleasant things, and hang on to what you have.*]

D. What *spot* do you mean because, *as you said,* the last time, there are a number of *spots* where you had *wrecks*. There was the one where your first little brother was *born* and *died;* and then when the second one was *born*; and then when *mother died*; and then when the *girl* turned you down in Washington; and when your *wife* turned you down before going overseas; and when you *left* the Service; and when you *came home.*

[*The relevant units of this material are brought into focus, in order to use them in a concentrated form for the confrontation.*]

P. (Interrupting) And tried to get in bed with my *wife* and got the *brush-off*. I even got it last night.

D. And even when you tried to get your promotion which came at the same time you got turned out of your house, and then your baby came along, another mouth to feed; so really there are all kinds of *wrecks* along the road, and I wondered which one you meant.

[*All wrecks in life are one and the same: the mouth is hurt.*]

P. Well, I really don't know because all those wrecks seem to be *one and the same wreck* in some ways. They seem like *hurdles,* and each one seems to be a little *higher.*

[*His anxieties tend to summate faster than he can handle them.*]

D. How do you mean the same type? You mean *competition* with a *newcomer* and *rejection* by the *mother,* and feeling *down* at the *mouth* and getting *funny feelings* in your *stomach?*

[*Weaving in additional words of his.*]

P. Yes, it is like the summer of 1950. There was another thing that was important too. I don't think I told you. My boss was giving a conference and he wanted me to help him, but he was, really the *whole show*. The result was that I felt I was being completely *outdone* when I compared *myself* to *him,* which was all very silly, and I tried to think it was silly at the time, but it didn't work.

[*New and important material can also be integrated—it was in the summer of 1950 that he broke down.*]

D. He was an older man?

P. Yeh, he's gone now. He went out to the *West* Coast and is probably making quite a figure now like *you*. (Chuckles)

D. What do you mean?

P. Oh, five figures and all like that. (Chuckling. Long pause) Well, that was one of the big factors that brought me in here, just about the time everything was at a low ebb, work, living with the in-laws and everything. Do you know I had an automobile *wreck* on New Year's Eve?

D. No, I don't believe you mentioned it. Tell me about it.

[*Another loss he had never mentioned*]

P. Well, we were out New Year's Eve.

D. Who is we?

P. My wife and I and another couple. I went home and it was an icy night and this car was coming in the other direction. I ended over to the side of the road, but still the car *hit me.* It wasn't my fault, luckily, or I would have been more shaken up than I was. At the same time, my *poor little car* which I had had for around *ten years* was pretty badly *messed up,* and that on top of everything else nearly *paralyzed* me. That's why I turned into the hospital. It's the first *wreck* I ever had in my life, although there was an accident, another accident, in my life which was also significant too. There was this girl. This was when I was *fifteen* or *sixteen.* She was named Barbara Allen and she was well known, almost as an *easy mark.*

[*The figures must have some significance and may refer to other wrecks when he was ten. In the interview, he is now turning from an oral to a phallic, competitive, aggressive level after releasing enough anxiety from the passive side. Shifts from the feminine level to a phallic one during an interview are often expressed in a symbolic way, using parts of the body: like tooth versus stomach, or head versus chest. It is a kind of balancing of passive and aggressive tendencies.*]

D. An easy target for your gun?

[*Referring to his war experiences as an artillery observer, of which he said, "I fought the war with a phone and my mouth." (See Association Chart 2.)*]

P. (Chuckling) That's right. In fact the general talk around the high school was that all you had to do was have one date with her and "you were in." Well, of course, I didn't dare to get mixed up in anything like that. I also heard these stories that a boy used to go over and sit on the front porch and *play* with her. You could do *anything* you wanted with her, *anything* you wanted to do. Well, one time I went out shopping with the *car,* went downtown to buy some *groceries,* and I had the bright idea that I would try to find Barbara and take her out in the *car* and all that. I felt with a *car* I'd be all set up. It was the *family car,* of course.

[*He has previously talked of little Eddy playing with the older girl.*]

D. Father's car?

P. Yeh, father's car. So I stopped there and talked her into going for a *ride,* which she did.

D. Without anxiety on your part, huh?

P. Oh, my God, tremendous! Well, we started to cross a *bridge,* and the bridge was the type where it had railings which seemed to start all at once, big metal ones. I don't know how to describe it properly. It goes along as a regular bridge and then all of a sudden you have these *big steel things* on the sides which *stick out* almost squarely. Well, there was *another car* coming anyway, and in a place where the bridge was a little bit narrower than the rest of it, and these things came in and there wasn't any leeway to get over *out of the way*. Well, I thought to myself, this is going to be bad. There wasn't anything left for me to do but either *hit her* or turn right to *avoid her,* so I turned *right* and ran the car right into the side of the bridge, *smashed* up the fender and cut up the tire. It was just too bad; that is, it wasn't too bad an accident, but I was scared to *death* of the whole situation. Here I was with this girl, apparently a *whore.* I'd gone there with the specific intention of trying to get into her *pants,* and then that happened.

[*Another bridge; he is using a complex symbolism, suggesting that his turning to his sister and father came to grief. He had previously talked of his sister's smelly pants, and guilt over sexual games with both sisters.—It is striking how the whole tone of the interview changes when he begins to exhibit his superior masculinity. The weaning procedure of the interview leads to aggressive strivings of independence.*]

D. You felt caught?

P. Yes, I was *caught,* so I immediately, well, we weren't more than a mile from the place where she lived, so I told her to get out of the car and walk on home, and I'd take care of that. I was *scared* that if anybody else had come up and seen me, huh. The other girl didn't even stop. She kept on going. She probably didn't even know what happened. That girl was a tomboy, the rough type, almost like my *big sister,* the kind you might *get into* but you wouldn't want to. You might find the muscles down there so big that you'd get *strangled.* (Chuckles to himself)

[*There were two girls, the older sister was a tomboy. He had fantasies of the vagina as a mouth, and ejaculatio praecox. (See Association Chart 2.) He uses the "dirty" talk of the boys and is amused.*]

P. Well, anyway, I lied about it when I got home. I told them about the accident but not the circumstances, and that was the beginning, well, let's say, not the beginning, but just one more of those things that seemed to make all the hurdles bigger for me.

[*All wrecks are the same: the mouth feels hurt, and that makes the next hurdles bigger, as he said before.*]

D. You mean that was a pretty dangerous proposition?

P. You said it! Here was the first time that I got the courage to approach a girl, and look what happened.

D. And you were with your wife and another couple in the accident?

[*To unravel the meaning of the present accident.*]

P. This time, yeh.

D. What couple was that?

P. Some people named Smith. He had a very *pretty* wife. He has since moved away.

[*He intimates the lady-killer attitude.*]

D. He had a *pretty nice wife*?
P. Yeh, she got a little *hurt* in the accident. She bumped her *head.*

[*What kind of "women" are those who bump their heads? The explanation follows, when he says those who have no children and bite or snap at the "man," i.e., who use their mouths to hurt what they get into it.*]

D. How do you mean by nice?
P. Yuh. She certainly was. In fact, come to think of it, I had been comparing her with my own *wife.*
D. Better than your wife?
P. Well, more so, in most ways, yes.
D. What do you mean?
P. Well, that's hard to say. She *never had any children* and she looked better then. Yet there's quite a lot of resistance in her too, a kind of a girl you'd figure—well, you go up behind her and put your arms around her to surprise her, and she might turn around and *bite* at you instead of being just *surprised* and *glad,* if you know what I mean. Some girls are like unbridled colts. They almost *snap* at you. (Chuckles) Whereas, others aren't that way.
D. You mean, some girls are dangerous like your sister?
P. Yeh.
D. You were afraid of her?
P. Yes.
D. You mean for what she did or tried to do to you?
P. Yeh, that's right, she tried to seduce me once, but I was afraid of her and she was *smelly.* At least I thought so then. At least there is one thing I'll give my *wife* credit for. She's *clean* as a whistle.

[*He had talked of "smelly" before.*]

D. How did you know that your sister was so *smelly*?
P. Well, I'd been around her bedroom long enough and had seen her old *dirty pants* hanging on the closet door. My youngest sister wasn't too clean either. I guess at that time my *ideas* on that subject were pretty well fixed. Of course, I liked the youngest sister best. She was much more *receptive.* Of course, it was the other way around there. I tried to *seduce* her but it didn't work. At least she never got *mad* at me when I tried anything, even though she might not have liked it. But this other one in the car there, I had the idea if you tried anything with her it would have been *dangerous.*

[*All of this material is linked with the original rejection and represents an effort to work it out, as well as his ambivalent attitude to mother and sisters. Here he equates the girl in the car with a sister figure.*]

D. After all, it was. You got in an *accident.*
P. Ha, ha, ha, that's right. (Long pause) Well, I haven't had a car *wreck*

now for a long time. (Another pause) In fact, I never *really* had a *bad* wreck. (Pause) See that *scar* on my head?

D. Uh huh.

P. That's the one I got when my *brother* was driving. I was in the *back seat* then. That's the one I took the *blame* for him for. Apparently most of the car *wrecks* I got in were where I was trying to make some *good love*.

[*We remember it was the girl who got her head bumped. Now we see he played the girl in relation to his brother. Making love leads to a wreck: the male and the female are hurt, i.e., mouth and head.*]

D. You mean it's *dangerous* to make *love*?

P. It seems to have worked out that way. (Pause) What do we gather from all this?

[*Getting anxious.*]

D. As you said, the only time you got into *wrecks* was when you tried to make *love*. It's as if making *love* is *dangerous*.

P. Of course it is if you get so *absorbed* in it you don't get *going*.

[*In the early stage of therapy, he was afraid of being absorbed (swallowed up) by people, literally.*]

D. What do you mean?

P. Well, the smart thing for me to do is: do my own *driving* and do it right, not let somebody else *drive,* while I concentrate on *love*. I get so *absorbed* in trying to *get there* and get *into it,* that I don't pay any attention to what else is going on. That's about the whole story.

D. But, of course, in the accident the *girl* got hurt.

[*The girl part of him.*]

P. Yeh, that's so. It seems as though when you make *love* someone is going to get *hurt*. I really have felt that way too. I was *afraid* of my *sister,* afraid of what my *father* would say if he caught me with that *girl* when I wrecked the car; yet there are other guys, now take Hank Martin, he is the other extreme from me. He could get away with anything. He used to tell me about how his father *went away* and they had a colored maid that stayed there. So his father came home, took the bed apart and found this rubber in the bed. They had been using the old *man's bed*.

[*Hank Martin is what he would like to be. Now he sends father (West) away again and takes over in this fantasy or screen memory.*]

D. Father found it?

P. Yeh, used, and in the bed. He had been *screwing* the *colored maid,* and all his father told him was, the next time you do that, use your own rubbers and don't use mine. (Patient laughs loud and long)

[*This is the kind of a permissive father he wants, who tolerates anything.*]

D. Your father wouldn't have done that?

P. Boy, I never gave him a chance. He would have told me, keep it in *your* pants.

D. You wish you had such a father?

P. Sometimes it's better for a father to be that way. I guess I *envied* him in some ways. That happened to be my *boss's son.* Remember I told you about when I was working in the bookstore. Well, his father's *dead* now and there's an angle about that that *bothers* me. When I see a guy like that who *died,* I think maybe it's because he lived that way he *died.*

[*A double envy: Hank is himself, just as the boss is father. He is talking about various aspects of his own ego. The punishment for doing bad is dying (going away).*]

D. And you mean he should have led a *nice clean* life if he wanted to *live?*

P. Yeh, keep away from *women* and *liquor* and *things like that.* They tried to get me to work for them, that is to work for the company instead of going to Washington to school. They even went so far as to invite me to a *party* at the best *fraternity* on the campus, and that night he took me aside and asked me to stay and work for the company, and I turned him down. But he now, Hank Martin, Jr., now he runs the company. Gee, even last year I always felt that when things came to the worst, I could always go back to Hank and he'd give me a job.

[*"Things like that" refers to infantile pregenital elements. Adolescent asceticism demands complete renunciation. "Fraternity": the brothers ask him to stay with them and to keep away from women. He reacted like a prudish girl. Now he feels that he can always turn to father and the men.*]

D. When did you *lose him?*

P. Why do you say when did I lose him?

D. Because when you spoke about him, tears came to your eyes.

P. Well, I have a *soft* spot in my heart for him because he was the guy who, well, he always treated me *swell.* If he didn't have any use for you, he'd tell you so too.

D. A real nice *father?*

[*The ego ideal of a father. This also reflects the positive transference and his sorrow at losing his therapist.*]

P. Well, yes. Not only that, but he treats you like a *friend* and an *equal.*

D. Not like a *little boy?*

P. Yes. No matter what you had done, well, if he found you had passed out in the gutter he'd pick you up.

D. Like a *father* should be with his *son.*

P. That's right. He was proud enough of me to invite me to his fraternity *party,* the *best* one on the campus. (Tears flow freely) Also he was the kind of a guy if you came there he'd come over and make you feel at home, say hello to you, introduce you around. You were as *good* as anyone else.

D. You mean you ordinarily wouldn't feel that way?

P. Well, you know me, not always.

D. He was like father should have been?

P. And there was another time, well, one of my best friends I had all the way through high school, two of his older brothers belonged to a certain fraternity, and I knew both of the brothers as well as him; so when the time came to pass out bids, they didn't give me one. Not that I would have joined it anyway, but I would liked to have had a chance.

[*He had never felt "in" with father and brother and had to turn to his sister.*]

D. That hurt?

P. Darn right. It was later on in college that I was invited to that party, but earlier in college my sister had to go to one of those dances. This boy took her, but I don't think he liked her very well. I don't think he wanted her because the boys in the *fraternity* he was in didn't ordinarily date the girls in the *sorority* my sister was in. So she went to the trouble to get me invited over to that fraternity, but when I went over there, why, they didn't give me much of a welcome. I remember when I was invited over to that other party, of course, I was a senior then and he was only a junior, but he was *real nice* to me.

[*"Brothers" don't ordinarily have affairs with sister.*]

D. You mean like a *nice brother?*

[*The ego ideal brother.*]

P. That's right. It was quite a triumph.

D. So I guess your brother didn't treat you like that?

P. No, and I guess I didn't treat him like that. *I* wasn't a *good older brother* to him either. I remember buying a sailboat and he had more use of it than I did, and I remember lending him my car. He always *abused* the privilege whenever you'd let him have it.

D. You mean, you tried to be sort of the good father to brother, as you wanted your father to be to you, but it didn't work.

[*Changing through magic imitation as a forerunner of adult behavior.*]

P. Exactly; all he'd do though is make *fun* of me and call me good old Ed, the sucker. (Laughs) It seems *funny* now but it didn't then.

D. You couldn't even show how *mad* you were?

P. No, that's right.

D. You could only feel *down at the mouth* and get those feelings in your *belly.*

[*Linking up the new material with that from the beginning. The interview had gone ten minutes overtime.*]

P. That's right, and get *tears* in my eyes. (Laughs) What time is it getting to be? I guess I've gone over my time.

D. I didn't notice. Well, it has been good to see you.

CHART 2

SHOWING RELATIONSHIP OF THE MOUTH TO THE MOTHER-CHILD RELATIONSHIP

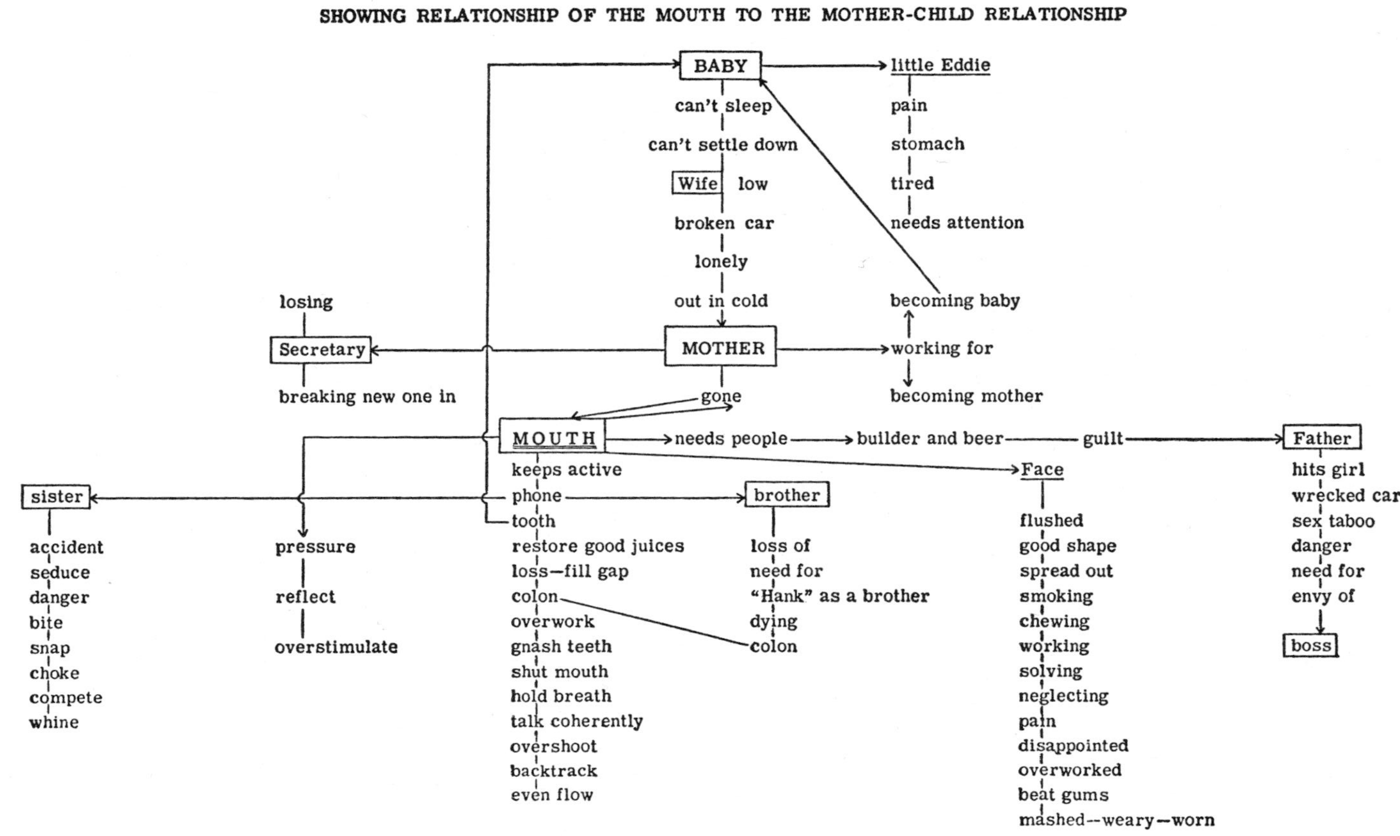

P. Same here, Doc. I hope I can help you sometime. See you next month. [*The interviewer is the good father-brother in the transference relationship, who permits him to compete and accepts him on an equal footing.*]

D. Okay, so long.

Discussion

A glance at Association Chart 2 will show how feelings in relation to the body image of the mouth are linked with his interpersonal relationships both in the past and in the present. The patient's symptoms can be seen, among other factors, as a frantic attempt (1) to restore by a form of infantile magic the good feelings which were a vital necessity to him in the past; (2) to handle anxieties continually resurrected by the distortion of his present relationships, due to a failure in his psychosexual development which made oral dependent needs and fears excessive; (3) to deny anxieties connected with the loss of a mother, pregnancy fantasies and castration fears.

Three months after this interview he called and asked for an appointment, which will be dealt with in Part 2 of this chapter.

Part 2—The Overburdened Mouth

Introduction

In this interview the patient is led into the past and to his mother; the material is kept around the loss of her, and his attempt to find mother substitutes. The interview is concerned with vital interpersonal relationships and frustrations which are now out in the open, and the mouth subsides into the background, being no longer of primary importance.

Interview 2

D. Well, how have things been going?

[*Three months have elapsed since the previous interview, and the patient has been seen monthly. Lately he has been told that his services are no longer required at his job (due mainly to his having been "ill" for such a long time). He is to give a speech at a conference and is taking active steps to obtain a new job.*]

P. Well, events are *breaking* fast and good.

D. What do you mean? What has happened?

P. Well, well, the first thing, of course, the job is over except for a few months. This thing at the convention, you know, this speech, it's still in the wind. That's got me a little *anxious* from time to time, but I think I'll go through that all right. It isn't clear yet exactly what *role* I'll play. We just got a refusal from one of our speakers, and the result is, there may be some readjusting of people on the program. (Pause) Last night I was down at a dinner meeting for a business organization. You know the way I feel the *pressure* somewhat is . . . there's a lot of talk going around now about how much I'm doing for this *organization*. Practically everyone I meet now, they want to shake my hand and say gee whiz, that's a swell job you're doing on this, and I haven't done much of anything anyway. You begin to get that *funny feeling*. Everybody starts coming around and *recognizing* you.

[*He has expressed anxiety in the past over the roles that he played in terms of passivity and activity. In the last interview, the content of the associative material had shifted from passivity to activity.—The family is the primary organization.—He is afraid of the demands that will be placed upon him as an adult man, as his concept of himself in this role is still not firmly established.*]

D. What do you mean, *funny feeling?*

P. Well, you wonder kind of whether you will be able to live up to all their *expectations.* Most of them know darn well that when you actually get down to the *dirty work,* the *glad-handing* has nothing to do with it, and you just got to *sweat it out.*

[*He is afraid of being exploited and rejected again, as he thought he was in the past (father-mother; boss-secretary).*]

D. You mean you are afraid of being "good old Ed" again?

[*"Good old Ed," he called himself once, when he looked at himself as the little, fearful, discouraged one.*]

P. Well, I don't know just what you mean by that.

D. After all, that was one of your difficulties in the past, never knowing what role you were going to play, and playing that of "good old Ed."

P. That's right. Then you get *discouraged* and you get *mad* and you get *depressed.*

D. Mad at yourself?

P. (Laughs) Yeh, and *mad* at any authority figures around me.

[*Here he means the therapist. He is in a seemingly good mood and very confident of himself. He does not want to face the old anxieties and would rather forget them. The interviewer is in the position of the surgeon who realizes that all pockets of the abscess must be drained before healing can be permanent.*]

D. Feeling too much is demanded of Little Ed?

P. Yeh, but this particular speech shouldn't be hard because it is about my own work which I know exactly all about. I've gone through the literature on the subject. There is some nice stuff out.

D. Surely. You know it's your field, and you know it's a good one, and that your knowledge is perfectly adequate.

[*The interviewer pushes him in the direction in which he is already moving.*]

P. Yes, and the more I *talk* to guys, the more I realize that damn few know half as much as I do.

[*He is overconfident.*]

D. You compare their *knowledge* with your knowledge, and you find yours is *big enough,* even *bigger* than theirs?

[*In the past, he was continually comparing his body and bodily products with the rest of the family (organization), with deep feelings of inadequacy.*]

P. (Chuckles) Yup. (Laughs) That makes you *anxious* too, when you find out it's *bigger* than theirs. You don't want to take advantage of these guys. You know what I mean!

[*A wishful fantasy. He now reveals what he wanted to do to his family and what he felt they did to him.*]

D. What do you mean?

P. Well, you get in *conversations* sometimes with people and you're *talking* about a subject, and you bring up something you've read about or this or that case, and pretty soon you find out the guy doesn't know beans, and there's no doubt about that, and it's a *temptation* sometimes if you are feeling a little *aggressive* to kind of lord it over him a little bit, at least to give him the *needle* to some extent.

D. To stick it into him?

[*Revealing the phallic aggressive nature of his wish.*]

P. Yeh.

D. You mean it can go too far?

P. Well, you know you can get a little bit *megalomanic,* and that you've go to watch against.

[*This sounds like a piece of insight, but is rather a part of his infantile defenses and anxieties.*]

D. Because there is always someone who has a bigger one, as you said.

[*He said before that few know half as much as he does.*]

P. That's right. And someone will say, well he thinks he's an awful hot shot, we've got to get rid of him.

[*Like he got rid of brother whom he frequently accused of being a show-off and who lorded it over him.*]

D. You were familiar with that feeling in the past?

P. Not very often. I haven't usually been in that position. I've always been very *careful,* perhaps overly careful to make sure not to be a *show-off.*

D. You mean you wanted to *show off* but you had to be *careful?*

P. Well I had to be *careful* because I didn't dare get into a *vulnerable* position, you know, and have somebody knock you down a peg, if you stood up a little too high.

[*Afraid of having done to him what he wanted to do to brother.*]

D. And *showed what you had?*

P. Yeh, I felt a whole lot *safer* in being little Ed, little me who doesn't amount to much. You get very *uncomfortable* when you get these *swollen* feelings, you know, of being important.

[*He cautiously moves forward, revealing the phallic nature of his rivalry and anxiety.*]

D. Because you wondered how it would *compare* with the others?

P. Yes, you wonder that, and then, of course, you have to use your own *head* and you can't be *dependent* upon anybody else. That's one phase of it. I'll give an example. Last night I was *talking* before I went to the meeting with a couple of guys who are in other fields about possible *speakers* to replace the one who had *refused,* and these fellows were ones who should know something about the field too, and I asked them and they didn't have any *ideas* at all that were any good. In fact, they had very *little idea.* That put me in a position of realizing that, well, it almost goes into *contempt* for them, just like saying, you guys don't even know, you don't know *shit.* When you get that *feeling,* you turn around and it's *dangerous*; you might *express* it. What you really do is sort of *apologize* and *weasel around* and you try to sort of line up *good feelings* about them even though they haven't told you anything.

[*"Dependency" is the source of his original anxiety.—Now he brings up the old competition in a different guise. The "contempt" he felt his family had for him. He brings "contempt" and "shit" and "back" side together. He plays the passive role of "good old Ed," afraid of his aggressiveness.*]

D. You mean not to let them know?

P. Yeh. I didn't want to show any feelings of *triumph* or *scorn.* I had, I had to *butter* them up and *pat* them on the back, sort of, to *assuage* the situation.

[*He tries to assuage the "backside" of those for whom he has contempt, like he pats himself.*]

D. And not let them know how much *pleasure* you got?

P. (Chuckles) Yeh, I suppose so. Well, you do and then you feel *guilty* as hell, at least I do.

[*He feels guilty when he shows his contempt as he did in the past. All of this general material must now be made specific by further confrontation.*]

D. What do you mean?

P. Oh, I don't know why. I just do. I think the reason you feel *guilty* is because if you go into the whole—this is my theory—if you go into the whole project with them with too much of a *self-interest* and "I'll *show them*" attitude, the minute your efforts begin to succeed, you are bound to feel a little guilty, because your effort has been more or less to *show them up* and be the *big shot.*

[*This is a recapitulation of what happened in the past, except that he had more reasons for feeling guilty; i.e., the baby rival died.*]

D. You mean like in a *family* where a *child* wants *mother* all to himself and isn't willing to *share* her with brother and father and sisters?

[*Confronting him indirectly, but he is not quite ready.*]

P. And then the thing to do that I discovered is, you can work the *thing* around and go at it with a sensible attitude, and not do it from the standpoint of attempting to *outdo* someone else, but from the standpoint of someone just *doing his job* and doing the right thing in your own interest.

[*"Working the thing around" means to overcompensate the ill feelings by a "sensible attitude," which spares guilty feelings.*]

D. Surely.

P. Then those *guilt feelings* don't crop up.

D. That's right, but as *you have said* so often, this is what your trouble was in the past, wasn't it? You were being "good old Ed" and you were trying to cement your relationship to mother and be the one shining light that would show up your brother and your sisters as lazy, good-for-nothings; and you felt very *guilty,* and when it didn't work you were full of *rage.*

[*His conflict of the past was his need for aggressiveness and the pangs of conscience because of it, i.e., guilt feelings. Behind his passivity lay fantasies of ultimate triumph and displacing them the way he had been displaced.*]

P. That's right. It just leaves you between a shit and a sweat all the time.

[*Being left between "shit" and "sweat" means, between contempt and anxiety.*]

D. And then you *hated* the others and thought they were laughing at you for being "good old Ed," so it didn't work very well, as you said.

[*Bringing him back to his previous general statements.*]

P. That's right. (Coughs) But you see also (coughs) one of these fellows that I was *talking* to the other day is being *let go* and I feel very *sorry* for him, because next month it will be me they *let go.*

[*"Pity" is "self-pity." Doing so helps him to deny and rise above his predicament in a more adult way.*]

D. It could be anybody?

P. That's right, it could. (Pause) But thanks to you, now I'm going ahead at full speed and my colors are high on the *mast.*

D. Thanks to your own *self,* that's your *own mast.* Now you feel more confident about it?

[*To diminish any anxiety he might feel over being attached to the interviewer, and to boost his ego, the interviewer proposes to him equal rights.*]

P. (Laughs) I do, and I've got this speech to write. Then I've got my organization duties to do, and I'll try to have them done by the end of the summer. At the same time, I'll go through this conference thing without too much slip-up, I hope. I don't think I'll be sidetracked. (Pause) Of course, now I'm *settling up* things at work and *settling up* things *always* provokes strong *feelings* in me. When I go to work, I'm practically like Jimmy Durante. You know, first he takes his coat off, then he puts it on, then he takes it off. This ambivalence you have about *giving up something,* giving up your friends, and so on. They're good *kids.*

[*"Settling up" means getting ready to leave. Now he begins to think of leaving work, which is like the family to him, and reopens thoughts of going away and mother leaving. The interviewer seizes upon the opportunity to develop the theme of the loss of a mother. The ambivalence of the three-year-old period is condensed with the baby arriving and going away, and mother leaving.*]

D. *Leaving* your *children?*

P. Yeh, leaving your *children* and the people who have been your friends.

D. It's like *going away* from *home?*

P. It sort of leaves you feeling kind of *sad* and also you're wondering whether you *finished* the whole thing right. These feelings of *nostalgia* come up. I hope to settle them in a few days. I used to get the same feelings when I'd leave the lake up in New York. The day before we'd leave I'd take a long walk up and down the shore almost as if this is the *last time* I'll ever see it.

[*He had produced a great deal of material about himself, mother and his siblings at their summer place on a lake. The lake is symbolic of mother, as he will demonstrate.*]

D. When you were with *mother?*

P. Yeh, up in New York. I'd look around the shore and look at all the places I was so fond of, and *get a big lump* in my throat, and the *pressure* would be on you to get ready to go, and your feelings would be *yelling* for you to stay. You'd feel *torn.* It's the same sort of thing.

[*He had complained of torn feelings in his jaws.*]

D. You mean as if a nice *part of you* were being *torn away,* those nice, warm, summer days?

[*Leading up to his relationship to mother.*]

P. Yeh, and all the things you were so attached to. You know, they had some *tugs* that would go across to the other side of the lake *towing barges* with limestone that they dug out of the bottom of the lake, and they had *three tugs* and one was named *Helen,* and that was my favorite tug, and I could tell them all apart like you can tell your *children. Other people* didn't seem to know the *difference* between one and the other, but I knew them.

[*Three tugs stand for mother, older sister, and stepmother at one level; at another, the three brothers. He played the role of the good mother. Who is Helen?*]

D. They were your *children?*

P. Yeh.

D. And *Helen* was your favorite?

P. Yeh. Well you could call it my girl friend or even my mother in a sense, you know, a feminine figure like.

[*Helen probably is also himself as a passive little girl child.*]

D. But *mother* was with you? You were her little *barge?* She towed you along. She took you with her to the *lake.*

[*Sticking to the mother sector.*]

P. Whenever I'd see that tug go by I'd break out into *tears.* I just would somehow.

[*Why tears? Mother developed her terminal depression at the lake, but he had no reaction, completely denying and repressing all feelings of loss when he talked about it previously.*]

D. Did you break out into *tears* when that *mother* tug left you, the real one?
P. No.
D. She died up by the lake, didn't she—when you were twelve?
P. No, I didn't *cry*. Why, I don't know. Well, I had the *feeling* but I didn't cry. I was just all *choked up,* that's all. (Here his eyes fill with tears)

[*The memory has changed! He has begun to accept and work through the loss.*]

D. The name of the tug was *Helen?*
P, Yeh, that was my favorite name. I don't know why. Anyway, I did at that time. (Pause) We had a *baby sitter* at one time whose name was Helen.

[*The good mother he needed.*]

D. How old were you? Do you remember?
P. Oh, I must have been less than *ten* when we had her.

[*Ten! a critical figure.*]

D. Do you remember?
P. No, not very much.
D. They told you that?

[*Trying to get more material from a different angle.*]

P. Yeh. We had *two or three* girls. In fact we had a *half dozen* girls in the course of *ten years,* and they played a fairly *important role* in our upbringing, I guess. One of these girls came up and stayed all summer with us at the lake. Her name I've forgotten, and then we had a couple who used to room with us. They were college girls. We had them at home. I was *very attached* to them, like I would be to any other baby sitter more or less. I imagine I got some pretty *strong attachments* to those girls.

[*Now he can reveal feelings about mother indirectly and with less danger of an affective outburst. The pressure the interviewer put on him by continual guidance within the mother relationship sector, pays off.*]

D. You imagine?
P. Well, I think I'd be the kind of guy who would. Little boys do get quite strong feelings.
D. Do you remember them?
P. Well, I don't remember them as well as *others* I was the same way toward later.
D. What do you mean?
P. Well, my fourth grade school *teacher,* I was *crazy* about her. She used to have a watch that hung from a chain around her neck upside down, and I was enamored of that. I watched it all the time. I had

all kinds of *desires* to be with her, you know, *her little boy,* I guess. In fact, once I used to go over there. She didn't live *too far away* and I'd go and see her, and I'd conjure up something about wanting to learn how to draw. I didn't give two hoots about learning how to draw. Later on, even when I was in college and working in the drugstore, there was one of the *women* who worked there in the store too, who was very nice. She was about *thirty* at the time. I was *seventeen or eighteen.* That was after my *mother died.* I was very fond of her. I used to take her a *plant* on Christmas or went to see her and all that sort of thing, and I've done *that sort of thing* off and on to, well, as many as a *dozen.*

[*Teacher is a substitute for mother. He displaces his interest in breasts to the object on her chest. Now he begins talking about a series of mothers. He has avoided the problem of giving up mother by having an ideal one around all the time.*]

D. Be their little barge and get *towed* along?
P. Yeh, just to go to *see* them and to have them be *nice* to me, and I'd be *nice* to them. (Wipes his eyes)

[*He drifts deeper into the past when his longing for the mother was thwarted and the search for a substitute always failed.*]

D. And you had to *give them all up?*
P. Yep, *give them up.* (Pause) There is one of them I *still write* a Christmas card to, *two or three* of them.
D. Really?
P. Yeh, this is a Sunday School *teacher* I had. If I were to go back to New York, boy, there would be at least *ten* around there, women like that, if I were to complete the list.

[*When he was* ten! *The critical figure appears again.*]

D. That you write to?
P. Oh, no, I don't write to any of them now, but I'd go back and see them.
D. *Ten mothers?*
P. (Laughing) Yep, ten. One is just as important as others. Well, I've *never* really given this much thought, but in *each stage* of my life there has *always* been a *mother* or someone that you kind of turn to. (Pause) Right now, well there are *two or three* women who fill that bill, or maybe I've switched to some nice *men,* and I could do just as well with them, or better. They'd be a sort of *good father.*

[*Now he is working through and comprehending the loss of mother. Tears are in his eyes as he is reliving the grief placed at its correct source. He doesn't know which role to play, in another sense.*]

D. How do you mean?
P. Well, sometimes a *father* gives a son a *hard time.* He really wants to help him, and I guess it is necessary.

[*He wanted a motherly father and also to play a feminine, passive role.*]

D. You mean sometimes father seems to be hard with the little boy, but it is really necessary to immunize him to hard times he'll get later on, huh?

[*Suggesting a new attitude.*]

P. Yeh, but right now these mother figures would be, well, some of the "nurses" around here—Miss B., and uh, my wife's sister, and that's about all.

[*He needs to suck and be nursed, and turns to "men" and "nurses" and the womanly sister.*]

D. Your wife's *sister?*
P. Yeh.
D. And not the wife?
P. My *wife* doesn't seem to want to fit *that bill.* I don't know, I guess she's uh, well even figuratively speaking she won't allow me the privilege of resting on her shoulder for a while.

[*She is like father in one sense and the mother in another.*]

D. You mean she wants to rest on yours?
P. She won't even do that. She wants to rest on it figuratively speaking, but not literally. She wants me to be the strong figure, but she doesn't want to come around and put her head on my shoulder.

[*He projects onto his wife his inability to be either passive or active.*]

D. How come?
P. I don't know.
D. That would be nice if she did.
P. (Wipes his eyes) That would be nice. (Pause) I don't know.
D. You mean you have ideas but you don't know which is the right one?
P. Well, at times, I wish that she would be, well that she would *break down* and be *weak,* but she won't. She always puts up a *strong front,* not in a *really* strong way, but in a sort of *cross-bearing* kind of way.

[*Now he begins to get on more familiar ground. He has described mother at one time and himself at another time as having a martyr complex. The interviewer tries to remain in the mother sector and not take up his narcissistic identification with her.*]

D. Like mother?
P. Uh huh, *exactly,* almost *exactly.*
D. Which made it so that you had to go out and find *other mothers,* huh?
P. That's right, and I still do. Even now, if I come home after a hard day, I sort of just want to sit around and relax for a while, and maybe talk with her or even do a little complaining about things that are bothering you, and she says: "Well, don't go on and on about that. *No other men* have to go on and on like that the way you do."

[*Mother says, "Don't be a baby." He continually wondered if he were like others with his "whining."*]

D. She says that?

P. Well, it's partly *true.* Now, for instance, I was over at the M——'s the other night and they were arguing about some *small point* that he is having trouble about, and they got the *thing* pretty well settled, and she was *sympathetic* with him. A little *argument,* but it cleared the air, and they got those things *settled,* and they felt *fine* the next day. Right now when I get a little *worried* about things at work, she just doesn't want to hear anything about it. She says: "Oh, they won't let *you go.* What are you worrying about?" (Chuckles)

[*As a child he needed and kept asking for reassurance from mother and various other members of his family concerning what he felt was his misshapen body, penis, stools, head, etc. His brother took advantage of his fears and played upon them. The underlying fear, which he was able to express, was his feminine desire coming true. For many years, he felt his sister had a deformed, small penis. Yet he felt she was a better man than he.*]

D. Was mother like that too? You said "exactly."

P. Well, that was a little overstatement. The only time I ever remember really having a clear-cut case of that was at my mother's one time. I came home and I was kidded about being *bow-legged,* so I told my mother about it and I was quite *upset* and she got quite *upset.* I told her, you know, "Why in the hell do I have to be bow-legged?" and she says, "Well you aren't *bow-legged,*" but she didn't say it in a nice way. She just *whined* and *scolded,* and I was. . . . God, you only had to look down and *see it.* (Chuckles) So that didn't *satisfy* me. If she had only said, "Well, sure you're *bow-legged,* but it isn't going to do any harm."

[*Mother whined like he does with his wife.*]

D. You mean she should say, I'll love you anyway.

P. Surely; I can *love* you with your being *bow-legged,* that's what she should have said, and it wasn't until I got quite a bit older and after working it out with I don't know how many *thousand men,* and looking at their *legs,* finally I came to the conclusion that a *lot* of them do have *bow-legs* and they don't do so *badly.*

[*He continually compared his bodily parts and products with other boys.*]

D. That's the same way you felt about your *penis?*

P. Yeh, it's the same thing.

D. You compared your penis, and your semen, and your feces, all of those things, and wondered why do I have to be this way, there's something wrong with me.

[*Confronting him with the past.*]

P. Another good thing that happened was last night, this *builder* called up. You know, the one I've been *working* on the *house* with. You remember I had a figure from one builder two or three weeks ago. I thought it was a little high and I was holding it on the shelf.

One of them that I was doing a more careful estimating job with, well, he called up about a week ago, and he came out and saw me, and last night he called up and said he could build a house at a contract price for $13,500, i.e., to my specific specifications which is $2,000 better than the last figure which I think is good. Of course, that doesn't mean anything to you. You've probably got a $30,000 house anyway, but to me this $13,500 means the whole house, including the land.

[*The builder represents the therapist who works with him to build a better, less deformed edifice. His optimism in the therapeutic situation is reflected in his plans for a new house.*]

D. But that is not *excellent?*

P. Yes, a three-bedroom house, brand new, custom built, and he's going to do everything except the fixtures and the fixture hanging. I'll buy my own light fixtures and put them in myself, and dig the dry wells for the gutter, and then put in the hook strips and some of the closet shelves, but everything else will be done. That's absolutely perfect.

[*It is more than a house. He is using it as a symbol of wiping out the bad past and beginning anew.*]

D. Surely.

P. It took almost two months' work negotiating, etc.

D. Why, of course, it means you can be perfectly happy without a $30,000 house.

P. (Triumphantly) And not only that, he is a *competent man* and he'll start on March first, and I won't have to look at that project until it's done and completed. I won't have to lose a wink of sleep over it.

[*He has realized an old fantasy of finding a father to whom he could turn—who would rescue him from his dependence on mother.*]

D. Surely.

P. So I've got the figures all down and I've got the contract. (Chuckles)

D. It would have been nice if you could have done the same thing when you went to *mother,* it's as if you could have said, aw, my *bow-legs* aren't so bad, I'll fix things up *myself,* or I'll go to *father;* but you didn't go to father then.

[*Trying to bring him back to mother or at least get him back into the past.*]

P. Nope.

D. Why?

P. Oh, I don't know. He was the kind of a guy if you said anything about yourself that was *bad,* he wouldn't *listen* to you, at least you felt that way. You felt you had hurt his *feelings.*

[*The simple act of listening to him has been reassuring.*]

D. How do you mean?

P. Well, in general, my feeling was that my *father* wouldn't *listen* to anything about his children except what was *good*. In other words, I was scared to tell him anything that wasn't *good*.

[*Father too is a perfectionist.*]

D. Anything that was *bad?*
P. Yup, so if I did anything *wrong* or anything you did that wasn't quite *up to snuff*, that wasn't anything you told him.
D. What would happen if you did?
P. I'm afraid he'd *disapprove* of you. He'd make you feel *bad*.

[*He felt abandoned on two sides.*]

D. You mean he had *disapproved?*
P. Well, he hadn't *disapproved* to much actually, but his whole *manner* was one which I interpreted as being that way.
D. You mean you had to be *good all the time?*
P. That's right, you had to be *good all the time*. All his conversation talk was about the *younger generation* nowadays isn't very *good*, they don't *work too hard*, they *fiddle around*, and I don't know what's *wrong* with them. They've got it so *damn easy*. (Chuckles) It was really *tough* when I was a *boy*, so on, and so on. The only way you feel you could *please* him is to make things as *hard* for yourself as they apparently were for him.

[*Good means hard working. Now we see his hard work was an effort: (1) to force fate to be good to him and build up a fund of credit; (2) to beat out his siblings (show them up); (3) at an identification with mother; (4) to win favor with father and mother; (5) to become ultimately like father.*]

D. That's not the way you are going to treat your "little Eddy"?
P. Well, I'll try not to.
D. But do you *feel* that way?
P. Well, sometimes you do, yes. My *wife* sure does now, and I hope to get a chance to *straighten* her out. Of course, the thing that is happening right now is both *good* and *bad*. I don't want to *malign* her too much because she is doing a *wonderful* job, but she is *busy* with the *baby* all the time as would be expected, and so far, the main thing that is happening to Eddy is that my wife is making him do *twice* as many things for himself than he did *two* months ago. He's got to go to the *bathroom* himself; he's got to dress himself. He doesn't, but she tries to get him to do it. In other words, she's putting him on *his own*.

[*Not he, but his wife, tries to make things hard for "little Eddy" by pushing him into independence, but he decided to change her. He returns to the mother sector.*]

D. And he doesn't like it?
P. He doesn't like it at all, and he begins to *rebel*. He says, I can't unbutton this. Of course, he can. He even *knows* he can, but then my wife will fall in the trap of arguing with him about whether or not he can button it, which, of course, is beside the point. He just wants her to do it for him.

[*The present repeats the past.*]

D. Like you?
P. Yeh, he really does.
D. All little boys hate to leave their mother?
P. That's right, and he says, come in and help me to go to the *bathroom.* Actually he just wants the *reassurance* of someone being *near* him. You have that *feeling* you know. Well, I don't want to go so *far* as to try to make up for the *mother,* you know, but that's the sort of thing that causes the *disturbance,* and my own feeling for the moment is that it is not until that becomes *centered* on the *new baby* that he'll actually have any feelings of *jealousy* toward her. At this stage of the game, he just knows he is *not getting what he used to get.* Of course, later he might blame the new baby. Then again he might, well, he might eventually need her all the more later on.

[*In this manner his perspective is sustained and enlarged. He wants to make up for the mother. This is the focal point of his trouble; i.e., he really does, and being mother means, among other things: (1) being overworked; (2) becoming depressed; (3) dying.*]

D. Of course he is a lot older than you were when the same thing happened to you.
P. Well, yes. He's four and a half.
D. And you?
P. Well, I was one and a half when the first one, and then three years when the next one came, and then there was a girl who came when I was five, so there were three of them who had come along.

[*The three tugs.*]

D. A triple dose of losses?
P. Uh huh.
D. You lost three mothers and you got ten to take their place?

[*Weaving the interview together.*]

P. (Chuckles) That's right. (Long pause)
D. It was not easy to give them up?
P. Well, the hard part comes when they begin to *multiply* and you try to put someone else, a mother *substitute,* in their place. Then when you are *rejected* it's worse than the one you got from your *mother.*

[*All his love affairs with girls had failed in the same repetitive manner, with terrible feelings of depression, and he had to leave them, i.e., "go away"—symbolic of dying.*]

D. How do you mean?
P. Well, you try to attach yourself, say, to an *old maid* down the street, or *somebody else's mother,* or the mother of one of your boy friends, or a school *teacher,* or a girl *friend,* or a *baby sitter* or a *governess* or whatever you call it, and so on, and naturally it's going to be impossible for them to be as *personal* with you as you would *like* for them to be. So you may wind up being *hurt bad* or even *worse,* when you can't get what you want with them, as you were when you were in the original case and you couldn't get what you *want*

from your mother; so that things begin to multiply, and each one leaves another lump.

[*He now uses the present tense. His insight is markedly increasing. He has clearly integrated into his conscious the material which was uncovered in the mother relationship sector, and the weaning process relived in the transference promises to be less painful.*]

D. Enough to give you *indigestion.*

[*Weaving this interview in with some of the other interviews.*]

P. (Chuckles) Uh huh.

D. Because, *as you said,* you felt it in your *stomach* and in your *colon,* that empty, *hungry feeling,* and you tried to restore the *good juices* with your *tongue* and your *fingers* when there was none of those *mothers* around, no Helens.

[*Sucking the fingers was a magic act restoring mother (see Discussion).*]

P. Uh huh. No Helens. (Pause) I later had a girl friend named *Helen.* She was the one, remember I told you about, who got *drunk* when I was with her.

[*What does drunk mean?*]

D. Got *drunk,* how do you mean?

P. Well, I must have told you this before. Well, anyway, I was in college. I had this girl in my French class, and I began to date her. One night I took her out to a place where you can *drink.* Well, I poured out a *drink* and I went upstairs. There were some people I wanted to see up there, and when I came down she had *drunk* that drink and poured herself another. Even I had sense enough to know she was going a little *too far,* but I had never seen her *drink* before. Well, as it turned out, about fifteen minutes later I was *dancing* with her and I could tell that she was getting *weak in the knees.* She was clinging to me like a *dead weight,* so I came to the conclusion that we had better *get out of there.* Well, at that time, I was a pretty, well, I had a pretty *good control* of myself as far as making an *incident* out of that sort of thing. I know what to do. I was no *babe* in the woods.

[*He had not mentioned this incident before, which means it is important. Here drinking is sexualized, and he takes an incident out of the past to serve as a screen memory for a fantasy revolving about mother when he was the drunken, little weight clinging to her.*]

D. How old were you?

P. Oh, I was *twenty* or *twenty-one,* but I knew how to take *care of things,* so I took her out to a rock quarry (chuckles—then *sniffs*) to give her some fresh air and to *walk* her around a bit. Well, gradually I got her *sobered* up and after she had *sobered up* some she told me, she said, you could have done *anything you wanted* to me a little while ago, which I didn't do, much as I might have *wanted to,* I didn't do.

[*He comforts himself with "I could have if I had wanted to—she would have let me."*]

D. Well, of course you wanted to, because when you said it now you immediately took your finger and put it in your ear (patient had put his right index finger in his left ear), as if you were wishing you had.

[*To fill up the gap, the sexual act continually reassures him—it is a nursing, oral, drinking act.*]

P. That's right. I did take her to a rock quarry and not to a hospital.
D. Why did you take her there, had you an idea?
P. Oh yeh, part of me had it anyway, but I *didn't dare.* I took her back home and got her in all right. Everything was okay. Strangely enough, later on, out in R——, she was there. She moved there. I wonder if that was one of the reasons why I went there to *school.*

[*Helen is a mother representative which should not be touched.*]

D. To be with Helen?
P. Maybe. Well she was *married* then already.
D. A *mother?*

[*Keeping it tied up.*]

P. Well, she was just a *young girl.* I never thought of it before, but maybe that was the reason I went there, but I'm not sure, even now that I knew she had gone to R—— before I went there. Maybe subconsciously I knew she was there.

[*He is continually projecting the two roles:—(1) the little passive girl child; (2) the mother—onto reality figures and making screen memories in order to aid the denial of the painful past.*]

D. You mean you wanted to *make up* for what you *hadn't got?*
P. Well actually when I went to R—— I had an offer for a fine job teaching Math. I won't say that I wasn't aware of it though, I don't know. I was thinking a lot of teaching then too.
D. You mean if you couldn't be with the *teacher* you were going to do the teaching yourself. (Long pause) Because, as you said, when you couldn't find a mother, sometimes you had to be mother to yourself and restore your own good juices with your fingers and your tongue. And as you said, when you left schools you would get that old nostalgic feeling that you had in connection with mother and the lake and Helen and the barges and the teachers and all of the other girl friends.

[*He is continually confronted with the similarity of the past and the present, to add more and more memories and increments of insight.*]

P. Yeh, that's true. You know I've had some *dreams* about the *Army* lately. Last night I had a *terrible fight* with my *wife* in a dream. I wanted to join the Army and she didn't want me to. It was something like that.

[*He wants to give up the disappointing mother and turn to the boys and father.*]

D. It was in the Army?

P. Uh huh. (Long pause) Well, I'm supposed to be to a luncheon at twelve o'clock.

D. You mean you've said enough.

P. (Laughs) Well, really no, no, I mean that. I'm not kidding you. There's a business group that have a luncheon, and strangely enough it is about hiring new men, that is, I'm a party to hiring *my own rival.* (Chuckles) And you have to kind of *grow up* to do that.

[*His insight has expanded.*]

D. That's right, to *accept rivals.* When you can do that, it takes care of all that *ache* and *longing* to be a *child* and be *mothered* and *fathered.*

[*Another general confrontation.*]

P. I hope so.

D. Sure. You've done it.

P. Well, strangely enough, I have been going over all these applications. First I did it with a sort of *fear,* wondering does that *guy* have *more on the ball* than I have. Gradually, I came to two conclusions: first of all, that not very many of these guys have any more *training* than I have; and secondly, there is not very many of them that are even interested in the *kind* of a *job* that I want anyway. So the result is that you can forget all about that stuff and take a more sensible course about *picking* out a guy, the kind of a guy you want to have around with us. That's all there is to it, and that's what you have to think about.

[*You don't have to long for the breast. You can accept brother.*]

D. Surely, as you said, there are lots of *mothers.* There are *ten* of them, and like there were lots of alma maters, there's lots of bosses and jobs in case you ever get rejected by one or even more.

P. (Chuckles) Yeh, I got *three* of them and I'm not satisfied yet.

[*Referring to the fact that he had gone to three colleges.*]

D. And you could have had more of them, and if they had rejected you and you had wanted to leave them, there were always others that you could have gotten. The world is full of jobs too.

[*"Jobs" means also "mothers."*]

P. (Rises)

D. Well, it was good to see you. Let me know when you wish to see me again.

P. I will. I'll be seeing you. I'll probably be over two or three weeks from today. By that time my speech will be done.

D. I'd like to see it.

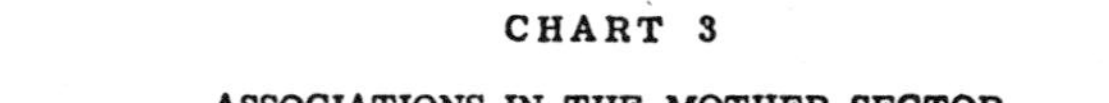
CHART 3
ASSOCIATIONS IN THE MOTHER SECTOR

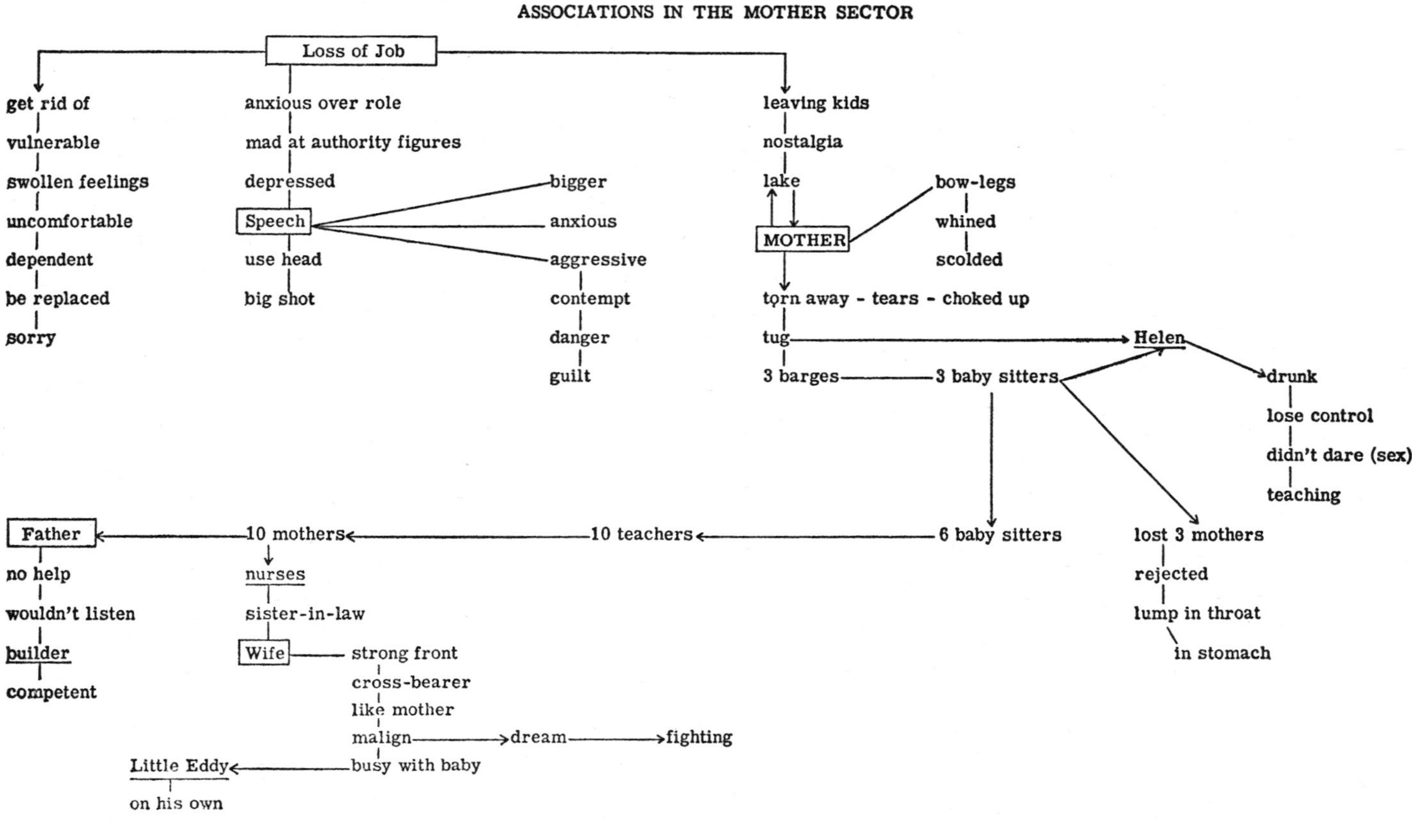
Loss of Job
get rid of
vulnerable
swollen feelings
uncomfortable
dependent
be replaced
sorry
anxious over role
mad at authority figures
depressed
Speech
use head
big shot
bigger
anxious
aggressive
contempt
danger
guilt
leaving kids
nostalgia
lake
MOTHER
bow-legs
whined
scolded
torn away - tears - choked up
tug
3 barges
3 baby sitters
Helen
drunk
lose control
didn't dare (sex)
teaching
6 baby sitters
lost 3 mothers
rejected
lump in throat
in stomach
Father
no help
wouldn't listen
builder
competent
10 mothers
10 teachers
nurses
sister-in-law
Wife
strong front
cross-bearer
like mother
malign
dream
fighting
busy with baby
Little Eddy
on his own

Discussion

Association Chart 3 shows that the loss of the patient's job led to feelings connected with the old loss of mother and the various mother substitutes he gathered around him to replace her, and also with her earlier loss to a rival. He expressed his sorrow and need for mothering, and disappointment in his mother, father, and wife, his rivalry with his siblings and empathy for his little boy. All of the material was linked up so he could see it as a long-standing pattern of behavior.

A different series of problems led to the exploration of a different sector three weeks later, when the next interview took place.

Part 3—The Overburdened Mouth

INTRODUCTION

Three weeks later, in this interview, the therapist explores the sector of the patient's relationship with father, and aids him in the settlement of his disappointment in father and of his fears of losing his therapist as the therapy draws to a close. He also evaluates the effects of the treatment.

INTERVIEW 3

D. How are things going?
P. Well, I feel pretty *confident.* I should have brought in the speech to you to let you see it.

[*He is five minutes late, although ordinarily on time, and looks a little defiant.*]

D. It looks *good* to you?

[*This remark reduces the anxiety.*]

P. Well, I've tried to avoid this business that I used to be so full of . . . of . . . *look, see,* is it *all right,* is it *okay,* is everything fine. I don't want to *tag around* after you like a *little boy* all my life.
D. You mean—"Is that all right, *Daddy?*"
P. (Laughs heartily) Yuh, that's it.
D. Because, as you said, father was never satisfied by anything unless it was *perfect.*

[*He is being threatened by his old dependency needs to attach himself to someone. This is a difficult situation. We must allow him to express aggression but maintain enough of a positive transference, so he will accept our confrontations. This is now done by deflecting onto figures in the past.*]

P. Sure. And what if you do *slip up* on a word here or there? (Pause) I noticed a few times I get a little *scared;* like last night when I walked into the meeting, I felt a little *weak* in the knees. But I wasn't so *bad.* (Pause) *Everyone* has been very *nice* to me this year. Of course, I don't want to go over a balance in my *loyalty* between any of these *groups.* (Pause)

[*Competing with father figures scares him—the weak, bad child.*]

P. It's very tempting sometimes to make *singular attachments.*

[*It is a mistake to interpret the transference without the proper perspective.*]

D. Like you did in the *past?*

P. Yes. First to *Mama,* then *Dad,* and then all these other girls. Yuh, I was *always* afraid somebody else would *outdo* me. But then twice this year I've sat at the *head table* at business luncheons, and it has made me get used to it, and I've been to quite a few committee meetings, and all those things just *raise* your *morale.* You see *all those guys* around you, and they aren't much *different* than you are; and it is as easy to do those things as it is anything else.

[*Dad is like Mama. He feels accepted, but is still overawed.*]

D. You don't have to be a superman and ahead of everybody any more, huh?

P. Yes, and even one of the *speakers* at the meeting called me up the other day. He's worried about his *speech;* so I felt he was more like I am, that he was one of the *weak sisters.* He wanted to know what the other guys were going to say so he could *compare his* with theirs.

[*Not much "bigger"; this also refers to his sisters and his confusion with the sexes. Anyone who worries is a weak sister—a natural lead into the past. Here, voice is like phallus.*]

D. Like you used to compare your *productions* with everyone else's, and every part of you as well.

P. Yes. I guess it's more than his *speech* he is worried about.

D. What do you mean?

P. I remember when I used to go back and double check it. Boy, it sure is a lifelong racket.

[*He refers to his boyhood comparison of his feces with other members of the family in outdoor privies.*]

P. By the way, one thing that came up, uh, I wish you could shed some light on this for me—this insurance man who has been pestering me for five or six years to buy some insurance, well, about a month or so ago he came in, and I promised I'd buy a policy for my *daughter* from him. I've always thought it would be a good idea to have $1000 ordinary life policy on everyone. It's a sort of recompense in case anything happens. My little boy has one.

[*A recompense is for a loss. This is overdetermined in meaning, but a hidden death wish is implied.*]

D. The little boy has one, and the little girl should have one also?

[*A "weak sister" should have what a boy has.*]

P. (Laughs) Well, you can say that. Then it was my *father's* idea. Whether it's *good* or not, I *don't know.* Maybe you're covering your subconscious desire to get *rid of them,* I don't know. (Laughs heartily) But that's not the main feeling.

[*At this level, the death wish is condensed with his wish to give up his child (penis) and play a passive feminine role.*]

D. What do you mean?
P. Anyway, in the process I tried to find out what my insurance possibilities are now. So he went through the procedure of making *inquiries*. Maybe it was handled through you.
D. No, I haven't heard of it.
P. Well, anyway, he gave me this long song and dance of how the records got mixed up. But anyway, the *company turned me down.*
D. Turned you down? It stirred up all those inadequacy feelings, didn't it?
P. That's right. Whether it's the *speech*—or life *insurance,* or *anything else,* they all tend to hit me there. One other thing that stirred me up a little bit—it's this *new place* we live. You know we've moved. The general *social* level where we live is a little *higher,* that is, higher than the district where I lived near my *father*-in-law. There, a lot of *them* have an *inferiority complex* about themselves.

[*Meaning himself.*]

P. So there has been a certain amount of jokes directed at me since I've moved. They say, oh, you're over in the high-class neighborhood now.

[*Turned down is related to being in a new place, i.e., the old conflict where a birth pushed him higher and into a new place.*]

D. You mean, a *big shot* up at the head table.

[*That is, with father. When his little sister was born, he had to turn more to father, and compete with his brother and older sister.*]

P. (Laughs) Yes. It just means that you're less secure. There is more *competition.* Also, there was *one boy* in the neighborhood who acts a little *snooty* toward our *boy.* So that's sort of stirred up a little *anxious* feelings in myself and my wife. I don't even think the boy is aware of it yet.
D. So you've got to go out for the sake of your *little one* and *prove things,* huh?
P. (Laughs) Yes, I suppose so. I know what you mean. So I go around trying to be good old Ed all over again, and furthermore trying to avoid being *snooty* at the same time. I don't want to *bend over backwards* too much, and I don't want to be too *aggressive.* I've always avoided at all cost having anyone think I was *high hat.*

[*In the past, he tried to show them up and was "snooty" himself, but disguised his feelings. At this level of psychosexual development, there are only the passive feminine and aggressive masculine positions.*]

D. What you mean is, you want to be high hat according to real values, and not too aggressively.
P. Well, I want to be well *respected,* but not be *snooty,* at least aggressively so.

D. You mean like you did with the fellows in the hospital? You really thought, ha, ha, you're still in the hospital and I'm out, but at the same time you felt sympathy, too.

[*In the session preceding this one, he had talked about his sympathy for the patients who were still here, with a note of triumph in his voice.*]

P. (Laughs) Yes, I guess that's true. When you say it, it doesn't sound so *bad,* and it *really* doesn't sound as *bad* to me now as it would have in the *past.* By the way, they hired one man to come in part time at work. I guess part of me still wishes it could *hang on;* part of me even goes so far as to secretly hope they may change their minds and say, we really want to keep you.

[*He is being replaced here by other patients.*]

D. You mean that is possible, as they must see now that you're a *different person.*

[*Reinforcing the adult ego attuned to reality.*]

P. Well, even if they do, I don't know what I would do. I don't know whether I would *really* want to stay. Of course, it depends on what they offered me. If they offered me a two-year position without any guarantees, I'd turn it down. Well, then also, they've got a *fellow* coming up there next week, who is the son of one of the top bosses. (Grins)

[*Another rivalry situation.*]

D. Why do you grin?

P. (Laughs) Well, three weeks ago I asked about this guy—that is, some of the fellows at work—I asked them whether he was any good. Well, they more or less wrote him off. Well, when this fellow wrote to my boss, he made out that his father was very *ill* and that he wanted the job because he wanted to stay in this area. So I guess they feel it would be nice to give him a chance to stay here for two or three years. His father is *sick* and liable to *die.*

[*A complex alter ego figure as well as a rival. He lets father get ill; he is thinking of breaking off the relationship and getting rid of a father, as he inferred early in the interview. Another part of him would like to remain two-three years.*]

D. So he is *anxious* and wants to *stay* around with his *father.* He doesn't want to leave him?

P. Yes, that's right.

D. Well, in a way, it wouldn't be too bad if his *father did die.* He wouldn't be a *little boy* then any more. He'd be the *head* of the house.

[*His anxiety-laden ambition.*]

P. Well, yes.

D. All fathers have got *to die.*

P. Well, that's looking at it from *his* point of view. Well, from my point of view, I feel sort of *funny*. Here they're going to bring in a man who is one of my replacements.

D. It's almost as if you felt, "Why can't they do this for *me*? After all, I want to stay around this area myself."

[*A confrontation with the more obvious relationship.*]

P. Yuh, I feel, why can't they give me the *same break*?

D. And then again, your relationship here is sort of *dying*.

[*Another obvious confrontation.*]

P. *That's right, that's right, that's right.* (Laughs)

[*The anxiety is apparent and mixed with relief at being understood.*]

D. But you and I know that it's not really so, and that you can *come back* anytime you wish.

P. (Laughs long and loud) Well, I guess I can *get along without you,* but at times I *don't like to.* (Long pause) By the way—I had a dream last night about my boy. I dreamed he was sucking my penis. I hate to talk about it. Now for Heaven's sakes, what does that mean?

[*He now brings out one of the sources of his aggression. His sexualized, oral-dependent need for the therapist as a motherly father is too much for him.*]

D. What do you think?

P. Oh, I don't know.

D. Well, if we think of it in connection with what we have just been talking about. It might be that the *little boy* is yourself—the *little part* of you, the *little boy* in you. If that is the case, whose penis is that little boy sucking?

[*This relationship can be handled indirectly.*]

P. (Laughing) *Daddy's,* I guess.

[*To ease his anxiety, he laughs.*]

D. And who is his *Daddy?*

P. (Laughs loud and long) Don't ask me that question!

[*He understands; anxiety is released by laughter.*]

D. It sounds like you're going to be your own psychiatrist.

[*The most acceptable version, but he knows better.*]

P. Yes, and it might mean the wish to go on with the *old* relationship. You know, I never thought of it in those terms.

D. You remember when you were so sick and when your mouth was going and you'd *suck* your *fingers* and you'd look down on me, and one time you said right out loud, "This doesn't mean that I want to suck your penis." Do you remember?

[*Integrating one aspect of the illness with his present insight.*]

P. (Laughs loud and long) You know, it really makes me feel embarrassed to talk about it. (Long pause)

[*A more healthy ego attitude!*]

D. You mean there's a part of you that feels full of shame, feels like a little boy?

P. Well, you're right, and I feel like a little boy when I tell you these things. (Pause) Well . . . . (The patient begins to fumble and smacks his lips, and starts working his mouth a little bit)

[*A difficult place in the interview, and somewhat too much for him.*]

D. Well, anyway, you no longer think of restoring mother's *good juices,* but father's, huh? This seems to go hand-in-hand with the desire to get rid of father and *cut off* this substitute relationship.

[*Acceptance of his hostility minimizes the anxiety.*]

P. You know, it's like this business of "old soldiers never die". . . .

[*The phallic aggressive nature of his psychosexual level is apparent.*]

D. Do you mean that sometimes a younger soldier can feel, why don't they *die* and move over and make room for the young and vigorous?

P. (Laughs) That's right. You feel torn between love and the wish to displace.

D. But the little boy was like that. He wanted to have Mama all to himself; he wanted to have Father all to himself. He didn't want to share anything; he wanted to *kill* all his *rivals* and . . . .

[*Helping him to master the feared wishes by reinforcing the ego split. His wish to kill his rivals had been hinted at previously, but never accepted by him.*]

P. Yes, he wanted *everything,* but he was *scared to death* of the consequences.

D. And they are afraid when they sit up at the *head table* and need someone *bigger* to lean on.

P. Well, it's twelve o'clock. (He gets up)

[*Only half the interview was over. His aggressive wishes were making him very restless.*]

D. What's the matter—are you getting uneasy?

P. No, but I'm always afraid to wear out my welcome, because then you might not let me come back. (Laughs heartily) Then sometimes you get a bit ashamed of yourself, and you want to get rid of that part that has to *suck around.* Just about the time you get to the point where you are awfully ashamed of your weaknesses, you seem to *realize* you *still have them* (Pause)

[*The aggression covers an intensified need.*]

P. The two best things that have happened to me this year are: first, I've had enough exposure or contact with my associates on a different basis where I feel fairly easy, and I don't have to *suck* around *them* any longer, and secondly, I can take my wife's criticisms with a lot more sense of humor. I've got enough kindness in my soul now, so I can—well—I can be kind about it.

[*He can be this way, since all these feelings are concentrated in the transference relationship to the therapist as a good father.*]

D. You mean now you've gotten enough, so you can afford to be kind, and you feel strong enough?

[*Keeping him in the father sector.*]

P. (Pause) By the way, I haven't told you, but I haven't missed *church* once since Labor Day. I haven't brought it up in here much. I don't know just *why,* but you know, I've *enjoyed* it, and I think it has *helped* me a lot this year. As long as I don't—well, as long as I get the proper perspective on it and don't have that *compulsive* frame of mind.

[*A new feature: he is able to socialize with less anxiety. Why hasn't he brought it up? Is he fearful of going too far?*]

D. What do you mean?

P. Well, in the past, if I didn't go to church, I felt so miserable for not having gone, and then I depended too much on the fact of *going* to church, rather than on the *over-all perspective.* In other words, my efforts should have been more to integrate it, rather than to become just *dependent* on it.

[*"Going" to church had the magic aspects of a ritual warding off punishment and atoning.*]

D. You mean on the act of going to church? It's like coming here, going to work, or anything else. You mean you shouldn't use it just as an act?

[*Using material from previous interviews.*]

P. That's right. You should integrate it into your life experiences, so you get more perspective, and . . . . and I should be more plastic, and I think I am. When you can't go, you just stay home and do the things you have to do, and go the next time and not get *upset.*

[*These ideas are a big advance for him, based upon identification with the therapist. However, one must not overestimate the extent of the change.*]

D. I think you're right.

P. I think I've gained a great deal from church this year, and you know I also listen to Reverend X . . . . I don't know whether you've heard of him or not.

[*Reverend X is a bishop who speaks over the radio.*]

D. Oh yes, I've heard of him, but I don't know much about him.

[*To get* his *ideas.*]

P. Well, I don't know whether he's a *crackpot* or not, but I've *enjoyed* him. Somehow the things that they talk about don't seem so *crazy* now. Our own *minister* is *good.* The things that he says don't seem as *tough* as they used to. I used to go to church and *blame* myself a lot, because I hadn't lived up to the standards they were expounding, and I felt like such a darn *sinner,* all the time, and I looked at all the people around me and I felt, why can't I be as *nice* a guy as they are.

[*He is more tolerant toward father, the therapist and himself. A modification of his superego has occurred.*]

D. You mean nobody else might have bad fantasies?

[*He had talked about this with guilt feelings in a previous interview.*]

P. (Laughs) Yuh, that's it. I'd feel these people haven't done the *horrible things* I have in my time. I'll never get *forgiven.* I'll never be a *proper member* here.

D. You mean, I'll never be accepted by *God* or by father?

[*God is seen as a father.*]

P. That's right. (Pause) Well, it seems as though maybe I *have.* In fact, sometimes now I look around and I feel that maybe I have more *right* to be there than some of the others. (Laughs loud and long) Anyway, now I see that there are just as many *sinners* in the world as any other kind, and that they're just as *bad* as I am, in fact *worse,* many of them. I think on the whole, this attitude of mine has been quite a *gain.*

[*Trying to reassure himself.*]

D. And you aren't so *angry* at them, and you aren't so *angry* at yourself?

[*Returning to his aggressive fantasies.*]

P. That's right. In fact, I even see places where I feel the minister is *off the beam.* Sometime I think they just *expect too much.* The other day I noticed he made some cracks, well, mostly about *business men,* as though their life was completely devoid of spiritual things, that they're always just pursuing the *almighty dollar* and don't think of anything else, and they never find it necessary to seek spiritual guidance. Well, that just isn't so. Everybody has to seek spiritual guidance of some kind. And I know lots of business men who do plenty of it, and even some of the hard-hitting ones, and when this Rector stands up there and says these guys don't, it makes me *sore.* Of course, I don't know what the Rector is worrying about—maybe where his next dollar is coming from. Maybe he's worried about his own concern over money and is saying to himself, well, I don't need it, it's not important. And then he goes to the other extreme and gives everybody else hell for thinking too much of money.

[*He can stand up to father. The patient is a business man. At this stage, money signifies phallic power to him. The "Rector's worries" are obviously the patient's own concerns.*]

D. You mean ministers don't get much?

P. (Laughs) Yes, that could have been the case easily. It's like statisticians. They have to get along on much *less* than other people usually make. They *don't mind it,* too, most of them, but they have to *live.* It sure is a *relative* thing. You know another thing, I'm getting along much *better* with the wife and I'm ashamed to say it

— it's partly because I'm not *interested* in her as much as I was.

D. You mean you're not as *dependent* upon her as you used to be?

[*He has turned from the mother to the therapist in a fatherly role.*]

P. Yes, that's it exactly. Now, for instance, last Sunday I had a good long *sleep* in the morning, something I haven't been able to do for a long time. I had a few papers to do that day, but I felt I could do them easily, and I just stayed in bed. You have no idea what a *change* in me this represents.

[*Another sign of a modified superego.*]

P. I haven't been able to *sleep* Sunday mornings late and in a *sound manner,* oh, for ten or fifteen years. Anyway, I decided what the heck, I'd sleep. In fact, I stayed in bed until 7:45, and my wife usually gets up at 7:00. By the time she got up, boy, was she *sore.* So she started in and began to *rail* at me for staying in bed, and boy was she *sore.* She didn't *speak* too much directly to me. She was just sort of *moping* around.

[*As he had described mother and himself.*]

P. Luckily and fortunately I felt pretty *good.* (Chuckles) And I knew what I had to do as far as my *work* went, and I was pretty *sure* I could get it *done,* so I wasn't very *sensitive* and I had everything under *control,* so I just let her *rave,* but a few times I got *disgusted* with her and said, for gosh sakes, you mean just staying in bed for forty-five minutes longer is worth all this *fuss*?

[*The harsh maternal portion of the superego is projected onto his wife.*]

D. You felt more *tolerant*?

[*Introducing a new word for him to take over.*]

P. Well, it's true. I do feel more *tolerant,* and then I have more *confidence* in my *ability* to do my *work* when I'm up.

D. So the wife behaved more like you used to behave to yourself in the past?

P. That's right. And of course, part of that which is in you comes from being around people like that.

[*He accepts the confrontation and adds to it.*]

D. Yes, as you said, your *wife* is exactly like your *Mama.*

[*This helps to impress the newly won insight.*]

P. More so right now, because of the size of the family. Actually from the point of view of *sleep* throughout our whole married life, she's been a lot *worse* than I have. At least I have been more *overconcerned* about getting the proper *amount* of sleep. I noticed that during the past month or two, I've been the one that *stays up later* and has more *energy,* but prior to that, that is during most of our married life, she has been the one who kept me up. In many ways, I seem *stronger* now and I don't need as much sleep. Of course, she used to keep me up late in the past, which had a lot of disadvantages. I'd be *angry* at her, and when she came to bed I'd be feeling *sore* because I'd be lying there and I'd be wanting to get *laid,* but now the shoe is on the other foot. She gives me *hell* for keeping *her up,* but there's no point in *arguing* those things. You just set your own course. (Pause)

[*Another therapeutic change: (a) he needs less sleep; (b) more energy available for daily tasks, formerly utilized for countercathexes enforcing repression.—Sleep and intercourse are treated as oral derivatives; less need for mother means less need for them.*]

D. Was father like that?

P. Like what?

D. Concerning sleep.

[*Returning to the father sector.*]

P. My *father* was always *against* sleeping late. My brother and sister were *terrible* about *sleeping* late, sometimes even until 12 in the morning, and my *father* would start in at mealtime and talk, my gosh, the rest of the week. He would make *snide remarks* about my brother and sister lying around doing nothing, and here I was, good old Ed, getting up at 6:30 and 7:00 in the morning.

[*It appears that the wife has taken over aspects of the bad father! He can be more like brother and sister. He had to get up for father to show he didn't need and want mother.*]

D. Trying to *outdo* them?

P. That's right. (Laughs) So I developed into a somewhat *torn* individual on that point. Part of me had a terrific *longing* to get *adequate sleep,* and the other part felt so *guilty* about such a thing, i.e., getting enough rest, you know. All through college, time and again, *when I went out nights,* I'd *worry* about *getting enough sleep,* and my *guilt* and *anxiety* about *sleeping late* the next morning would just spoil the *date* for me. No matter how late I was, that is, out late that night, I'd wake up early in the morning and have to get up. I did this over and over again. That's why it seems so *wonderful* now to have thrown that off and to *forget* about it. Now I can—well, if I need the rest, I can *take it,* and I'm through *kicking* myself in the behind over little things. For instance, when I was coming over here, I realized I was supposed to be at some meeting which isn't very important. Well, I can remember the time when I would have been very much *concerned* about it, and I know darn well a *lot* will be missing from it with not half the reason I have.

[*His longing for sleep is really a longing for love and attention from mother. Sleep too was sexualized and laden with incest guilt feelings. He associates sleeping with dates.—He gave himself a punishment to fit the crime, i.e., in previous interviews the anal connotations of sex were obvious.*]

D. Just like church?

P. That's it. You know I find myself—that is, part of me thinks that if you're not there at that Committee meeting, it's just one more *big, black* mark against you, and they're bound to *send you away*. Yet I know that is a lot of *hog wash*. Actually the more you're *absent,* they probably think you've got *more important things* to do.

[*Going away is like dying.*]

D. How do you mean?

P. They might even think, what the hell, haven't you got anything *better* to do than to come to these *meetings*? (Long pause) Last time my wife and I had *intercourse* was the night after that big meeting. For about a week after that, she was either too *tired,* or I was staying up late nights working, and lately she's been kind of *sore* at me. She seems to think I've got it a little *easy* and she's got it too *rough* with the two kids. So she takes sort of a dim view of *man* at this moment.

[*He wonders if he is going to be left out in the cold again.*]

D. But as you said, you don't care so much about it.

P. Well, I don't. I wish there was something I could do to *help her* out a little more, but then she tries to do things just as *well* and just as *perfectly* as she did when she had no children at all. She got an automatic washing machine, but now all that amounts to is, she washes things just about two or three times as often as she used to wash them before.

[*He was constantly trying to placate mother by helping her, but she was never satisfied. He had become like her in this respect also.*]

D. You mean she is doing things like you used to do?

[*Confrontation. He identifies with Mama and rages at the man.*]

P. That's right. She's always *cleaning* and vacuuming things. *Two* or *three* times a week she *cleans* the whole house. Then when we have breakfast, she has every one of the small dishes out that you can possibly use, which is very nice but it makes a lot of *work.*

[*He continually uses the numbers 2 and 3, which refer chiefly to the younger siblings who displaced him.*]

P. When we moved to our new location, she insisted on doing the curtains so they would be clean when she put them up, but I kidded her about it, saying that she spent more clock hours on those curtains than on the entire rest of the place, which was true; and we had an awful *squabble;* of course, there's another side of the thing too. I'm *no easy guy* to live with, and especially when I get under pressure, ha, I make it very *hard* on other people, because I used to be so *hard* on *myself.*

[*The interviewer attempts to reinforce his insight by tying it all together.*]

D. So you mean that a guy who is *hard* on *himself* tends to be *hard* on *others* and to marry a wife who is *hard* on *him,* and *hard* on *herself,* and finds a *God* who is *hard* on *people*?

P. Yes, that's true, and it can get pretty *rugged.* The funny thing about it—it all seems to be because he feels his *parents* were *tough* on *him.* He takes it out on *himself* and on *everyone.*

D. Now you can see those things?

P. Well, I *hope so.*

[*He's somewhat uncertain.*]

D. It's nice to be able to see those things?

P. Well, you not only have to be able to *see* them, but you have to be able to take certain steps along the line to *catch yourself* in the *act.* You have to be able to *shift* your *balance.* I'm still pretty *rigid,* but I'm a damn sight *better* than I used to be.

[*An excellent statement of the situation.*]

D. It takes practice?

P. It sure does. Like learning how to play a *new game* with a whole *new set of rules.* It's funny—when I married my wife, I thought she was pretty *normal*—(chuckles) even *better* than normal. Now I can see that in many ways she's just as *neurotic* as I am. She's got her own neurosis, anyway. (Long pause) Just the other night we were talking about how I did get better.

[*He can see her more realistically; i.e., he sees himself.*]

D. What do you mean?

P. Well, I started wondering how did I get *better,* and it's very hard to put into words. (Long pause while he frowns and looks off into space) Well, it's kind of hard to reconstruct. I think the *first* thing that helped me, and this is—well—it's hard to know how this does help you, but anyway I did a certain amout of *moaning* and *groaning* about the *things* that bothered me and *rubbed* me the wrong way, and you know you just tend to get that stuff out of your system. Well, that's the *first* one. I think the next thing that helped me was that I found out there were *certain things* I *could do,* and I found I *wanted* to do them, and that kept me going. And then with *your help,* I sort of seen the various *choices* that a man has, things *you* can do, how if you can't *jump* over a *hurdle,* you can go *around* it, and jump the next one. I don't know, it sort of gave me a new *approach* to things, and also from the beginning of last year at this time, up to this time, they told me about I wouldn't get my job back—well, just about everything I did went *well* or *seemed* to, and that hit me and gave me more *confidence,* and also somehow I seemed to get a *sense of humor* and feel better, although once you begin to feel that way, you want to *keep at it.* You know something is going on that makes you feel *better,* but you just *don't know* what it is. You just *thank* the *good Lord* that it is that way, and you keep it up.

[*He begins a discussion of his own ideas regarding the therapeutic process. (1) Abreaction ("getting it out of your system"). (2) Reassurance by doing things. The second month of therapy, he went into the O.T. Department and made a stool. (3) Identification with the ther-*

apist in a kind of teacher-pupil or father-son relationship ("with your help"). (4) Increased perspective ("new approach"). (5) Ego support and substitution by the therapist for loss of previous figures ("more confidence"). (6) More adequate defenses ("sense of humor"). (7) Restoration of the good parent-child relationship ("thank the good Lord").]

D. And you felt better?

P. Yes. You just don't know how, but through all this process you find there are certain things you seem to do that can *help,* and certain *attitudes* you can take that *help.*

D. But your trouble with your *mouth* was your main difficulty when you came to the hospital.

[*Trying to integrate material concerning his chief symptom.*]

P. Well, I was *aware* of that a *little bit.* In fact, I am even as I'm *talking* here now, but not enough to really *bother* me or keep me from *saying* what I have to say. I'm just trying to give an honest account of what happened, but you can't really be *sure.* Occasionally, when things seem to *fall out from under me* and I begin *grabbing* at all these little *crutches* that I've used along the way, well, some of them *don't.* You never can really *depend* on them.

[*The mouth is no longer overburdened. His defenses have been broadened and redistributed.*]

D. What *little crutches* do you mean?

[*Substitutes for what, in the last analysis, are his parents.*]

P. Oh, crutches—uh, well, like last fall. I got sort of a *fixation* on a *lucky half-dollar.* I used to feel that I always had to be carrying one of those in my pocket, and then I was—then there was Harry D. . . . I noticed he had one of these that had been *damaged*—well, I've been carrying this, you know, since it's a *lucky piece,* it has narrowed down to this one now and that's all I bothered with. (He pulls out a half-dollar that is dented and banged around, and shows it.) But there was a while last fall when I damn near thought I had lost it. Well, that's one *crutch.* Then there are certain *clothes* that I didn't want to *wear,* oh, that seemed to b*other* me—or that I *wanted.* For instance, for a long time I wore that *Army belt.* Now I've got a *new belt* (laughs) and I'm able to *live* with it, and that if I can keep it up and not go back to the *Army belt,* it will be quite an achievement. We'll see how that goes.

[*Dependence on the magic of the compulsive-obsessional individual. The lucky piece is a symbol of himself. As long as he cares for it, he will be cared for and protected from losses. The "new belt" is a new identification with the therapist.*]

P. (Pause) I have some *toothpaste.* (Pause) These are very little things. (Pause) Well, I bought it in the other hospital [*where he received shock therapy*] and I see it on the shelf there. My wife is using it now. I use another kind. Well, I've avoided that toothpaste like *poison,* although this morning I slipped up and used some of it, and it *bothered* me so much I *washed* my mouth out and used something else. You know, little things like that. And uh, this *pencil,* I had it given to me at this meeting I flew out to at C——. I'm very careful not to lose that. There are a lot of little *superstitions* that are attached to this. Well, those are some of the *crutches.* Some of them have been a little more *abstract.* I've taken a certain amount of pride in doing things *carefully,* yet in a little *different* way than I've ever done it *before*—just to keep alive the idea of *something new.* I seem to get *pleasure* out of that word. In the past it was *different.* I wanted to grab hold of the *old things*, I didn't dare to go in any *new* direction for fear I'd get into some kind of trouble, I don't know what. I just didn't do it.

[*The "poisonous toothpaste" is representative of the bad, sucking, oral need. He tries to turn from an oral to a tenuously phallic and genital relationship. All this material is new and untouched by the therapy. Another point: a new orientation to his problems. The regressive process has been halted.*]

P. This year when I had done my work, well, it used to be that whenever I was feeling *real low* I'd pick up my *old notes* and try to do something real *simple* and real *easy,* something I was sure I *could do,* and I was sure that if I could do something *easy*—that, well, uh, I'd feel right then. But this time that's *worse.* It's *worse* to do that than it is to just *throw your old self away,* and well—do it differently. Oh, you're bound to do it in some ways like you've done it before, but your effort is to do it without having to go back to the old way and *slavishly copy* it and match it with the *past.* Not only that—but you bring up all the old *bad associations* with the *past,* and they keep making you worse. I just don't do it any more.

[*The regressive process itself arouses anxiety. The old self has now become the bad self or parent he wants to discard.*]

D. So now you're not *living in the past* so much?

P. Not so much. Then there have been other things. I have gone to church every Sunday. That seems to have helped. I don't seem to be quite so *hard on myself,* although it seems lately, it seems I'm a little bit *harder* on myself than I was back in the fall. Oh, I don't know whether that's good or bad. Like yesterday, on this business I told you about of hunting for a job. Well, it seemed to *bother* me a lot yesterday. (Pause) So that's the way things have been. Then, of course, I've had a *baby,* and that's one of the things I was thinking about when I said, by and large *everything has worked out right.* I just didn't have any major setbacks at all. We're living in *new quarters now* and that helps. I'm *driving* to work a *different way,* and all that *sort of thing.* And all those things help. So I'm able to *pick* and *choose* between the things of the *past* that are *good,* and avoid the *things* which were kind of—kind of *bad,* or at least things you *don't like.* You don't have to *live through them again.*

[*Increased socialization with less anxiety. On the other hand, anxiety leads to more productive efforts in keeping with reality. He can work through his infantile anxieties by being a good parent himself and project his infant needs onto the baby. At a deeper level, his unconscious wish to have a little girl baby (like part of himself) by father has been gratified while in the therapy situation. He was reborn the way he wished it, with the therapist as a strong, good father.*]

D. You don't have to take them indiscriminately?

P. No, I can pick and choose and separate them better, and it seems to *work better.* Also there's this business of *dressing.* I used to be *afraid* to wear something as *flashy* as this (pointing to his tie). Now I get pleasure out of it, but if anybody ever said to me, ha, ha, you're looking pretty *sporty,* I'd feel awfully *bad* for a while. But no one has.

[*His powers of discrimination are better; i.e., his ego is more mature. He dares to exhibit himself—a red, cheery tie; his previous ties had been brown or dark.*]

D. How do you mean, *bad*?

P. Well, it used to be that I was very, very *sensitive* to any criticisms about being considered *flashy.* I was ultra-*conservative* in dress and so on. I think that's my father's influence. I got it from him. He was *always* that way—not necessarily *conservative,* but never wanting to put himself in the *limelight.* Well, he wasn't, well—that is, he never seemed to *dress* or do anything for his own *pleasure,* so I just never did it myself. He wasn't one to come home with a *necktie* or a new *coat* and *strut* around and act as if something good had happened. He was more the kind of a fellow who if you got *something,* he'd say to you, well, look at me, I've had this *suit* for five years—that sort of a guy.

[*"Flashy" refers to phallic exhibitionism. Father forbids showing things, and one shouldn't get more than father.*]

D. He made you feel as if you were doing a *terrible* thing?

[*This refers to his guilt over oedipal competitive strivings.*]

P. That's right.

D. So you're much less harsh on yourself, and less demanding?

P. That's right.

D. And you don't mind being a little *sporty* or a little *sexy*?

[*The same thing!*]

P. (Laughs heartily) That's right. I might add on the *sex* angle too, that my intercourse experiences of late, well, huh, maybe I'm getting old, but I'm getting so—well, I used to worry about getting through too *quick.* Well, last week, which is the last time that I had intercourse, let's see, it was a week ago last night—at any rate, the last few times I've been the *slow* one. In fact, I've almost gone an *inordinately long time.*

[*His ejaculatio praecox is gone, but he is still anxious.*]

D. How do you mean?

P. Oh, maybe *five minutes.* (Laughs) In some ways it's *pretty good,* but then I think that I'm either *getting old* or I'm getting *no control,* or I'm *losing* my *interest,* or I don't know what, but for some reason or other that's the way things are.

D. And your wife?

P. Well, she seems to enjoy it, more I guess, although a couple of times she seemed to complain that it was a lot of *work.* Of course, she's still a little *sensitive* about being *hurt* because she had those stitches when the *baby* was born. (Laughs) Well, I know it's *healed* down there.

[*His anxieties are revived about being hurt or overexcited like mother; this was her original complaint. He is talking about himself as well as his wife; i.e., his wound is healed.*]

D. You *enjoy* it more?

P. Oh, yuh, sure.

D. But in spite of this—you still get anxious?

P. Some, yuh.

D. First you're anxious about being too *quick,* and then about being too *slow.*

P. (Laughs heartily) There are *dangers* on both sides. I guess I'm never *satisfied.* I guess I'm always *anxious.*

D. You mean it wouldn't make any difference. You'd still feel there's something wrong down there?

P. Yuh, that's right. I have to have everything *just right,* and it *never* can be *just right.*

D. That was the *old* feeling?

P. That's right. I got to the point where whenever I do something *right,* I get *anxious* and think I must have done it *wrong.* So you're always in the soup.

D. It's not a difficult world to live in?

P. (Laughs) That's right, I'm *less concerned* about it. In fact—I know so.

D. Not in too big a *hurry*?

[*One of his most troublesome symptoms had been his inability to wait; like to a hungry baby, waiting seemed an eternity to him.*]

P. Most of the time. Sometimes I get *impatient* and a lot of times *irrationally impatient,* but I have a hell of a lot to show on the *positive* side of the ledger.

D. You're in the *black,* huh?

P. That's right. (Pause) Well, I'll see you in a month or so. I'll call your secretary.

D. I'm always glad to see you.

Final Discussion

Association Chart 4 shows how the material in this interview was kept centered around the father. The patient revealed his passive feminine wishes to suck, and his struggle over these tendencies with his

CHART 4

SHOWING KEY WORDS AND ASSOCIATIONS IN THE FATHER SECTOR

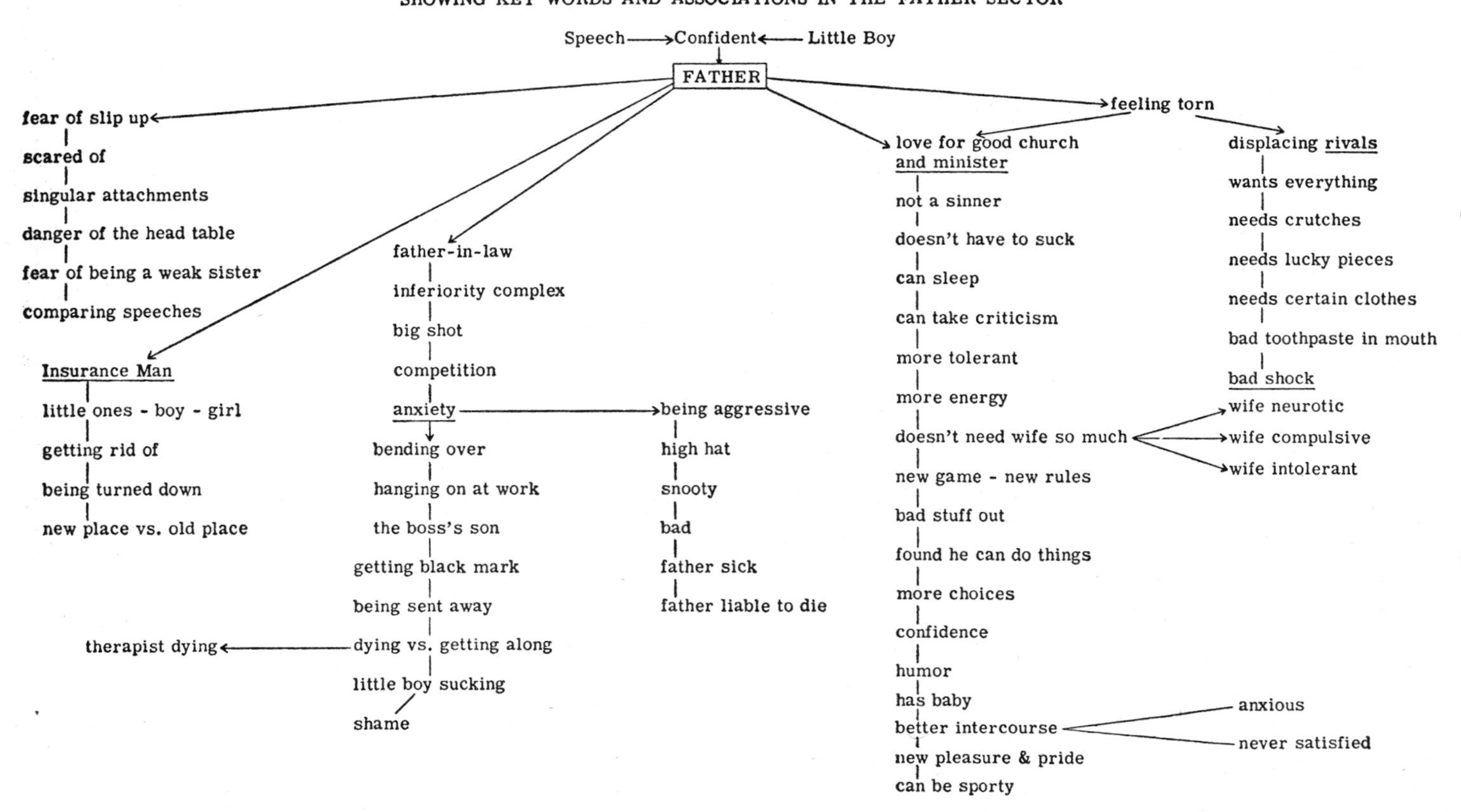

aggressive masculine desires to displace father, his fears of losing the good father, and his anxiety over his "singular attachment" to father.

It is apparent from this interview, that in his fantasy everything has worked out all right. At a deep level this refers to the gratification of a fantasy that he—via his wife as his feminine part—has had a baby girl by the good father, as represented by the therapist through his identification of his masculine side with the therapist. The baby represents himself reborn, and his feminine wishes are gratified. Now he is tolerably free to project his feminine fantasies onto this baby, and to play a masculine role.

Follow-Up

The patient terminated his therapy of his own accord, following this last interview. One month later he called to state that he had obtained employment at a higher salary than he had received previously, and held a much more responsible position. Three months after the above interview he phoned to arrange for an appointment, but was unable to keep one because of his "new business responsibilities." At that time he stated that he had no particular problems, but would like to report on all the "good things" that had occurred. Eighteen months later a Christmas card was received, informing the therapist that he was doing very well and that his wife was again pregnant.

Two years later he was still adjusting well at work and at home, and had been elected to a responsible position at his place of work. Three years after that, his status was still the same.

CHAPTER VII

Sector Therapy of a Psychosomatic Disease (Essential Hypertension)

Part 1—The Color Barrier

INTRODUCTION

An interview of a case with essential hypertension should be made with the purpose to prove that the premorbid personality needed and used in its development certain parts of the body and bodily functions for the expression and solution of emotional conflicts, and that later they may become a part of the symptom complex of the organic disease. This means that the subjective bodily sensations serve simultaneously as symptoms of both the neurosis and of the organic disease. Moreover, in such an interview one should be able to demonstrate that the subjective symptoms of the disease followed a pattern laid down in the personality make-up.

What remains to be explained is the question of whether in these psychosomatic entities common libidinal conflicts and their concomitant organic responses which are normal, but transient in other individuals, meet from the beginning a less resistant organic, perhaps constitutional, condition which paves the way for the development of a specific personality and for the later disease.

Essential hypertension is a pathologic condition of which *one* symptom is high blood pressure. It has been suggested that a certain personality structure is apparent in cases with this disease. The question arises whether and how the specific personality has contributed to the functional vascular disturbances. It has been established that these patients are highly narcissistic, sensitive, easily offended persons with a great need for (bodily) activity, and who carry within themselves a pent-up hostility and resentment which they are unable to express sufficiently and effectively.

The premorbid personality of the hypertensive during its development uses inherent organic functional pathways or erotogenic spheres to express certain repressed libidinal elements, i.e., guilt, shame, anger, narcissism, because of a compliance of these pathways with the other needs. This compliance exists in every human being. In this condition, the repressed, and therefore hypertrophic libidinal elements of such patients are linked with a hyperirritable vasomotor system ideally suitable for the expression of these repressed feelings. Such a person blushes sooner than others, (1) because of the hyperreactibility of his vasomotor system; (2) because he is pathologically filled with shame; (3) because he has repressed anger excessively; (4) because he is afraid of being exposed. The need to keep his desires suppressed as well as repressed stimulates the vasomotor system into action. Organic manifestations thus become the representatives of the repressed drives. Finally, what was transient becomes permanent and the vasomotor system remains in the hypertensive condition, independent of the repressed emotional factors, and due only to the inherent functional condition. "The demons which he called—he can't get rid of again. . . ."

The hypertensive condition itself would not be perceived if it did not serve as a vehicle for the repressed drives which are stirred up simultaneously. Therefore, the treatment should make repression superfluous. If that is achieved, then the hypertension may remain, but the subjective sensations will no longer disturb the patient, or they will at least not be of paramount importance to him. He might then become ready for surgical treatment, if necessary.

Case Presentation

The patient, whose five successive therapeutic interviews will be discussed, was a thirty-two-year-old, white, single male. He worked as a mechanic, and was admitted to the hospital because of problems centering around an underlying hypertension, with complaints about headache and palpitation unassociated with effort. He was a slender, well-built, tall person who showed a rather embarrassed behavior, but tried to cover it up by smiles and laughter. He blushed frequently and became increasingly flushed during the interviews. His neck showed deep redness, and his face often became faintly covered with purplish-red spots.

The patient's past history told only about a pneumonia and empyema at the age of one. Fours years ago he was first informed of his hypertension, when a complete study was made at the O.P.D. of the hospital.

The family history revealed that his father, age fifty-five, also had hypertension. His mother, age forty-nine, was the worrying type and dominated the household. There was a sister, three years older, and two brothers, three years and fourteen years younger, respectively.

The essential findings in the physical examination were normal retinae and blood pressures ranging from 150-170/90-100. The cold-pressor test was positive with an increase of 20 mm. during systole. The cardiac examination was entirely normal. The blood pressures were not influenced by postural changes. Repeated urine tests showed specific gravities of 1010, 1014 and 1015 and were also otherwise negative. In view of his hypertension, the patient had been rejected from military service. However, a doctor had suggested the psychotherapeutic approach rather than resorting to sympathetic surgery at this point, particularly since the major organs and the peripheral vascular tree were still intact.

Preliminary Discussion

The interviewer had no previous information concerning the emotional problems of the patient. It was therefore decided to guide the associations—after the key words were assembled—into the sector of the father relationship. Then—relying on the concept of the personality pattern of cases with essential hypertension as previously mentioned, according to which they are narcissistic, aggressive, sensitive persons who overcompensate their passive trends and are unable to release sufficiently their pent-up, repressed hostility—it was planned to establish consciousness of the presence of this pattern through the associatively connected verbalizations, and then to stimulate the discharge of the withheld aggression against the father image.

Interview 1

D. Dr. X sent you here?
P. That's right.
D. And asked us whether we can be of any help.
P. I hope so.
D. Can you tell me now—what in your opinion makes it necessary to treat you?
P. Well, I suppose you know about the blood pressure.
D. I heard.
P. As far as he can find—as well as other doctors can find—there's *nothing physically* wrong, yet I seem to have it all the time. I seem to be always *tied up*—always *tied in knots.*
D. You yourself?
P. Yes. I'm in a *nervous sweat* all the time. Perspiration under the arms —I don't know. I can't seem to put my finger on anything definite why I should be that way. Yet everything I do, I *tighten up.* As to why I do, I don't know.

D. You said *nervous*?

[*"Nervous" is chosen as the cue word, implying "tied up in knots," and "perspiration."*]

P. Maybe it is a *nervous* condition. Just what's causing it, I don't know.

D. What do you mean—nervous?

P. That's what I don't know. I can't seem to find out just what it is. I've done things over and over again, and I still feel that tightened up feeling all the time, no matter how many times I've done it. Yet I'm not shaky. Outwardly I seem to be all right. Everybody tells me I look good. It's *inside*. It seems to be all *inside*.

[*The repeated expression "I don't know" is a defense against and a cover for the fear of becoming conscious of the cause of his condition. What are "things?"*]

D. What do you mean by "inside?"

P. It seems to be internally. There's nothing I can find to *relax*, so to speak.

D. You can't relax?

P. That's about it. The things I like to do that may relax, like *dancing*. I like to dance, but I find the exertion of dancing seems to bring up the pressure. I feel awfully *tired* and *exhausted*. I feel very *warm*, probably because of the pressure. It makes me *perspire*.

[*"Dancing" is one of the "things" for relaxation, but it makes him hot, sweating and tired, i.e., something about this activity is forbidden.*]

D. You like to dance?

P. I do. But I get so *tired* very easily. I like to—but I don't enjoy it. I mean I do *like to dance*, but when I do, I get so tired and so exhausted that I'm almost panting. It's exertion for me. I don't know why I should be *nervous* about dancing. I've done it so many hundreds of times. It's always there. I think of going and I know I'm going to enjoy myself, yet I have that *tightened up* feeling.

[*Dancing makes him "nervous." What does "dancing" mean?*]

D. You said you've been dancing hundreds of times?

P. That's what seems funny to me. I can't see any reason for it. I can see maybe if you were doing something new, you might be *nervous* about doing something new—but here I've done it hundreds of times, so to speak. I can't see any reason why I should have that tightened up feeling. If I was trying something new—yet it's always present.

[*Anticipation of some kind of failure makes him nervous.*]

D. When you're doing *new things*, you get nervous?

P. If it's something different I were doing and I was in doubt just what it would be, I could see the reason for being *nervous* at something like that. But there are a lot of things I've done time and time again. Yet I still have that tightening up feeling. As Dr. X wrote, when I went up for my Army physical—he said that I don't seem to be fully relaxed. I can see it, but I don't seem to find anything that would be causing it.

[*Denial as defense against the exposure to the "unknown": "I can't find anything that would be causing it."*]

D. But you said, if you're in doubt whether you can do something, then you get *nervous*. . . .
P. I can see the reason for that.
D. When?
P. Well, I guess the ordinary person—I should think—if you're trying something new and are in doubt about it—I think it would cause it. Maybe I'm different, but I should think if somebody was trying something new, something different—and is in doubt, he'd be *nervous*.
D. For instance?
P. A new job. Different type of work. You might not be able to do it or something like that. Then I can see the reason why a person might be a little nervous about doing it. But doing the same thing, and you know you've done it before—I don't seem to be able to find out just what it is that makes me feel that way. Yet I always have that feeling. Outwardly I probably don't show it. It's inside of me, so to speak. It seems to be internally.

[*He is trying to ward off his unconscious anxiety by externalizing and rationalizing it.*]

D. You mean you feel it internally?
P. Yes. I try not to show it. That might be causing the tightening up.

[*The threat comes from within.*]

D. How do you feel internally?
P. In a knot, so to speak.
D. In a knot, as you call it. Is that how you always feel when you're in doubt about doing something new?

[*Returning to the first cue word to prepare an opening into the past.*]

P. Or even things that I've done before. I find myself that way, too.
D. Do you?
P. Yes. In the case of dancing. Before I even get up to dance, I feel that sort of *tightening up* feeling. I don't know anything it might be. Maybe I've felt that way before and kind of wonder if I'll be feeling that way again.

[*Fear of failure when "moving toward" the forbidden object.*]

D. You mean the first time?
P. When I did go.
D. You felt shaky?
P. That might be it.
D. Do you remember?
P. Maybe there's something in that. The first time I did go, I was a little bit nervous, but still it comes back to the same thing. I don't know

why it should be—it *should be* something I like to do. Yet there's no reason I can see why I should be nervous.

[*This suggests his liking for dancing is somewhat forced. The pressure into the past continues against resistance. When did dancing achieve the meaning of the forbidden activity?*]

D. Do you remember when it happened the first time?
P. No, not in dancing particularly. I don't seem to recall being nervous the first time I was going dancing. (Pause)
D. What kind of feeling was it?
P. What?
D. What kind of feeling was it—what do you call internal knots?

[*Returning to one of the original cue words.*]

P. Tightening up. Just in a knot, so to speak. Tightening the muscles. Not fully relaxed. Sometimes if I was going out, maybe there might even be a *nausea* feeling.

[*"Nausea" as if the tightened muscle knot were in the stomach. A new cue word.*]

D. Nausea?
P. *Nervous* stomach, perhaps.
D. Did you have it?
P. Nobody ever told me I did. Are there any symptoms for it?
D. You mentioned nausea.
P. Your stomach seems to be turning over from nervousness. More than anything else I think it would be. I don't know if it's any symptom for a nervous stomach. I've heard of a nervous stomach.
D. What did you hear?
P. I heard the thing "nervous stomach." That's what I would call maybe this feeling I have when I go out or something like that. Sort of a sickening feeling. (Pause)

[*In this context, "dancing" means taking something wrong into the stomach (through the mouth), which leads to nausea. His difficulty is with the passive or feminine aspect of the dancing relationship.*]

D. And what was your reason for going to Dr. X?
P. Well, one time when I gave blood, they told me my pressure was high. I've known it was high for about four years, when the doctor over there. . . .
D. Four years ago you gave blood?
P. That's the first time I knew my pressure was high, but one of the times when I gave blood, the doctor suggested where I was so young, it shouldn't be that high, and I should investigate it. I was sent to Dr. X to see if he could find *anything wrong* or what might be causing it. I've been up to him three times. As far as he can see, there's nothing physically wrong. I went through a complete physical at the hospital about three years ago. They came to the same conclusion. They called it essential hypertension.

[*The fear of having taken something wrong into the stomach, leads to high blood pressure.*]

D. Essential hypertension?

P. That's what they called it. There are other doctors who came to the same conclusion and gave it the same name. Yet where does that get me? Sometimes it seems there's nothing wrong physically, yet I don't feel right. I never even feel comfortable.

[*"Essential hypertension" as the expression of the pathological conflict solution. It is the result of having done something wrong; it is the punishment and atonement for it.*]

D. But you said four years ago. . . .

P. I was working in the American Express. I started to work. I worked there about a week or so and they gave me a physical. When I went up there, he took my pressure and he felt it was high. He thought maybe I was tired from work. He told me to come back again. I went up to the hospital. I went through this complete physical and all kinds of tests. They came to the conclusion that it was "essential hypertension." Since then two or three other doctors came to the same conclusion. There's *nothing physically wrong* with me, yet the pressure is there. They tell me to rest a while longer and go into consultation. I tell them I know it's high. I've known for three or four years. But I've gone through that physical. I've had other examinations from different doctors. Nobody seems to be able to find anything *physically wrong*. Yet the pressure is always there. It's higher than it would be from just nerves, I think. No one has ever told me.

[*"Physically" wrong, versus mentally wrong.*]

D. But you have that feeling.

P. I presume that is why. One doctor suggested an operation for high pressure. I thought, before I went into any surgery, that I would look into it a little bit. The reason I was recommended by Dr. X is because he saw all the examinations and X-rays I went through there. He has contact with the doctor who does the operations. That was the reason I went to him. He still wouldn't suggest the operation. He thought something could be done without surgery. (Silence)

[*"Surgery" means cutting off the wrongdoing part, and preventing the ego from using the body for the solution of the conflict. He waits hopefully that the interviewer may take sides against surgery. Instead, the interviewer responds with the associative key word "nervous."*]

D. Have you always been *nervous*?

P. I guess I have.

D. Yes?

P. I believe so.

D. In which way?

P. There doesn't seem to be anything that I can put my finger on to make me *nervous*. I know nothing that should be causing it. No reason why I should feel that way. That in itself may be causing me to be nervous. It's sort of a vicious circle.

[Being afraid that his inside may become exposed, makes him nervous.]

D. As I see, you're a little. . . .
P. Fidgety.

["Fidgety" means to him trembling in the hands. What did he do wrong with his hands?]

D. A little bit nervous now.
P. Talking to you, I know I shouldn't be.
D. You are?
P. I am.
D. Why? Nothing here is bad, nor good.

[The benevolent impartiality of the interviewer is stressed to ease the tension in the transference relationship.]

P. In fact I think there should be no reason at all why I should be nervous, because I'm trying to find something that's bothering me. I'm trying to help myself.
D. You—yourself?
P. I'm trying to.
D. You yourself?

[He against himself.]

P. (Laughs) I'm trying to help.

[A welcome laugh; it indicates a positive transference. He tries to help himself by hiding what is inside.]

D. But, as you said, it bothers you to be this way.
P. Naturally it bothers me, feeling this way. I don't feel comfortable in anything I might do. I *always* have that tight feeling. On exertion I feel all hot, warmed up, sweaty sort of feeling—that nervous tension.

[The effort of hiding creates "nervous tension."]

D. Always?

[Returning to the past.]

P. I can look back and see times when I first got out of high school. I can remember doing things, and any sort of exertion would cause me to have that *flushed-up feeling.*
D. In high school?
P. I remember after high school. One of the first jobs I had was a shipper. *Lifted things,* I remember. Got a flushed-up feeling when I exerted myself.

[At last he dares to expose the flushed-up feeling of the schoolboy after "any sort" of exertion, but as an undercover he refers to the adult occupational activity of "lifting things."]

D. You worked as a . . .?
P. Shipper.
D. As a shipper?

P. It was after high school. It was the first job I had. (Pause)

D. That you felt so *hot?*

[*Using the more obvious word.*]

P. Yes. Flushed up easily. Even apparently for no reason, I'll just be talking to someone. . . .

[*Hot, flushed up, when talking. Working, dancing, talking, are equated.*]

D. Talking to someone?

P. Yes. Nothing embarrassing. You might say I'm *blushing,* but it's just ordinary conversation. I get that *tightening up* feeling. I find myself flushed.

[*"Blushing" as the exposure of the "reddened" head.*]

D. Talking to someone whom you don't know?

P. No, no. With anybody. I don't think I'm shy.

D. What?

P. I don't believe I'm shy. I like people and crowds.

D. You like them?

P. Yes, but because of the way I feel, I'm somewhat—I don't have the ambition to go out and do it the way I'd like to do it. I don't feel comfortable doing it. I do go out occasionally, but I'd rather be by myself when I don't feel right. I'm not exactly sick, but I'm not comfortable doing the things I know I'd like to be doing.

[*Afraid of liking people, but also of being disliked. He withdraws, afraid of giving himself away, i.e., his active masculine desires.*]

D. So you prefer to stay alone?

P. I'm by myself quite a bit.

D. You are?

P. Yes, although I do like company. I find when I feel so uncomfortable all the time—not because of the company, but personally— I seem to go off by myself.

[*The term "going off" has a double meaning.*]

D. Although you would prefer. . . .

P. Not maybe to disturb them or embarrass them. I find that I may be doing things or saying things where I don't feel comfortable—that I *might hurt them.*

[*Afraid of insulting people by talking.*]

D. Might hurt them—their feelings?

P. Yes. I've been told a few times that I've insulted them.

D. By whom?

P. By people themselves, by things I've said to them. I would say them in a joke. Maybe they take it in the wrong way. I'm afraid sometimes maybe to say things to them after that.

[*Who are "people"?*]

D. Not to insult them?

P. I don't like to hurt anybody.

[*He "goes off by himself"—afraid of being disliked for his aggression.*]

D. You don't like it?

P. I like people. I like to associate. I like to have fun, but feeling the way I do, I don't feel up to it, so to speak. If, say, I went out to a party, and *I dance,* I get *this flushed up feeling.* My heart begins to pound, palpitation, because of the exertion, and I feel uncomfortable. I don't feel just right, so I keep away from them.

[*Fear of "insulting" people leads to flushed-up feeling, heart pounding.*]

D. You do?

P. Yes.

D. Do you remember people telling you that you hurt their feelings?

P. Yes. People have told me that.

D. How did you do it?

P. By things that I've said.

D. For instance?

P. Well, *one girl* where I work. She's rather *stout.* I made a statement. She was just sensitive about it, maybe. She got awfully mad.

[*Insulting a "stout girl" by making fun of her. People are "girls"—the feminine part of himself.*]

D. What did you say?

P. I said something about "Meat must have been awfully cheap when they put you together." Something to that effect. She got awfully mad. She told me herself she's very sensitive about her size, so I've been very careful not to talk to her along that line since then.

[*He is not aware that he is making fun of himself, and that it is he who is very sensitive about the size of his "meat."*]

D. You felt with her? You mean you can understand it?

P. Yes. Well, she told me herself that I had hurt her. That she was sensitive about that. So I don't mention anything about that from now on. I don't like to hurt anybody knowingly.

[*Identifying with a "stout" girl makes him feel flushed up. His symptoms represent the anxiety-laden relationship of a small boy and a big (stout) woman.*]

D. You wouldn't do it knowingly?

P. Yes.

D. You never did it knowingly?

P. No. I was just kidding around. Just thought I was smart, maybe.

D. You were never. . . .

P. I never did it intentionally. She just happened to be sensitive about that and took it that way.

D. Have you been sensitive, too?

P. No, I don't believe I have. I don't think so.

[*He cannot admit as yet that he is like "a girl."*]

D. Not you?
P. No. I don't think so. I think I take it the way it comes, and forget it as quick as I can. Why should I be insulted when *something like that* happens? I let it go over my head. *In* one ear, and *out* the other, if it should be something I didn't like.

[*What is "something like that?"*]

D. To be hurt?
P. Yes. I forget it as quick as I can.
D. You mean you try?
P. Maybe try. Then again maybe I *bury* it, so to speak, *unknowingly.*

[*He tries to "forget" when he feels hurt. Denial as a defense.*]

D. Did other people say you were easily hurt?
P. I? No.
D. I mean people around you.
P. I think it may sound like bragging—but I think I'm well liked. A lot of people enjoy my company.

[*Afraid of being disliked.*]

D. But I mean—they thought you are easily hurt.
P. No. On the contrary.
D. On the contrary?
P. I think I take everything in its stride. Pass it off, if it should be something that they shouldn't have said to me. (Long Pause)

[*The interviewer does not interrupt the silence. Apparently the patient became aware that what he tries to "bury unknowingly" is the voice in him which ridicules his "meat," as he did to the girl. "Meat" is the insulting part which he uses in dancing. Therefore, this key word is introduced again to prove through the associations that "dancing" stirs up the threatening wish of "insulting."*]

D. For instance—about your dancing?
P. It should give me pleasure, because I do like to dance, but it's the pressure I have. The exertion from dancing seems to build up the pressure which causes me to be very uncomfortable about it. Feeling flushed up, palpitation. I feel the blood boiling through me, pounding through me, where it should be something which I should be enjoying. I know I like to dance. *People tell me I'm a good dancer.* Yet when I do it, I don't feel comfortable. I can't seem to see any reason why I shouldn't be comfortable at doing something which I like to do. I find swimming—I find I like to do that. I think swimming is about one of the things that I can put my finger on. One of the particular reasons I joined the YMCA was to continue swimming in the winter. I like to swim quite a bit. They say swimming is one of the exercises you use all your muscles. Yet I find I enjoy it.

[*Doing "things" which he likes to do makes him uncomfortable (flushed up, warm).*]

D. You always like to use your muscles?

["*Muscles" equals meat. Muscular activity means masculine activity.*]

P. Yes. Active things. Yet when I do active things, it seems to affect my blood pressure, causing me to get flushed up and warm, uncomfortable.

D. You don't like to be too hot?

P. You don't feel comfortable, all sweated up. The way I feel sometimes— don't know if you've ever been down at the race track. You see a horse after the race, practically steaming. I feel as if I was all flushed up like that and breathing hard. Feel as if I were steaming like a race horse that just finished a race.

["*Race horse" versus "stout girl." Whom is he racing against?*]

D. A race horse?

P. That's the feeling I have. I feel so warm from the exertion of dancing. Yet it's something I like to do. Yet when I do it, it makes me feel that way. I don't see why I should be nervous about dancing. I've done it so many times. Yet I have that same tightening up feeling when I do it.

[*His symptoms appear now to be warning signals against masculine activity on an adolescent level.*]

D. Since when?

P. High school. Not too much in high school. I don't go too much dancing. Since the last four or five years, I haven't gone to any extent. Probably once a week or so.

D. Also when you were in high school?

P. No. Maybe I didn't have a chance to do a lot of *things* I wanted to do.

[*There were many kinds of races and competitions.*]

D. Why not?

P. My *father* had a place on the beach. While other people were enjoying things, I was working.

[*At last his resentment against father is revealed.*]

D. When?

P. As far back as I can remember.

D. How far?

P. We all *worked* together. He had a stand. A place where they sell refreshments on the beach. My mother tells me when I was in a carriage they used to have me down there. We all worked. I went Sundays. When other people were enjoying themselves, *I was working the hardest,* because that's when the business was on Sundays and holidays. I never got out much. Through high school, even after high school for a couple of years, I never did the things the ordinary high-school kid did.

[*Father forced him to exert himself. Father is responsible for his condition; that relieves his guilt feelings. He has an alibi that the hard work as a kid made him sick. Father prevented him from doing what other kids did. He was racing with father.*]

D. And you couldn't go?
P. I couldn't go. My father was down there for twenty-eight years—so he was there before I was born.
D. On the beach?
P. Yes. He hasn't been down there the last five years.
D. No more?
P. He isn't down there any more. He got sick.
D. Sick?
P. He got sick and had to give it up.

[*Give up the "race".*]

D. What do you mean?
P. Same thing. *Blood pressure.* He thought at first it was his *heart* that went bad. He had to give up the long hours of work. Long hours of work down there. Early mornings to late at night. People like to enjoy themselves. They come down on different hours of the day. You stay with them and suffer for it.

[*Father suffered from high blood pressure because he had to serve the people who enjoyed themselves.*]

D. He suffered?
P. Yes. I guess so. He was down there for so many years—it took it out of his health. He got sick and couldn't do it any longer. There was a chance for me to get out of it. I went looking for a job. Little by little I got away from it.
D. So you shouldn't become like him?
P. Like him. I wasn't doing the things the other kids were doing. I always had to be down there, and when they were *out enjoying themselves,* I was working the hardest.

[*Father prevented him from joining the kids when they were out enjoying themselves (with the girls).*]

D. You had to do it for him?
P. That's it. We all helped.
D. And you resented it?
P. I was more or less confined. Never went out much. At high school they had parties. I never was part of them. Well, this time of the year it usually starts, about April. During the week probably there wouldn't be nothing down there, but Sundays people start coming out, and Sundays is *when other people are out enjoying themselves.* That's the day we would be working. Even when I was going to school, if I was going to school now. During the week I'd be going to school, then Saturdays and Sundays, when the other kids would be out playing, having a good time, that's when I'd have to go down there and work. So I missed all that.

[*The sight of people enjoying themselves became forever tied up with father's prohibition to do the same.*]

D. How did you feel?
P. There were bars in front of the place. You felt as if you were in

prison. Everybody else was enjoying themselves, and here you are working. I felt as if I missed that part.

[*He felt like a prisoner in chains when he could not do what he liked.*]

D. You felt bad?
P. Yes. In high school. I didn't do the things the other kids did. Not all of them. Some of them might have had to work during the summer. It was more or less voluntary. Mine was more or less necessity.
D. You couldn't get away . . .?
P. That's it.
D. Father didn't let you?
P. I felt it was part of my duty, so to speak, to be with him. It was their livelihood. Before I could be out front, I was in the back doing things, helping out, preparing things, getting things ready.
D. All of you?
P. Yes. We all worked. The whole family.
D. Who is the whole family?
P. Father, mother, my sister, myself—and I guess my little brother got out of it. He got out before he was old enough to get down there.
D. Your little. . . .

[*The baby brother got the things the patient wanted and which father wouldn't let him have.*]

P. Yes. My smallest brother. There's one younger than I. He was down there for a while, too. I guess we lost out on a lot of things that the ordinary kids used to do because of that. I think so, anyway.

[*Resentful against father for having made him miss what other kids used to do.*]

D. You lost out?
P. This time of the year when you *dance* and socials are going on, the other kids always went and I didn't. I won't say I missed them all, but there were a lot of times when I wanted to go and couldn't.

[*Father did not let him "dance."*]

D. And you never complained?
P. No. Maybe that's the reason. There's something in that. I don't complain because I felt it's what I should be doing.
D. Tried not to show your resentment?
P. There were things I would have liked to have done; but I found that first I don't know if I was right or not.

[*Enjoyment is wrongdoing.*]

D. Not right or wrong, but you felt that way.
P. It's something past. Maybe it's something in the past.

[*He would like to forget.*]

D. But today you feel that you've missed. . . .
P. Yes, I missed something there somewhere.
D. I'll see you again.

CHART

CONTAINING THE ASSOCIATIVELY CONNECTED KEY WORD COMPLEX WITHIN THE CHOSEN SECTOR OF THE FATHER RELATIONSHIP

SYMPTOMS:

Nervous tension; flushed up, hot feeling; blushing; heart pounding; feeling tied up in knots in muscles and in stomach; nausea.

What caused the symptoms?

Talking; dancing; working; muscular activity; exertion; insulting people; exposing his inner self; anticipation of failure; fear of not being liked.

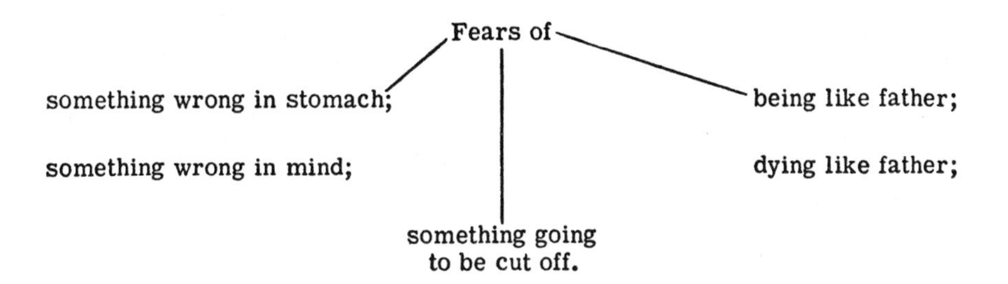

What relieved the symptoms?

1. Avoidance of their causes;
2. Going off by himself;
3. Identifying with females;
4. Putting the blame on father;
5. Dissociating from father;
6. Playing the role of a Gentile;
7. Releasing the repressed resentment against father.

Discussion

The first interview developed according to plan. The patient presented his symptoms in their meaningful interrelations, expressing on different levels the fears which motivated them. He revealed the type of defenses he had to use against these fears, and also what pattern of behavior could relieve the symptoms (denial, withdrawal, rationalization, hiding his passive wishes, being ingratiating).

By and large, the therapeutic task of this interview was the assembling of the key-word complex and the release of some of the infantile resentments toward the father. Against the attempts to uncover the unconscious motivations of his condition, the patient reacted with anxiety which needed to be handled carefully. For instance, the interviewer had to remain unpartial when the patient asked him to take sides against surgery.

It transpired that the symptoms were warning signals against masculine activities. The patient's relationship to the interviewer in the role of a permissive father enabled him to air his old grudges against the forbidding father.

(*Note:* the patient's blood pressure after this interview was 168/110.)

Part 2—The Color Barrier

INTERVIEW 2

D. How are you?
P. Pretty good, sir. Now what?

[This statement is a sign of transference.]

D. Now what? Did you think about our conversation after you left here?
P. The impression I got was that you would ask questions and maybe bring out something hidden, *so to speak,* and I got the impression that you more or less studied me more than anything else.

[He suggests that something is hidden.]

D. That's right. Only in this way can we find out the real source of your problem and can try to remove it.
P. Well, we found there is nothing physically—*so to speak;* I presume I was sent here with the idea of something in that line.
D. This was also *your* idea; wasn't it?
P. Yes—where I've been examined by Dr. X and other doctors, and there's nothing wrong physically, maybe something, as *you* say, something in the past or something emotional.

[He calls the "something" hidden the "YOU," so to speak, and projects it on the interviewer who turns it back to him. He accepts it that the "YOU" is he himself.]

D. As *you* told me.
P. Yes.
D. I mean—*you* referred to certain events. Do you remember?
P. Yes.
D. Events which stirred you up and—as we saw—brought tears to your eyes when thinking of yourself as a boy who went through so much hardship. Am I right?
P. Yes. (Pause) It's not along the same line, but last night I went dancing. As I explained to you before, I've done it so many times before. Yet I seem to have that feeling—nervous feeling. There's no apparent reason as far as I can find out. Yet I always have that feeling, doing things I've done before.

[He went dancing due to the transference feelings toward the interviewer. "Doing" is identical with "doing wrong" and with "dancing."]

D. You went dancing?

P. I went dancing.

D. And?

P. I had a good time, but yet. . . . I still had that tightening up feeling, not fully relaxed. There's no reason for it as far as I can see.

D. *Dancing?* With whom?

[*"Dancing" is repeated for a continual confrontation with the "wrong-doing."*]

P. There were a few people that I work with. People that I know, associate with quite a bit. Nobody that I should be nervous about. I know them, talk to them every day. Yet that feeling was there.

D. People whom you see every day?

P. Yes—work with. That's what seems funny to me. To be associating with people every day and yet have that feeling—tightening up. One of them was telling me—I was talking to a girl and she said *I get awfully red* for no apparent reason. At other times I feel as though my face was red and no one ever mentioned it. As though mentally I thought my face was *red.* It feels like I'm *flushed* up many times. Yet this particular time I had no feeling that I was *blushing,* so to speak. Yet she tells me I was.

[*The "girl" becomes aware of what he is hiding: "the reddened head." "Dancing" leads to red face. "Blushing" is reddened face.*]

D. The girl?

P. One of the girls that I was up there with last night.

D. Do you know that you blush easily?

P. Not that I know. She said it was the first time she ever saw me. Yet there are a lot of occasions when I thought I was, and I felt I was.

D. When?

P. In conversations. I get that tight feeling. I feel flushed up. I always thought my face was red on a number of occasions, but no one ever mentioned it to me. Yet this time I felt perfectly at ease. I thought I did until she told me my face was awfully red. I was conversing with her. (Pause)

[*"Flushed up" turns into "blushing." What comes first?*]

D. That surprised you?

P. I mentioned it to her. I had no feeling that my face was red at the time. It did surprise me. I mentioned to her that sometimes I feel flushed up, but no one had ever told me so. She said it was the first time she had ever noticed it. I don't see why it should be.

[*"Flushed up feeling" from dancing serves as a cover for "blushed feeling" from exposure.*]

D. Because . . .?

P. It was ordinary conversation.

D. You mean, if it had been another type of conversation . . .?

P. Yes, then I could see a reason for it. Yet she said my face was red.

D. You mean you might understand getting a red face if you had another conversation?

P. Possibly. If I were embarrassed, then I could see a reason for it.

D. Are you easily embarrassed when you talk about things which could embarrass someone else?

[*The interviewer proceeds cautiously.*]

P. I don't think I have. I don't know. They've never told me about my face being red.
D. Who are "they"?
P. People I work with. If you're talking and you do get red, they usually mention the fact to you, I suppose. They say you are blushing. It's very rarely they haven't told me so. This particular girl said it was one of the first times she ever saw me. (Pause)
D. You mean you expected to feel it when you blush?
P. I guess there's some reason. She told me she feels it when her face is flushed up.

[*Girls feel it when they blush. He again equates flushed up and blushing.*]

D. She said so?
P. Yes. She told me, when she blushes, she knows about it. I suppose I'm no different than her. On this occasion anyway. I don't feel any different than I ordinarily do.

[*If he were a girl, he could admit his blushing.*]

D. She said she feels it?
P. She feels it when her face gets red and embarrassed.

[*Girls have reason for getting red.*]

D. So that means you must be different from her?
P. I suppose so; yet I felt as normal, so to speak, at the time I was speaking. Just a couple of days ago that happened. Last night I happened to be talking about it. Up to that time I didn't know when I was blushing. I didn't feel it.
D. Are there times when you thought you were blushing?
P. Yes. They don't tell me. Maybe I feel it. My face feels warm and flushed. Maybe it's natural that my face should be redder than anyone else's. Maybe it's because my face is red more or less all the time anyway.
D. Is that so?
P. I don't know. How does it look now?
D. Do you feel it now?
P. Yes. My face feels more or less flushed now.

[*The admission that he feels flushed now, implies that he feels like a girl in his relation to the interviewer. The transference situation permits him to reveal this feeling, by blushing. In relation to the other sex, he hides his masculine wishes, apparently afraid of being a failure.*]

D. Yes, but it is your color. It's the color which is somewhat reddish. As you said now, being here with me, you feel it.
P. Right at the present time I feel as if my face is somewhat flushed.
D. You mean it is different from the feeling you had when you were with the girl?

P. Yes.
D. Are you embarrassed?
P. No. Maybe it's something I haven't done before. As I said last time, something new.
D. As if you were in a situation that is new?
P. This lull in conversation *embarrasses* me a little bit, not knowing what to say or what to do.

[*He contradicts his former denial of embarrassment.*]

D. A situation where you don't know what to say or what to do—is that a situation which could be called an embarrassing one?
P. Not exactly—but it makes me feel uncomfortable. Like you and I talk here. We both talk. It seems as if we were both ready for one another to make the next move.

[*A meaningful statement. He is blushing like a girl in relation to the interviewer, with whom he "talks."*]

D. As if we both were moving toward each other?
P. The same, I guess.
D. The feeling as if each was waiting for the other to make the move?
P. As I said before, I like active things. When I'm still, I'm not moving or not talking. It's sort of that feeling—I don't know what you would call it—wonder maybe. I feel more comfortable moving around and talking. When we stop like we did quite a few times, I'm not exactly comfortable.

[*It seems as if he equated "dancing" with "moving" and "talking." "Being spoken to" means acceptance. Silence indicates the opposite.*]

D. That is, you mean if you could be active being with me?
P. If we would keep on talking.
D. Being active?
P. In a sense, yes. Then it counteracts any nervousness, or what's another word? When we're talking, I'm probably concentrating more or less, and it takes my mind off the empty space. That's why I like to do active things. I feel more comfortable at it. Like dancing. The exertion seems to bring up pressure.

[*Talking (dancing) with men counteracts "nervousness." What is the "empty space?"*]

D. The pressure?
P. It shouldn't, because *I enjoy it.* That's why I can't figure it out. Where I'm doing something I like to do, yet the pressure, the exertion brings up the pressure and I feel uncomfortable.

[*What he enjoys is forbidden.*]

D. Active? You mean dancing?
P. Well, if I can move around—not sitting around. I don't like to sit down playing cards, sitting around just talking. I like to get out and move around, and I feel much better. Just eating together—sitting down and eating, I don't feel comfortable.

[*"Sitting around" is like being silent, i.e., rejecting or being rejected.*

"Eating" is an association to the "empty space" from which he wants to take his mind off.]

D. You don't?
P. No. It seems, though I'm on the move, I feel more comfortable that way.
D. Always?
P. Active.
D. You should move?
P. Gypsy blood may be in me to keep moving.

[*Moving versus mouth activity.*]

D. Gypsy blood?
P. Maybe that's where I get it. (Laughs)
D. Have you always been on the move?
P. I try to, because I know I feel better doing active things. Maybe someone takes my mind off myself. I forget myself.

[*Moving to counteract the passivity, i.e., sitting around, eating together. Is "myself" his feminine part? "Someone" is the masculine part.*]

D. What do you mean?
P. I haven't got a chance to think so much about the way I feel. I talk, move around, haven't got time to think about myself.

[*He rejects the "myself."*]

D. Why should you not?
P. Well, if you're concentrating on something, it takes your mind off yourself.
D. For instance?
P. Talking. Then you don't have a chance to talk about yourself or think about yourself. Your mind is in another channel.
D. Which kind of thinking about yourself?
P. The way I feel, probably. It relieves that *lonely* feeling.

[*The rejected part of him feels lonely.*]

D. Is that the way you feel?
P. Yes.
D. Are you lonely?

[*Which "I" is lonely? It is the feminine part of him which makes him different from other boys.*]

P. I think so.
D. What do you mean?
P. I think I'm always alone. I was never really close with anyone in my gang. I used to go out with them. I used to go to parties and things like that. They seemed to like different things than I did. So I used to go off by myself quite a bit. I seem to never have been real close to anyone. Usually in a gang there are two that are closer than with the rest of the gang. They probably confide in each other, but I can think of no one I've been that close with, ever really talked to, I guess.

[*The two sides of him want to be close to each other, but cannot be brought into a unit.*]

D. Although you wished. . . .
P. Yes, unknowingly. Probably up to recently I never realized it.
D. You mean recently you have more. . . .
P. I became conscious of it.
D. And you feel more lonely, the more you wish to talk?
P. Maybe that would help a lot. I realize I do feel better. . . . talking takes my mind off myself.

[*He represses his feminine wishes.*]

D. But you were never close to the other boys or to the gang?
P. There was a gang. We used to do things together. I never really was close to anyone, any particular one. They were more or less mechanically inclined. One of the boys had a workshop down the cellar, and they used to spend a lot of time there. I used to go down there for a while. It didn't appeal to me, so I used to go for a walk.

[*"Walking" is like "talking," "moving" or "dancing." He did it with "himself."*]

D. Alone?
P. Alone. Most of the time alone. There were a couple of fellows I used to walk with or talk to, but mostly myself, alone.
D. Why?
P. Well, as I say. . . .
D. You were different from them?
P. No—I wouldn't say I was different from them. They liked different things than I did.
D. They liked different things than you did?
P. None of them liked to dance, and I always liked to dance. I went dancing and they used to be down in the workshop. I never got really close with any of them.

[*He felt disliked by the boys in his feminine role, went off by (with) himself, then projected his own feminine part on the girls, with whom he identified. He dances with them (with himself) or talks to them.*]

D. You avoided them, so to speak?
P. I guess you might call it that. I wouldn't avoid them exactly, but they weren't doing the things I liked to do, so *I went off by myself* in the sense that I left them. I went to dances. Of course, there were other people there that I talked to and danced with. I joined the Y here. Going swimming. I like to swim. Gym once in a while. The boys never went in for it. Just went off and did it. Found a different crowd and got interested in them.

[*Synonyms: dancing, talking, swimming, gymnastic.*]

D. And you preferred to dance?
P. Yes.
D. To dance with girls, or do you mean dancing alone?
P. No, with girls. Public dances at the Y. They had dances a couple of

nights a week. I used to go to them. But my gang never went in for dances. I used to like it.

D. What did they say?

P. They didn't say much. I just got tired of hanging around down the cellar and I would go off. Go to the dance by myself. I would go swimming for a while and then go to a dance. The peculiar thing about it is that most of them are married now, and I was the one who was going out with the girls. All but one of them is married now, and he's seeing a girl. I'm the only single one in the whole gang. It seems funny that I was the only one that did go out, and the only one that didn't marry. I don't know what it might be. Maybe I didn't go to the right places. I met a lot of nice girls. They didn't seem to be the right ones yet.

[*He went dancing "publicly" to cover up his femininity. The boys who were active in the cellar got married. Since he is different from the boys, he is looking for a girl who is different from other girls. The feminine part of him looks for a masculine girl partner.*]

D. You didn't think there was the right one?

P. Not anyone I would want to spend the rest of my life with.

D. You have met girls?

P. Yes. I know a lot of nice girls now, but as far as anything serious, I don't think I could. . . .

D. You don't have the real feeling?

P. Feeling toward them, yes.

D. You said it is surprising that you, who went earlier with the girls. . . .

P. I don't know. This might account for it—I'm Jewish. I don't know if you know that. It seems that I go to the Y—it seems I've been associating with Christian girls and fellows most of the time.

[*"Jewish" is another name for the feminine (defective) side of him, which makes him feel different.*]

D. Whereas the other boys?

P. Truthfully, they very seldom went out. One of them came down to the beach and met her down there. Sort of accidentally. They never went to *public affairs like dancing* or things like that. Maybe that's why. I've never given a serious thought to any of these girls I've met with.

[*A real man does not have to publicize his masculinity.*]

D. Because you found you're Jewish and felt different?

P. I think I have felt a little about that, too.

D. Being Jewish means to you something . . .?

P. I know that my mother wouldn't approve of my marrying a Christian girl.

[*"Christian girl" means to him a kind of "feminine girl" to whom his mother objects because she is different from her.*]

D. She wouldn't?

P. Yes. There are a lot of things that would have to be considered before there would be a mixed marriage like that.

D. You mean you wouldn't do it without mother's consent?

P. I won't say I wouldn't do it, but I know she'd feel bad about it. There are a couple of cases. People around our way that have mixed marriages. At first the parents didn't like it very much, but they came down to it—came around. I don't know if they approve of it, but they make the best of it.

D. You mean—you hide that you're Jewish?

P. No, I don't hide it. I pass very easily for anything but Jewish—more Irish than Jewish. When I do tell them I'm Jewish, they're surprised. And my age. I have—I won't say trouble—it's hard to convince them how old I am and that I'm Jewish. I don't think I'm different from any of the Jewish fellows.

[*If he is "Irish," he is "reddened" racially, and not from blushing. He can also pose as "Christian" without being ashamed of exposing his conflict.*]

D. You said you look more Irish.

P. Maybe where I've associated with Christian girls and fellows for quite some time, I more or less fall along their lines of thought. Probably that makes it, as I say—(Pause) gives them an impression that I am not.

D. The other boys look Jewish?

P. Yes.

D. So you looked somewhat different. A red face, red hair. That is, as you think, more Irish?

P. Yes. A lot of them take me for Irish. I associated quite a bit with Christian people.

D. Close to them in some way?

P. Yes—I think *I feel more comfortable* with them. I don't know if it's because I've associated with them, but I feel more friendly, they gather you in, so to speak, don't ask questions about you. You become part of their crowd without any questions asked. But you go to a Jewish dance. They seem to be in their little groups. They're sticking together. You can't break in, so to speak. High-hat.

[*The self-deception of being taken for an "Irish," lets him feel comfortable.*]

D. High-hat?

P. I like to get around. Like I say, I go out to a Christian dance. It seems as if they just take me in, not asking me questions. I don't know if it is with everybody, but I find it is that way. They don't ask questions.

[*Among the "Christians" he does not have to fear being asked about the cause of his redness.*]

D. They don't ask questions?

P. They don't ask who you are or what you are.

D. From where you come. . . .

P. They are there for a good time. You get together there for a good time without wanting to know why, who you are.
D. Who you are?
P. Maybe in the conversation you might come out with some of those things, but usually it is just ordinary conversation. What you do in your work.
D. You mean being asked the question: "Who are you?" is a little embarrassing?
P. No.
D. Remember that you said your father was a peddler?

[*This question aims at leading him into the past and at inducing him to reveal his feelings toward the father. The positive transference has progressed sufficiently that he can do it. He begins to expose the protest against the feminine identification. That is expressed at first by a distortion of the reality, i.e., the fact that he was classified for dependency in the Draft.*]

P. No. He was a tailor by trade.
D. On the beach?
P. He had a place on the beach during the summer, but he does tailoring. He works in B——. He's not too well. So just during their season, he goes into one of the big stores and helps out. Like before Easter. They call him in for a few weeks. He has nothing steady at the present time.
D. He has not?
P. That's why I've been around so long. I was classified that way for dependency in the Draft. That's why I wasn't taken before I was really called. I was called and put in 4-F because of the pressure, but because of that I was kept out at first for dependency. Then I had deferment in the work.
D. They're dependent on you?

[*The "high hat" image of being the head of the house goes back to the time when he—as a little boy—had those dreams of grandeur. The father was in his way, who did not let him play with the boys. He devaluates father as a sick man.*]

P. Yes.
D. On you?
P. Yes. That's the way I'm classified. As head of the house.
D. You? How?
P. I'm the main support.
D. What do you mean?
P. Well, my father got sick. I guess I've more or less always contributed more to the house. I'm the oldest son. My sister has worked, but girls are always buying clothes and things they need. She gives something to the house, but I've always felt it was my duty and I *always did give more than the rest of them.* My younger brother before he got married. . . .

[*He sees himself as the head of the family.*]

D. Younger brother?

P. Before he was married he contributed somewhat. But then he got married. That sort of added to the burden. There was that much less coming in, so that I've always given a good part of my pay to the house. I sound like a hero.

[*To offset his masculine insecurity, he has to inflate his ego and to pose as a "hero," a superman.*]

D. Like a hero.

P. I didn't mean to be bragging, but it's the way I feel about it. I have no regrets about it either. I mean at the present time I contribute to the house. Yet I have enough money to do anything I want to do.

[*This narcissism is, apart from his denial mechanism, his main defense. It becomes manifest in his interest in his appearance.*]

D. You have?

P. Maybe before I didn't have enough to do some of the things.

D. Because you had to give away?

P. Yes. But at the present time I can say I'm making enough that I have a few dollars that I find necessary to buy or do the things I want. Then again—I don't do too many things. There are not many things that I do need. *I have all the clothes I need.* A few dollars that I have accumulated by saving bonds. I don't spend money very easily. If it's necessary I have no regrets spending it, but I don't do it foolishly. I don't like gambling.

[*He is already out of bounds in staging the "hero." In the transference situation he sees himself as a man with self-assurance.*]

D. You don't?

P. No. I can't see it at all. It's for people who want to get rich quick. I don't believe in it. It's so foolish to me—to be getting a few dollars back. I've always said, if I was going to gamble, it would be all or nothing at all. If the opportunity should come up where I could steal enough money to live the rest of my life comfortably—either that or have it over with—go to jail for the rest of my life. I'd take a chance like that, but outside of that. . . . Dog track I don't see at all.

[*His self-esteem already borders on delusion of grandeur. The interviewer does not interrupt him.*]

D. You never did?

P. No. I always wondered how these people even went down there to the horse track. I can see the dog track, but these people who go down during the day, if they've got the money. They should be working to earn it, if they haven't got the money. Why aren't they looking for a job?

[*He avoids attending competitive races (dogs, horses), because they would make him aware of his own competitiveness. He declines to take chances.*]

D. That's right. The others looked on you as a hero. You felt yourself as the head of the family, with responsibilities.

[*These remarks are intended to stir up more of the infantile feeling of omnipotence.*]

P. No, I wouldn't say because of that. I just had no tendency toward it. It just never appealed to me. I'm not a gambler. Maybe it might be better to gamble. *I don't like to take chances.* I like to be sure of what I'm doing. If I can't do it right, I probably wouldn't do it at all. I hate to do a thing part way. I like to do it the right way, or not at all.

[*He has forgotten his previous statement about taking a risk in gambling.*]

D. Is everybody in the family the same way?
P. Everybody in my family—gambling?
D. Yes.
P. No. I would say my father is exactly the opposite. As far as horses, he's very strong for it.

[*The father image is still more demoted and contrasted with himself.*]

D. For horses?
P. Yes. It seems to me he takes away from the house. I suppose there are millions of others like him, spending money that shouldn't be spent that way. Maybe he could contribute to the house more: two dollars a week.
D. He loses?
P. Yes. Nobody ever knows when you lose. They only know when you win. Everybody in the city seems to know when he's hit it, but they never know when he loses. One time that he was down there, he was working. He got paid on Monday. Thursday he would be asking for a couple of dollars until payday. One time it burned me up. I wanted to send my suit to the cleaners. I went to borrow one of his pair of pants and I found $50 in it. I didn't say anything about it. It was his. But very shortly after that he asked me for a couple of dollars. When he asked me that, I immediately thought of the $50 that he had put away. When I had the opportunity, I went up to it. It was gone. I guess that's where it went. To anyone else he's sort of a Dr. Jekyll and Mr. Hyde. I don't know which is which now. Is Dr. Jekyll the good one? Outside he's well liked. No one really knows him, only the family, I guess. He likes to be a good fellow. He likes everybody to pat him on the back. That's the impression he gives outside, while in the house he does a lot of things no one knows about. Maybe if they knew about it, they wouldn't think so high of him, so maybe that's why we don't tell people about him. There are a lot of incidents that happen along the same line.

[*Exposing father as a braggadocio, a good-for-nothing, he gets even with him. The long repressed, pent-up hostility against father is now out in the open: he calls him with contempt a sort of "Dr. Jekyll and*

Mr. Hyde." Not he, but father, leads a double life. His contempt for father has no limits.]

D. For instance?

P. He's insured, of course. In the last two years he hadn't been working, but still he could have paid the payments on his insurance, but he never has. He's sort of given it up. I guess indirectly I'm paying for it. Should something happen to him, my mother feels he should continue the policy. He does gambling things. Wasting it, so to speak. To me it's wasting. He should be putting it to more legitimate things. Like paying for his own insurance. He has no expenses, so to speak. A few dollars for cigars, car fare, his lunches. Outside of that, there's nothing much to do. He has a home. Funny person. He always thinks he's right. He won't evade a question. He's right. You can't. . . .

D. . . . Argue . . .?

P. I call it debating. There's no question there. If one debates their side of the question and proves the other person wrong or right, then it's alright. But if something comes up and he says it's white, you can't even debate the question and try to tell him that it's black. He says we're always arguing with him. If anything like that comes up, we just skip over it and forget it as soon as possible, so there won't be any argument. One time—I wasn't home—but he had an argument with my sister. He said some awful things about her. She isn't married.

[*He rages on; these outbursts of resentment are reappearances of the little boy's helplessness against the dogmatic father who puts the law down.*]

D. She isn't?

P. She isn't married. Maybe she's along the same lines as me. Never got out much, about with people, get around, go to the high-school games. So she never met up with anybody that pleased her. She's very fussy—I'll admit that. So they got into some squabbles. He said some very bad things about her. Told her she went with anybody that would come along, which is quite the contrary. Fussy. She goes out, of course. You can't help what she's going to meet up with. He all but called her a tramp. No one knows about those things. We never tell anyone outside the house. It's none of their business maybe. He's got a Dr. Jekyll personality. Outside, he's well liked, but inside he's just the opposite. Hard to get along with. Don't help. He prefers the wrong way more than the right way.

[*Father did not let him act as a man, and his sister as a woman. His remark that the sister is along the same line as he raises the suspicion that they had some common childhood experiences to which a father might have objected. Father does the wrong things for which he blames others. The projection mechanism is obvious.*]

D. It burns you up?

P. Yes.

D. You mean . . . .

P. I can't say the same things to him that I would be saying to someone else. Where he is my father, I have a little respect for him, but not the way I should, I suppose.

[*He no longer conceals his contempt for father.*]

D. So you have to swallow. . . .
P. Yes.
D. You can't debate with him?
P. Can't debate with him? He's right. I don't say I'm always right, but I like to debate a question. Maybe that's somewhat the reason I was more or less quiet when I was in school. Whenever anything came up, he was right. We never talked about it. We never talked back and forth and tried to prove the other's point. So when anything came up, we just kept quiet. So I just became very quiet. When anything came up, I just skipped it.
D. When you were little?
P. As I look back, it might have something to do with it. I was in the last year of high school, I was fairly quiet. No one bothered me; I didn't bother them. I did my work and that was that. I wasn't a genius or anything. I was moderate.

[*The flood of rage begins to recede, as if almost exhausted.*]

D. All right.
P. I hope we are making some progress. I don't know.

[*His relief after the spell of hostility is obvious.*]

D. See you next week.

Discussion

In the second interview the positive transference brought the patient's passive feminine identifications to the fore. He could admit that he was feeling flushed in the presence of his interviewer, and revealed this by blushing. His repressed feminine wishes became apparent, and likewise his fears of being disliked by others in his feminine role. He was projecting his own feminine self onto the girls with whom he identified.

The patient recalled how he had always felt different from his male companions, and how he tried to solve his conflict by presenting himself as an "Irish Christian," thus by-passing the color barrier. Following this, he could freely express the disdainful feelings toward his father, for whom he had no respect and whose place he usurped at home. These devaluations of father as a sick man were encouraged by the interviewer, whereupon the infantile daydreams of the patient's high self-esteem could be verbalized. The long repressed pent-up hostility against his father burst through. Its therapeutic effect may already be predicted.

(*Note:* The patient's blood pressure after this interview was 170/110.)

Part 3—The Color Barrier

Interview 3

P. Kind of *cold* out.

[*The remark "cold out" is taken in its meaning as a relationship feeling.*]

D. Do you like the cold?

P. *I don't know*. I like the warm, too. *I don't know* where to begin. I had a very bad week. Didn't feel right at all. Pounding in my throat all week. All *tightened* up. Altogether a bad week. *I don't know* why. *Can't seem* to find out what it is. It shouldn't be there, but it is there.

[*Three times "I don't know" indicates that he is trying to fight off what he knows.*]

D. What do you call *bad?*

P. Well, I feel my throat—that *tightened up* feeling in my throat. *Pressure* feeling in my *head*. It isn't exactly a headache. Yet it feels like pressure. Then I get palpitation and pains in my chest. One of the three is always with me. I can't seem to completely throw the whole thing off. What seems to be causing it, *I don't know*. But I've found a couple of things. If I'm disturbed, maybe the *nerves* disturb me. Why am I nervous—I suppose it might have been something that was bothering me, something that was the basis. But I don't think that's it. I find that when I *eat out*—it seems to be the nervous tension of eating out.

[*He previously equated "eating out" with "taking in the wrong thing," with "sitting down," and with being passive.*]

D. Eating out?

P. My nervous system or something seems to turn my stomach over and then something along the line—I've never been seasick, but I guess it's something along the lines of seasick. You don't feel good and the thought of eating on top of not feeling good seems to make it all the worse. When I left here last week, I had an invitation to go out to eat. At first I thought it was a party. There was a girl who called. I had seen her the night before at a dance. She told me it was her *birthday*. She told me she was going to have a cake. When I got to work I got the telephone call. At first it sounded like a party, and then she happened to make a statement about the company going to be there. Actually I want to go to those things, yet when I asked her how many were going to be there and she said four of us, it seemed to hit me. The thought of sitting down and eating seemed to give my stomach a twist. I've known it to happen before. I always found an excuse not to go out. I worked around it, tried to think of something after I told her I was coming. I went back to work and began to think about it. The more I thought about it, the more it disturbed me, the thought of doing something that was going to affect me that way. I tried to think of something that would excuse my way out of it. Finally I thought of something. I couldn't get in touch with the girl, couldn't get connections on the phone. I finally gave up in hopes that she would call me. She finally did call. I was supposed to be there at 6 o'clock on Sunday. She finally called about 6 o'clock. I suppose I lied out of it, made up some excuse why I wasn't there. She didn't seem to be satisfied. I couldn't blame her for that. I knew why I wasn't there, but I guess I'm not too good at lying. So this particular girl—I work with her sister . . .

[*The danger is that if the stomach turns over, the "inside" will be exposed. There is always something hidden in his stomach. What is it? What does a "stout" girl have in her stomach? Previously he admitted his identification with such a girl. Eating together, sitting down passively gave his stomach a twist. Working versus sitting down. Being forced to sit and eat with the girl makes him panicky. He wanted to go off by himself as an escape.*]

D. Her sister?

P. Her sister. The next day when she came in to work, she told me her sister felt very bad about my not coming, disappointed. I sort of broke down and told her the real reason why I hadn't come. She suggested I come over alone. I thought maybe, feeling that she knew how I felt—it would help. So she did invite me over Tuesday night.

[*What did he claim as the "real reason" for his backing out? Was it "eating?"*]

P. Well, I thought maybe I could see whether the cause is not doing a lot of things, going out quite a bit. Those are the things I've been backing out on. I've always made excuses. I went over there that night. Maybe because I felt that they knew how I felt—the two sisters—made me think that knowing how I felt about it, it made me more at ease and I did get through the night. But that feeling was still present, eating. I had that nauseated feeling, that sick feeling. Yet since then I felt nervous about something. Then after it's through, I should think you'd feel it's over with now and you can forget about it, but it seems that just wasn't it. Unless I'm mistaken, it seems that I just haven't hit it. I thought that was something that was bothering me. It was bothering me, I know, but it don't seem to be *the thing*. I'm going to keep at it. I'm going to keep trying. That's what she suggested—to keep facing it, going out, forcing yourself to go out and *doing things*. Since then I haven't had occasion to go out. At the job they're planning some parties. I said I'm going, but even when I tell them I'm going, I have that feeling that I'm not going to be comfortable, and going to have that *nervous tension feeling.* That *nausea, sickness.* It really turns my stomach, the thought of going there. I have to force it on me, to eat. Even at home I find sometimes that I'm tightened up about something. I'm not eating comfortably. I seem to be *forcing it* in, knowing that I have to eat. I do eat. I thought maybe that was a big item. It possibly is, but it don't seem to be the thing. Like I say—it seems you might be nervous about something, but after it's over, you should feel relieved. But for a week now I've felt this way. Can't seem to relax.

[*He confirms that "eating" with the girls, or like a girl, nauseates him. "Eating out" means "doing things," i.e., a mutual feeding with forbidden food. Nervous tension, being tied in knots, and nausea sickness are equated. He forces "it" into his stomach, i.e., the forbidden food.*]

P. If I'm alone, I think too much probably, don't make me feel good. If I go out, I don't feel good. I thought if I went out . . . . like last night I went *dancing* again—figuring that going dancing and *talking* may be forgetting—but the dancing just seems to irritate my condition or whatever you want to call it. My heart seems to pound more and more from the exertion and makes me feel worse. There don't seem to be any happy medium where I can be doing something which will fully relieve me. I figured maybe sleep. I sleep well; it's the only time I actually do relax—when I'm asleep. Maybe if I sensed it, I wouldn't be sleeping. I do sleep very soundly and fully relaxed. It's the only thing that I know that I'm fully relaxed. I went to bed last night and had a good night's sleep, but that feeling is still with me. I didn't dance too much last night, because I didn't feel like it. I tried it for a while, and seeing it was not helping, I thought it was best to take it easy. So these two particular girls were up again. I sat down and was talking to one of them.

[*Dancing, talking, moving, versus stomach activity. Relaxation expresses the feminine wish of passivity, of taking "IT" into the stomach, to which the ego reacts with tightening of the muscles. Talking as a mixture of mouth and muscle activity is permissible.*]

D. To the sister?

P. The one that works with me. She and I have talked quite a bit. We find we have a *lot of things in common.* She didn't particularly care to dance either. So we took it easy. I thought maybe talking to someone would help, but this morning it's still there. That's the way it is. I always say maybe tomorrow I feel better. When tomorrow comes, it's the same thing all over again. Don't seem to know what to do about it.

[*He admits a part identification with the girl.*]

D. You have a lot in common with her?

P. Yes. She's very sensitive about certain things. I've talked about things to her, and I think I've helped her.

[*Both he and the girl have in common the insecurity about their respective gender.*]

D. In which way?
P. Well, she's a country girl.
D. What's her name?

[*The question about the girl's name is to test the transference. His readily given information proves his feeling of security in the transference situation.*]

P. Her name? Freda. She's married. She was married before her husband was taken in the Service. She lives with her sister or the sister lives with her. I suppose she likes to get out. Yet she's skeptical about going out, where she's married. She feels out of place. She feels she wants to go places and do things, but what she's afraid of is that people will talk about her. I can see what she means. People will talk that she's married. She shouldn't be going out but I told her she's limited somewhat, but there are places like public dances where she can go with a group, spend an evening, so to speak. I guess I did help her quite a bit. So that's why I talked to her at the time, knowing that she had *similar phobias,* so to speak. That's what I call this fear to go out. I guess you would call it a fear of eating out. She seems to have a phobia of going out and having people talk to her. She kind of always backs out. Last night I think she was kind of *lonesome* and melancholy, probably thinking of her husband. She didn't particularly want to go to the dance, but I suppose her sister thought if she went there she would forget what was bothering her, her melancholiness. When she got there she discovered she had a run in her stocking, and she was so afraid that *people would look at her.* It got so that every time the music got started, she thought someone might ask her to dance. She would run downstairs. They would play sets. Three numbers in a set. Every time the set would start, she would disappear. After the music got started, she would come up again—fear of going up and self-consciousness, maybe. I *guess I am, too.*

[*He now states quite explicitly the common phobia with the girl: "eating out" or afraid of acting like a girl as well as like a boy. Loneliness is like emptiness of the stomach, i.e., hunger for love. Either part of him feels lonely when it denounces the other one.—Does the "run in the stocking" reveal her wrongdoings? The fear of exposing the tabooed wishes leads to the delusion of reference and to the fear of being watched. The insight that the girl he is talking about is he himself shows the therapeutic value of the interviewing method.*]

P. She disappeared one time. I wanted to dance with her. I went downstairs and got her and I brought her up. I started dancing with her; I asked her to dance with me. She didn't like the idea of getting out on the floor. She was self-conscious, felt that someone would notice her stocking had a run. I started to dance with her. She began to cry. I told her, "If you would feel better sitting down, I'll sit down with you and we can talk—if you feel that people are looking at you." Well, she didn't exactly come out with too much, but a few tears fell. She said she didn't want to, she would dance. We got to dancing. I got her mind off it a little bit. She danced with me a couple of dances, but I don't think she felt comfortable. So when she wanted to go home, the sister didn't want to. She was having dances there. She was trying to convince her she should go home where she didn't feel like dancing. So I told her, "Well, you don't feel like dancing, I don't feel very much myself. We'll go somewhere to talk." We asked the sister. She wanted to stay and dance. We went over and had a drink of coca cola. I noticed she *spilled some.* It spilled on her dress; she became conscious of that. She began to sit down and put her hand over the dress, afraid people would notice it. We talked for a while downstairs. The sister came down and said she was tired. I suggested riding home, seeing that they were all tired out. I was walking up to the bus and put them on and went home. The reason I talked to her—I find in her someone who feels somewhat similar to me. She probably feels the same way, because I talk to her and tell her things.

[*She did to herself what she wished he would do to her: she spilled the fluid on herself, apparently on her lap. The girl wanted to hide her "leg," as well as her "lap." That girl is his feminine mirror image, hence the conversation with her is his monologue. This is an indirect confession, having a therapeutic effect. It encourages him to face his conflict, since the chips are down.*]

D. And you saw her crying. It's as if you were crying yourself—just as I see your tears now.

P. She's sensitive about those things, and I have things that I'm sensitive about. I happen to like talking to someone. I still haven't hit the nail on the head. It seems that something bothers me, but it still doesn't seem to be the thing.

D. You mean that people would talk about you, or see you?

P. I mean I'm self-conscious about it. I don't know. Maybe—what's that expression—what came first? The chicken or the egg? I don't know if the nervousness is causing the blood pressure, or the blood pressure is causing the nervousness.

[*He recognizes the sameness of his emotional and bodily symptoms. This is the right moment for tying the key words of the interview together and to weave the net of associations further.*]

D. You mean the feeling of *pressure* in the head, the feeling of *tightness* in the throat, and the feeling of *pounding* of the heart?

P. Yes. Like a vicious circle. I don't know which one is causing the other. Yet it's continual.

D. You mean when you said blood pressure, pressure in the head, tightening of the throat, pounding of the heart? You mean. . . .

P. Nervousness. It adds up to the same thing.

D. You said what you call nervousness is being afraid to eat. How is that?
P. I don't know. It's that I don't feel comfortable. That's what I can't seem to find out. I have that uncomfortable feeling, maybe more than the fear of going out. I don't feel comfortable when I'm going out and that adds to the thought of not being able to eat. So maybe I think about it.

[*"Going out" reveals a displaced sexual wish. Since "going out" and "eating" are equated, "eating" is also an expression of sexual activity. That is true for both the girl as well as himself.*]

D. People might see something on you like on the girl? There's something wrong with her, so people might know why she's going out?
P. That's what she feels.
D. And people might know why *you* go out? But you said it might happen at home, too—eating?
P. Eating at home, too.
D. What do you mean, at home?

[*He said previously that at home he was eating with mother and sister.*]

P. Just even eating alone. I feel that nauseated feeling, sort of sick feeling. As if maybe the nervousness is causing my stomach to turn over. It's really forcing myself to eat at times, even though I am alone.

[*He can take both roles: feeding and being fed.*]

D. Is it worse when you eat with someone?
P. No. When I go out.
D. At home?
P. No. At home I'm probably not so apt to be self-conscious, thinking people are watching me. Seeing how I feel, I actually feel sick. I might even perspire—a cold sweat.
D. Who watches you?
P. If I was out, that's probably the way I feel. I feel as if someone was seeing how I felt. That's what I told this girl. Knowing how I felt about it, she did tell me it would help somewhat, but I can't say I was comfortable.

[*His symptoms—as he sees them himself—are caused by the fear of being watched and of being found out. Either part of him suspiciously watches the other one, and each of the two is scared.*]

D. And who watches you at home?
P. Well, nobody. Yet I still feel that way. The only thing I might have had—something happen that made me nervous.
D. But who watches you at home?
P. Nobody. Yet that's what gets me.
D. With whom do you eat at home?
P. I usually eat with the family. Occasionally I eat alone.
D. Who is the family?

P. Mother, brother, sister, father.

[*It was necessary to repeat "eating at home" five times before he could name the incestuous figures of the past in the wishful but dangerous eating relationship.*]

D. Mother, brother, sister. . . .

P. Mother, father, brother, sister. Five of us when we're together. Like I said before, these things that I do time and time again. Yet I don't seem to be comfortable. Like dancing—I've done it so many times. Yet I'm not comfortable.

[*It now becomes evident why he can never master his anxiety although he has "eaten so many times with the family": eating means in the unconscious: sexual activity.*]

D. Like eating at home—you should feel comfortable.

P. I've done it all my life. Yet there are times at home when I don't feel. . . .

D. Comfortable with them?

P. Maybe not with them. Maybe just because I don't feel good. But it disturbs me. I feel more or less sick. I just eat and have it over with. (Pause) I was thinking about that. At the time when I backed out of the invitation. I thought maybe I should see you and talk to you and ask you what you might suggest, but then when I talked to the girl, she suggested that maybe after I had told her how I felt about it, I would feel better, her knowing how I felt about it. She invited me again and I told her I would go, even if it would kill me.

[*He no longer conceals what makes him feel sick. He is right: the girl, i.e., the feminine part of him, has to give the consent.*]

D. She told you . . . ?

P. She suggested that maybe you would say the same thing—try to fight it, keep doing it and doing it until it became natural.

[*The girl apparently felt that if she helped him to overcome his fear, and he did the same for her, there would be no further need to ask permission for doing what in his mind would "kill" him or for what he might be killed. If the interviewer gives his blessing for "doing it until it becomes natural," he could be free of guilt.*]

D. Eating out?

P. Yes.

D. The food which she prepared for you?

P. Yes. I don't know. Would you suggest that? If someone had a fear of doing something, would you suggest that they keep doing it, forcing themselves to do it?

D. Like dancing?

P. No, like me—here I seem to have that feeling. I call it a fear anyway—that fear of going out, so to speak. Would you suggest that I keep banging away at it, forcing myself to go out, and in that way possibly get over it?

[*He reveals unmistakably the meaning of eating the cake together, when asking the interviewer whether "they" should do it. It is advisable that the interviewer should keep the words exchanged on a symbolic level, as long as this is the patient's mode of speaking. "Keep banging away at it," is a good example; it stands for eating, talking, going out, dancing, and foremost for infantile sexual activity.*]

D. Going out is, as you said, in this case "eating out."

P. Well, it's anything you do. You're bound to have occasion to eat out, if you go to a show. My *sister* was going. We were going to the Ice Show.

D. Your sister?

P. My sister and my brother. Made plans to go out.

D. Your sister?

P. I thought that would be a good time to experiment in going out, but it seems that we didn't get together. I hadn't seen her since Sunday.

[*Finally, the "boy's" incestuous wish toward this sister, and on a deeper level "Mother," comes to the fore.*]

D. She's married?

P. No, she's single, but it's just that she works late Monday night. Tuesday night I was over at the girl's house. Wednesday night we were supposed to go and I left early in the morning. I was somewhat glad that I hadn't planned to go out, because I really was sick to my stomach. I felt really sick, not because I wasn't even going, but I had no plans. I got sick without having plans to go out, and yet—though I had thought about it, it would have been a good chance to try again.

[*"She" is to him now the sister as well as the girl.*]

D. With your sister?

P. With my sister. But it seems that she didn't get around to make plans about going out. I just met her and we went to the show.

D. Your sister?

P. Yes. My sister and my brother. There's a case there when I wasn't even going out and I felt sick. It seemed to me something else that was causing it. It wasn't just the thought of going out. It was an occasion where I had no plans of going out. Yet I felt sick all that day. The show itself was very good; yet I can't say I enjoyed it, because I really didn't feel well. I haven't felt well all week. I can't seem to find anything to account for it. I've been to doctors. There's nothing physically wrong. I've talked to you, but you haven't told me anything what was bothering me or what you think of me, of what kind of a fellow I am, or any suggestions or ideas that you might have.

[*There is no longer any doubt that he is already associating on a childhood level, without the mature ego control. It is the boy who sees in the interviewer a permissive parental image, to whom he can confess his sinful wishes toward the incestuous figures, as if they were not only fantasies. He has the stomach symptoms even before he was "eating out."*]

D. And you went with your sister?

[*The interviewer does not let the patient get away from this danger point, despite his plea for helpful suggestions.*]

P. I still didn't feel comfortable.
D. Going out with your sister, or eating?
P. Should be something natural.
D. Should be natural. In spite of that, it is. . . .

[*The emotional experience on this transference level has great therapeutic potentialities.*]

P. An ordeal for me to do things. It seems that everything I do or want to do disturbs me. If I stay at home, I get melancholy and lonesome. I want to do things, yet if I'm alone, I feel just as bad.

[*The interview has now to be kept on the level of the associations which fortify the strength of the ego's masculine part. Thus the interviewer's guidance in the transference relationship helps to make the flight into the feminine identification superfluous, and to overcome the incestuous, infantile fears.*]

D. If you're alone or with her. . . .
P. Either way I try, it still seems to be no good.
D. Is she younger?
P. No, older. She's the oldest, then comes me, then a brother in the Service, then a small brother, fifteen.
D. The sister to whom you talked?
P. No, I've never talked with her easily. That's something I never talk with anybody, how I feel about eating out. Maybe if I had talked about it to someone before, maybe by this time I would be over it. In fact, I've never really talked to anybody until I started to come to you. Telling people about these things that maybe are bothering . . . some things I've never told people—like the stories about my father.
D. Never talked?
P. No, because I didn't feel it was anybody's—maybe it was a personal thing. Family life. Other people aren't interested. I didn't think it was right to talk about it. Maybe I never found the right person that I could talk to about them. (Pause) I thought maybe you could suggest something or some ideas, what your idea might be. I would really like to hear what you have found, as far as talking to me like this. What you've found about me.

[*It is imperative that the interviewer should not give in to the patient's pleas, because only if he himself can verbalize the implications of his predicament can his improvement be reliable.*]

D. You mean—?
P. Well, I've confessed a lot of things to myself. I've admitted to myself that I'm nervous, self-conscious. . . .
D. Confessed?
P. No. Maybe I've kept them hidden and wouldn't even admit that I was nervous.

D. The girl thought what she was doing is wrong?

[*By "girl" the interviewer refers to the feminine part of the patient.*]

P. Right.
D. This girl who is like you, who has a sister, like you, she thought what she is doing is wrong—if she danced, whether she would be seen. . . .
P. Out with fellows, so to speak. She's afraid that people will talk about her, seeing that her husband is in the Service.
D. That she did wrong?
P. That she did wrong. That's what she's afraid of.
D. And since you said she is like you. . . .
P. That's what I want to know. What am *I* afraid of? I'm wondering if you have seen anything that would cause it?
D. Now—*you* said, you, who is like she, who thinks she's doing something wrong—*you* said what she thinks is wrong. If something might be seen on her. . . .
P. Makes her self-conscious.
D. She said, that it is wrong if she has a drop of. . . .
P. Soda. . . .
D. . . . . water or fluid on her lap.
P. Stain on her dress. It might have been anything.
D. Where was the stain?
P. On her lap.
D. People will think. . . .
P. I'm sloppy. I don't know what they might think.
D. What comes to your mind?
P. Not neat. Maybe that's probably what she was thinking. I don't know.
D. She could have other thoughts, too.
P. She just seemed to be very *conscious* of it. She wanted to cover it up so people wouldn't know, that people wouldn't know that she wasn't neat. Maybe she might have felt ashamed that something might have happened to her.

[*The girl is self-conscious.*]

D. Something happened to her?
P. Accidents will happen. She didn't do it on purpose, but I don't seem to be able to find. . . .
D. You yourself—have you always been very careful to be neat and clean?
P. Yes. Self-conscious, would cover everything, wanting to be neat and clean, being careful how you do things and what you did.

[*He is quite frank in admitting his identification with the girl.*]

D. You?
P. Yes. I think the word self-conscious would cover that whole thing. Maybe I'm extremely self-conscious.

[*He is self-conscious.*]

D. You mean extremely careful to be clean?

P. I mean that I'm self-conscious now. Maybe I never realized it before I started to talk to you, but now I do realize it. Like I realize I'm nervous. Someone told me I was nervous. It seems to be inside that I tremble. Maybe that nervousness has kept within. It reacts on my stomach which causes that sick feeling, that nauseated feeling. Maybe if I shook outwardly, I wouldn't feel it inwardly.

[*"I realize it now," is the most valuable term for "insight," if the patient uses it spontaneously. "Inside" is the feminine side of him, which is represented organically by the stomach, where he wants to hide the "wrongdoings." They appear outwardly as "spots."*]

D. And you were always so self-conscious that you shouldn't show any spot on yourself?

P. No, I don't think it would bother me that much. If I get a spot on my pants, probably for a minute I'd swear, especially if I had just taken them out of the cleaners. But I think I'd forget it fairly easily. But it bothered her tremendously. She's different in that way.

D. You mean—your spots are somewhere else?

P. No, not necessarily. I don't think a spot would bother me as much as the spot she got on her dress seemed to bother her. Made her more self-conscious than she was. It started with the stocking, then that on the dress just added to the fire, so to speak, and made her still more self-conscious. That's the word I'm using anyway. I don't know if it is the right word.

[*The spots outside make both her and him feel self-conscious and unclean.*]

D. Where do you have your spots which you want to hide?

P. Where?

D. In your face?

P. Huh?

D. You told me where you got your spots—red spots.

[*He is guided back to the key words, in order to test his degree of insight, and for a reconfrontation with his fears of exposure.*]

P. *Red* and *flushed up.*

D. You remember?

P. Yes. It seems that when I got the telephone call, they tell me I was very red, flushed up—blushing they call it. Yet like I said before, I had no feeling there was any reason for it. Yet I didn't actually feel I was blushing. If no one had said anything, I wouldn't have known I was blushing. When they said it to me, it brought back what we were talking about. At times I feel I'm flushed up, and no one tells me about it. Like you say, it looks like part of my complexion, but at the time I feel comfortable, they tell me I'm flushing. Yet there's no reason. Just a telephone call and I talk to someone. Maybe the only thing I can think of is, there are a few people that knew I was working on the second shift, and it might have scared me. They know the telephone number in the house. If anything should happen and they have to get in touch with me, I've left the telephone number at the house. When someone told me I was wanted on the telephone, I probably got nerved up, couldn't think who it might be. It caused me to get red more than the actual talking to the girl. That's the only thing I can think of. But they say I was blushing.

[*To whom could something happen at home? Is he afraid that his death wishes toward father may become true?*]

D. Who is they?

P. The whole gang around that saw me walk by. I could see no reason for it. It was just an ordinary telephone call, unless it was that it unnerved me to get a phone call there. I thought that something had happened at home.

D. What could happen at home?

P. I don't know. It's just if they wanted to get in touch with me. There wouldn't be any reason for an ordinary conversation. They wouldn't have called me there. It would be something special that they wanted to get in touch with me at work. If it wasn't very important, they could tell me when I got home. The only one I could think of was—my house knew I was working. (Long pause) It seems I did mention something about coming here, saying I was going to work the second shift, so that's how *she* knew I was there.

[*Apparently the long pause contains the silent thought: If father had suddenly died, mother or sister would call him and he could feel free to go to the "girl."*]

D. The girl?

P. Yes, the girl. I still can't seem to find what it is that's bothering me. Physically they say I'm okay. As far as I can find, there are things that bother me, but I haven't hit anything that would make me feel this bad. I thought this *eating out* thing was something. Yet like I say, I've done it and had it over with. I went through with it and didn't do such a good job at it. Yet that was Tuesday night, and here it's Friday, unless it disturbed me so much that it lingered with me.

[*He clings to the assurance that nothing is wrong with him physically —as a man. But as soon as he should act on the adult masculine level, he retreats. He cannot go further than acting on the infantile oral level, i.e., eating out.*]

D. This eating out?

P. This nervousness of *eating out* seems to affect me so badly that it stays with me for a length of time afterwards.

D. Eating out with your sister?

P. With anyone. Just *eating*. When I feel that way at home, I just say *eating*, so I can't seem to find out just what it is.

D. You mean *eating* at home with the family?

[*Eating together on this level means eating from each other, i.e., feeding each other.*]

P. Yes. Sometimes I feel that way. Just *eating* with the family. There's no reason for it. Is it because I don't feel well? If I don't feel well, what is it that makes me sick? It goes on and on. It's a vicious circle. Maybe not a circle in that sense. I jump from one thing to another, and there seems to be no end to it. No basis, no foundation for it. As far as I can find, there's *nothing physically wrong.* I've had not only Dr. X. I've been examined before. The complete physical at the Hospital. Every week another doctor taking my blood pressure. Maybe twenty-five doctors have looked at me. Found nothing physically wrong. I thought maybe you could find something that was disturbing me. Like I say—I admit certain things to myself, and a few people that do bother me—but that so far doesn't seem to be the foundation, the reason. I probably could talk for years and years like this, and never bump into it.

D. What do you mean?

P. I feel now that I've *cleaned out* any information of things that would bother me. Yet I don't seem to have found anything. In fact, it seems rather silly to be talking here and not getting anywhere. I don't seem as if I'm making any progress. (Pause) That's why I asked you if you've found anything, but you don't seem to say anything in one way or the other. When I came here, I thought you would ask the questions and maybe by asking me questions about different things, find out just what it is. It seems that I do all the talking and you do the listening. It seems as if you don't tell me anything, if you've found anything or not. It's probably insulting you.

[*Now the interview has reached the danger point where the transference relationship no longer suffices as a protection against the re-experience of the wishful thought of father's death. He becomes panicky about having to play the man's role now. Thereupon the resistance mounts. His anger with himself turns against the interviewer whom to insult and to devaluate he is encouraged.*]

D. Why not?

P. (Laughs)

D. Have you the need to insult me?

P. Talking like this, and you not suggesting anything or giving me any ideas of what you think, it seems to me a waste of time.

D. Waste of time?

P. Well, now I feel that I've talked to you and a couple of other people, and it seems that I have exhausted all the things I can think of that are bothering me and did bother me. Yet maybe I've mixed them up. Yet like I say, I might be talking and talking and talking and not hitting it. It seems that nobody I've talked to as yet don't seem to be giving me any help.

D. Have you been eating at home when you felt as badly as you feel now?

[*The interviewer channels the anger into the past by reminding him of "eating with the family."*]

P. At home?

D. Yes.

P. Well, like I say, with my mother, father, sister and brother. We usually eat supper together. Yet I have these spells when I don't feel well.

D. And . . .?

P. It seems to affect my stomach; my nervous system. Seems to give me that feeling. I'm forcing myself to eat. Yet sometimes I have a tremendous appetite. It's hard to swallow the food down. I've never been seasick, but it seems that's the way people would feel when they were seasick. I've seen pictures of it when a fellow would be seasick and someone would offer them food and it turns their stomach all the time and they have to run to the rail.

D. And you felt it at home when you tried to swallow it and force it down?

[*This remark refers to a previous statement about how angry he felt eating with father.*]

P. I don't know if I'm conscious of that.

D. They?

P. I don't know. They've never said anything to me.

D. They don't?

P. No. Maybe I *cover it up too well.* Maybe I've covered it up until recently. Now I feel that I've told everything I can think of—yet it's still there.

D. You swallow down everything—not only what you were eating, but also everything that you were thinking?

P. Yes.

D. And didn't. . . .

P. Didn't let it out.

D. And you swallowed it?

P. My thoughts and everything with it. I keep swallowing it down, keep it inside.

[*He confirms that he swallowed his anger.*]

D. And you now spit out part of it.

P. I think I've exhausted it as far as I know.

D. But you feel as if not everything is. . . .

P. I don't feel completely cleaned out. There seems to be something more.

D. You're right. Do you want to empty your stomach?

P. I think I have. Like I said, as completely as I can think of.

D. Didn't you say there was something more which isn't completely out?

P. There must be. In other words, you suggest that I keep talking, in hopes that I might find out?

D. Until you feel you've emptied yourself out.

[*What he is hiding, is in his stomach.*]

P. You've probably got as much patience as I have. I'm willing to try and try, but meanwhile I feel this—*it's like a little relief.* You don't seem to be able to give me any, and doctors don't seem to be able to give me any. Pills don't help.

D. Until you have emptied yourself.

P. I see what you mean, yes—but I still feel so uncomfortable not knowing. Until I feel comfortable, as you put it, I have to suffer. I can't seem to think of anything else. Like you say, there must be something there. Yet I can't seem to put my finger there.

D. Maybe you have the finger there already.

P. Do you think there are a lot of things that disturb me, causing it? That's what I want to know.

D. See you next week.

Discussion

The therapeutic situation after the second interview led to the expectation that the patient would begin to act out in reality his conflictuous sexual strivings which had been stirred up. At first, he wanted to go off by himself. He then reluctantly sought the company of a female, whom he found congenial on the eating (oral) level. They were feeding each other with forbidden food, so to speak. Being identified with her, he could reveal his insecurity and face his own sexual conflicts. He saw in the interviewer a permissive parental image to whom he could confess his "sinful wishes" toward the incestuous figures of his family.

The interviewer's guidance of the associations in the transference relationship revealed the patient's need of a flight into the feminine role. This became then the theme of the interview. However, he still wanted to be reassured that nothing was wrong with him physically—as a man—and the prospect of having to act on an adult, masculine level made him shrink.

In this panicky state he turned against the interviewer who had enticed him to enter the world of a man. The interviewer channeled this anger into the family relationship on the oral (eating) level, which facilitated the verbalization of the patient's resentment toward the father, which he had always had to swallow. This abuse of the alimentary tract for the strongly passive, but ambivalent, relationship to father led to stomach upsets and kindled his masculine protest.

(*Note:* The patient's blood pressure after this interview was 165/110.)

Part 4—The Color Barrier

INTERVIEW 4

P. Well, I'm feeling a lot better.

[*Four weeks have elapsed since the last interview. He does not refer to it in his introductory remark. The interviewer asks no questions as to why he missed his appointments. The patient spontaneously reveals that he had turned to a friend to obtain the "facts of life," as children usually do, since they don't trust the grownups. In the following it will be seen how freely and without any embarrassment the patient discusses these problems.*]

D. Do you feel better?
P. Much.
D. Much better?
P. Yes. I found one of my friends and had quite a conversation with him. We discussed it. He told me a lot of things I didn't know, about things I should have known, *as you put it.* Now the question is, how to go about it. I still don't feel too strongly about doing it, but I think more or less I would like to try it once and see what the reaction is, if it's something I feel I need, or just what it is.
D. You said a friend?
P. Yes. A friend of mine, married.
D. A girl friend?

[*The purpose of this question is to have him confirm that he chose a man for an ally.*]

P. No, a fellow.
D. What was the talk about?
P. He told me how to protect myself and what he thought would be the best way to use a safe.
D. Can you repeat it as if I were he?
P. Well, I told him I had never had intercourse, and he told me to come up to the house one night and he would tell me what he could about it. Where he was married, I thought he would be as good a person to talk about it with me. So I went up there the last of the week.
D. To his house?
P. Yes. And I told him I had never had it.
D. What?
P. I called it intercourse.
D. You called it. . . .

P. Yes. And he told me he thought I should be careful to protect myself by using a safe, and he told me little things—how to put it on, not to put it on too tight, so that when the discharge would come, there would be enough space, so that there wouldn't be any breakage. He thought it best—maybe some girl—probably all girls would say they never had intercourse. It would be best if you knew of some girl that had, they would know a little more about it, than taking a chance with someone who never had it. In that way, she would know some way to protect herself, as well as yourself.
D. Protect against what?
P. Disease, syphilis.

[*Syphilophobia as the rationalized fear of genital activity.*]

D. That means, you could become sick?
P. Well, I don't know. Where I've never done it, is it possible for me to have it? Is that the only way you can get it? *Contact* I suppose is a good way—by having intercourse. Is that the only way?

[*His previous fear of contact has been talking, dancing, eating together.*]

D. What do you think?
P. I should think it would be—what little I've read up on it. Intercourse would be what I think is the reason how to catch it—catch it or whatever you might call it.
D. You mean, you're not sure that you might not have something?
P. I think I'm clean, as far as that goes, where I've never had it before. But I'm still ignorant on the subject. I don't know if it's possible to get it any other way. Possibly by touching or by kissing. I don't know.

[*He reveals a determinant of his compulsive cleanliness.*]

D. By other contacts?
P. By other contacts.
D. A contact which you might have?
P. With a girl—possibly with a fellow.
D. With a fellow?
P. Touching something that they have touched.
D. Indirectly?
P. Indirectly.
D. Have you had such an idea?
P. I never gave it much thought until *you* mentioned it. I don't know. Is it possible to get it indirectly by touching something that maybe someone had who had one of these diseases, or even kissing or *something like that?*

[*Mouth contact with males or females may lead to disease. "Something like that" refers to intercourse.*]

D. Whom did you kiss?
P. There are girls that I've kissed of late. I don't know. Possibly they might have had intercourse and have had those diseases.
D. Indirectly from the man who infected her?

P. I should think the woman would have it just as well as the man. It isn't necessarily a man's disease—is it?

[*A disease leads to damage.*]

D. You mean this is an idea which you had, but you were not sure whether it's a possibility?

P. Well, until you mentioned it, I never gave it much thought. I would say the only way you could get it, you would have to get it by direct contact, by intercourse. But you can, or can you not, get it otherwise?

[*"Otherwise" apparently refers to touching oneself, i.e., masturbation and its consequences.*]

D. To be infected?

P. That, and maybe not knowing just how to go about it.

D. So you avoided it. . . .

P. So I just pushed it in the background. This fellow said as far as the actual intercourse—there's nothing to it as far as he can see. There's nothing hard about it.

D. He said. . . . ?

P. He said, you won't have any trouble as far as that goes—just be careful to use some protection. That's the only thing he knew of. He said, the first time you'll probably be more highly emotional and probably you won't last any time at all, but then after a while you might get so that you can control yourself. Maybe get more enjoyment out of it than just to do it and have it over with. *He told me* at first he was more passionate the first few times he did it. Before *he knew it,* he had discharged, but as time went on—he's been married about five or six years now—he can control himself enough to even go without a *safe.* As time went on, he just gets out. He suggested even with a safe, if you feel yourself coming—just get out. It's double safe that way by pulling out.

[*"Safe" is a protection against damage.*]

D. Was that his advice?

P. Yes.

D. He meant you could become somewhat emotional.

[*"Emotional" refers to "enjoyment" to which father always objected, as well as to the fear of losing or giving up "something" which he calls "control."*]

P. He said, at first he thought everybody would be more or less emotional the first few times. It might last fifteen seconds. I should think it would be at first, until you learn to control yourself so that you could probably go a little longer. I suppose it pleases the girl. I understand the woman is not emotionally so fast or heats up so quickly as a man. *I don't know* where I've read that.

[*"Women" need longer before they accept the loss, i.e., loss of control, as he calls it.*]

D. You read about it?

P. I heard about it somewhere. A woman isn't as emotionally fast as a man. Sometimes a man gets *emotional* quick and it's all over with, and she's not satisfied. He advised if I thought I would like to try it, he thought it would be best to find someone that probably has done it before, in order to make double sure that both of us were a little more protected than with someone who is inexperienced like myself.

D. Why?

P. He thought maybe we would forget ourselves. Let our emotions carry us away and forget to do the right thing.

D. Which would be wrong?

P. Stirred up so much that you would stay in. *I don't know* what you call it—to discharge and cause trouble.

D. Trouble—in which way?

P. Well, birth. *I don't know* what I'm trying to say. Pregnancy.

[*Fear of impregnation is another rationalization of his phobia.*]

D. Why is this trouble?

P. Well, when the boys talk about it, they call it a shotgun wedding, because you have to marry the girl because she's going to have a baby. Until I meet the right one, I wouldn't want that.

D. You were warned?

[*The therapeutic purpose of this phase in the interview is to let him express his fears on the masculine level, and to strengthen his ego by hearing them verbalized by himself.*]

P. Warned? About that? Yes, well, what he told me, he thought it would be best that way. That's one of the things I've been afraid of—I haven't tried it myself.

D. Did you know someone who got in trouble this way?

P. Yes.

D. Who?

P. A couple of girls down my way.

D. What happened?

P. I guess they *didn't know* how to go about it. That's what I think. Different things. That's another thing he talked about—menstruation period. There are certain times when you should keep away from her. A woman shouldn't even try to have intercourse during her period. He said it's not dangerous, but messy. *I don't know* exactly just when the woman is ready or not—the right state to become pregnant. *I don't know.* We didn't discuss that too far. *I don't know* if there's any special time.

[*The instability of his ego is obvious from the repetitive interlocation of: "I don't know."*]

D. How old was she?

P. I'd say she wasn't more than eighteen. (Pause) Is there any other advice you could give me? As far as he said, actually there's nothing to it. Just make sure that you protect yourself. It seems to be the only thing about it that he could give me any information on.

Actually there's nothing to the actual intercourse. Just make sure you protect yourself. That's the whole thing in a few words.

D. Who is he?

P. Friend of mine.

[*It seems suspicious that he leaves the interviewer in the dark about this "friend."*]

D. What do you mean—friend?

P. I've known him for quite a few years now. He didn't exactly hang around with the gang of fellows I did, but we used to hang around the store and got to know him. He was kind of sick when he was young and was away. *He had a heart murmur.*

[*Now it becomes obvious that "the friend with the heart murmur" is his male alter ego, and their alleged conversation appears like a dialogue within himself.*]

D. Heart murmur?

P. Yes. He was on a farm for quite a few years. He didn't come back until he was older. He worked in the store for a while, and then got a job in the Post Office. That's where he's working now.

D. In spite of the heart murmur?

P. I guess it's pretty well cleared up. He's pretty husky and he's put on a lot of weight since he's come back. He says he feels alright. It didn't bother him, I guess.

[*He feels assured, since the "friend" with the heart murmur has been cured although he is doing the dangerous things.*]

D. Anyway—he got married?

P. Yes.

D. And his heart gives him no trouble?

P. Not that I know of. I guess not.

D. The marriage didn't bother his heart?

P. In fact, I think it did him good. He got fat. *Maybe I could do that*—get fat. Could use some weight.

D. You would like?

P. I know I could use a little weight. Fifteen or twenty pounds wouldn't do me any harm.

[*The degree of increase of the ego strength can be clearly seen in his new argumentation that marital activity is good for the heart, as proven by his "friend." Therefore, he can feel safe, not having to share father's fate when following his "friend's" path.*]

D. Who said so?

P. I think I could use it. I'm thin. My father is thin. So maybe I take after him, but I guess I could use a few more pounds.

D. Can't you . . .?

P. I eat good, sleep good. It just probably isn't natural for me to be fat.

D. Did he know about your heart condition?

P. My heart condition?

D. Your friend.

P. My high blood pressure. Yes.

D. You told him?

P. My mother probably had gone into the store and discussed it. I guess I probably told him, too. He thought maybe where I had never had intercourse, he thought maybe that would help. He thought along the lines that we thought. That it would be *something to help me.*

[*The friend's voice decides: to act as a man "would be something to help him" against high blood pressure.*]

D. Your mother talked it over with his father?

P. No. I suppose she mentioned it to him.

D. To whom?

P. To the father.

D. His father?

P. Yes. She mentioned that I had high blood pressure and that's why I was rejected in the Service, but I don't think she ever talked about it deeper than that.

D. And mother thought it might be because you stayed away from the girls?

P. No. Where I've been going to doctors and they couldn't find anything wrong, I don't think she could make any decisions along those lines. Until I've come here and that subject came up, I never knew. It's only the past three weeks that we've talked it over.

D. Mother and you?

P. No. Us. *I feel a lot better.* I guess this is pretty near the end of what we've been looking for.

[*The insight he gained in the interviews made him "feel a lot better." However, such statements have to be taken with a grain of salt, since they are often only the cover for an escape into pseudo health.*]

D. Looking for what?

P. Just knowing that there's some basis for all this. That alone makes me feel better, knowing that I've something I'm fighting anyway. If you have any information or suggestions you can give me. . . .

[*The friend advised him to get fatter. How about mother?*]

D. You mean—mother always told you that you should get a little fatter?

P. She thought I could put on a few pounds. She feeds me well.

D. Does she?

P. Yes. I guess we always ate pretty well. The best of everything. I always say, no matter what it costs, it's good for your stomach. If it were good for my stomach, I would pay for it. I wouldn't question it.

[*The sector of the father relationship on different levels, in which the interview is carried on, has led to "eating." Therefore, any associations to the feeding aspect in relation to mother, have to be stimulated.*]

D. If it concerns eating?

P. Yes. If it is something for my stomach.

D. Did she know that your friend had a heart murmur?

[*Her image has to appear in agreement with the new eating plans. By implication, she plays also the role of his friend's mother.*]

P. I guess she did. But what has that to do with me?
D. You said you want to become fatter.
P. Yes. . . .
D. . . . so that you might become like him?
P. Yes. . . .
D. . . . who got married?
P. In other words, you suggest that I get married? You think that would help me put on weight?
D. You said he had a heart murmur, was sick, became married and fat, and you used him to get all this information.
P. Well, I had a topic to discuss, and that's why I picked him.
D. But he must also think that nothing is too expensive for his stomach.
P. Yes. He eats good, too.
D. You know him well?
P. Yes.
D. The only difference is that he is married and you're not, and he knows things that you don't know.
P. Yes. Well, he gave me information that I didn't know—so now I know, too, what he knows about it. Whatever suggestion he could give me, he gave. Now that we've finished that—what?
D. What are your plans?
P. Well, I suppose—like I said, I think I ought to try it.
D. What do you mean?

[*In the finale of the therapeutic interview, the confrontation of the adult ego with the immature one, has to be renewed.*]

P. Try intercourse once. Find out if it's something I want to do. It seemed to be something that where I haven't done it, I kept pushing it behind me. Maybe if I get it up in front and eliminate it, make up my mind if it's something I want to do or something I want to do without.
D. Why?
P. I guess I was ignorant on the subject, as *you* put it, and was afraid of it.
D. As *you* put it.
P. Yes. I just pushed it in back of me, put it far away. Never even talked it over with anybody.
D. Afraid?
P. I guess that's as good a word as any to use. Something you don't know about, I guess you're afraid of until you try it.
D. Which kind of fears?
P. Maybe fear of disease, maybe not only disease, but pregnancy on the girl's part. Where I didn't know how to go about it, those things might happen. Now that I think I know it and have an idea what it's about, I should try it and find out if it's something I want or

don't want. One way or the other, make up my mind. Have you any ideas?

[*He summarizes the realizations of his fears.*]

D. Why did you never ask before?

P. Well, I just talk about those things with the boys, and it got so that they thought you had intercourse, and you keep building them up on that preconception. After a while you build it up so high that you can't knock down your castle, and you can't tell anyone that you haven't, because they would laugh. They'd ride you for years afterwards. Some of the fellows in the shop where I work, they usually go out, go to parties with one girl or the other. They always get around. Ask you what you did. After a while it's hard to tell them that you haven't, so you let them think you have. If you told them you had never, you wouldn't live it down. Until I talked it over with you, I found it was bothering me, so I found someone who would talk it over with me and see my side. (Pause) He told me before he got married he knew as little about it as I did. *He saw a doctor.* He spent about half an hour with him, he told him everything that was necessary. Now he's passed it along to me.

[*He now puts his cards on the table and admits he has lived a life of self-deception in a pseudo reality. He feels relieved that he can give up his pretenses. The identification with his friend is complete.*]

D. He was afraid, too?

P. I guess he was. It was something he hadn't done before, and he didn't know how to go about it, like me. Maybe he wasn't so much afraid, but he wanted to know the right way, maybe. That's what I wanted to know. What was the right way? The doctor gave him the information and he passed it along to me. (Pause) Maybe you could tell me what you found.

D. You mean. . . .

P. Mentally.

D. You mean to find out more about your fears?

P. I don't understand.

D. What other fears you might have?

P. Do you still think I have other fears?

D. Have you?

P. I don't think so. I think I've discussed with you all the ones that I can think of. As far as I can see, there's nothing else. Just a question of fighting them. The things I was afraid of, that I've been fighting, like this thing here: intercourse. Go out and try if—and find out one way or the other, if it's something I want or need—or is necessary. I think I've discussed with you the difficulty about *eating, nervousness.* I force myself to go out and make *dinner dates.* Maybe by doing the thing often enough, I'll get rid of that. Those are a couple of the things we've discussed. I think *I'm fighting* them, doing them and trying to get over them.

[*The interviewer neither advises nor discourages him to act out the newly acquired masculine self-assurance.*]

D. Is that what you have in mind now—to fight?
P. Instead of pushing them behind—facing them.
D. All these different fears?
P. Anything that bothers me. To find out about them. If I don't understand it, find someone who can explain or talk it over with me.
D. All right.
P. In other words, I could come here any time I feel something is bothering me?
D. Whenever you decide that you're able to tell things which you are not able to tell today.
P. I was wondering if I could do it that way.
D. As you like. Goodbye.

Discussion

The subjective improvement in the patient's condition is not surprising. The confrontation with his feminine self during the interview had its therapeutic aftereffect in so far as he began to feel that he had given in too much to his passive strivings. He reacted by identifying with the male friend of his boyhood who had also a "heart" condition. After asking this married friend for enlightenment about the "facts of life," he received it as if he were in his prepuberty. Thus he shifted the responsibility for his contemplated adult sexual activity onto him. This progressive step made it possible to uncover in the interview the patient's rationalized fears of mature genital activity like syphilophobia or a fear of impregnation. He confessed this retreat into an immature sexual behavior.

The decision to follow his friend's advice is again supported by a rationalization, i.e., that "marital" activity is good for the heart and can even "cure" a "heart murmur." If that holds true, then to act like a man should help him against high blood pressure.

It is striking that this type of support of his male ego should suffice to strengthen it, and even to open the way for some insight. That could be confirmed in the interview when the patient was able to summarize the realizations of his fears. Obviously his understanding of the true reality had widened.

(*Note:* The patient's blood pressure following this interview was 165/110.)

Part 5—The Color Barrier

INTERVIEW 5

P. It's been a long time.

[*One year and a half have elapsed since the last interview. The patient had asked for an appointment.*]

D. Long time?

P. It's *years,* I think.

D. Years?

P. I think it is. I've felt well for a long time.

D. Well, and now?

P. That's just it. I don't feel any different than I did before. That's why I wanted to see you again. Still in a fog, like I was before. Still *don't know what I want,* what I want to do. I had a good chance in the last few years to do anything I wanted to do, yet I feel as if I'm in that fog, that I *don't know what I want.* Yet I work and got a good week's pay since the war in a defense plant. Now that it's slowed down, I don't know how long I'll be there. I should be thinking of something to do afterwards, and I *don't know* what it is I want to do. That's why I've come to see you and see what you might suggest. I still seem to be in that same rut, not knowing what I want to do.

[*"I don't know what I want," is the common expression of a person identifying with both sexes: one "I" is in disagreement with the other, which results in a feeling of being in a fog, or in a kind of depersonalized feeling.*]

D. You mean you can't decide between different things that you want to do?

P. I never found anything that I like enough to sink my teeth in, to hold onto, that I would like to follow it through. *Last week was my birthday.* I'm thirty-four years old and I still don't know what I want. It seems to me that I should have done something in thirty-four years—something that I was interested in enough to follow it through. But I don't seem to be able to concentrate. It's a waste of time. Like other things. I've done ordinary things that other people do. Yet to me there seems to be something missing, something that I don't seem to be doing, the thing I want to do. Seems as if I'm reaching for something—I don't know what it is. It seems there should be something somewhere that I'd like well enough. I feel there's something that I'd like to do. I don't like to hang around.

I know that. I still seem to grasp for something, but I don't know what it is I'm looking for. All these *years* it seems there should have been something that I took to. Maybe it's something I've done.

[*Where does he like to sink his teeth in? Birthdays are often an occasion for regressive behavior. The infantile oral needs recur. The feminine part of him feels thwarted when the male part got too much credit. As a result, he withdraws and goes off by himself.*]

D. Done?
P. Done. Everything I seem to *touch* don't seem to go right. I drop that, I try something else.

[*In the previous interview "touching" meant to him "using the mouth."*]

D. What did you touch?
P. I tried different things. I thought I'd like to go to school, learn a trade, radio or something. I went for a few months and I didn't seem to be getting anything out of it. Just listened and it didn't seem to sink in, didn't seem to be interested. I dropped it. It seemed a waste of time and money to go on like that. So I just dropped out of it. Yet I know I've got to do something. *What it is I want to do, I don't know.* I can't go on and on like that and not find something I want.

[*It seems as if what he is longing for is the utopic wish of being both a man and woman at the same time, a gender which does not exist.*]

D. You said you're now thirty-four years old and a thirty-four-year-old man should do what. . . .
P. Should know what I wanted to do.
D. What other thirty-four-year-old men are doing. What are they doing?
P. By this time they're married, have a family, settle down, have a good job. Maybe they all don't have good jobs, but they're doing something they want to do. And here I am still drifting.
D. You think you should do what other thirty-four-year-old men do?
P. I just want to find something that means a future.
D. You said a thirty-four-year-old man is marrying?
P. I'd like to be married, too, I suppose. That's life. I guess everybody looks forward to being married. *You* can't do that.
D. *You* can't do that?
P. You can't unless you have some foundation to work on.
D. Which foundation is necessary?
P. A job—a position that you can work up from. Something that you can fall back on.
D. To have a position?

[*Marriage would mean: "signed, sealed and delivered" once and for all; being a man like father. But father became a sick man.*]

P. Yes. I've been seeing a girl for about a year.
D. For about a year?

P. Over. . . .
D. How did it happen?
P. I've had my little loves. I can't think seriously. I don't think of anything like getting married—not until I've something that I can fall back on, something that I know is going to last for a while. I can't take a chance and hope it will turn out all right. I want something that I know will be for a while anyway. So I see her. It's a help—someone to do something with, someone to *talk* to. But as far as getting married—I can't see it, unless I had something that I'd be able to know it will last until I could support her, so to speak.

[*"Talking" is a mouth activity; previously he equated it with dancing, insulting, sexual activity.*]

D. To support her?
P. Yes. I wouldn't want to go in and take a chance. Right now it's very uncertain where I'm working. I don't know whether I'll be there a month or a day or a year. We were doing all defense work, Army and Navy. Now that the war is over, there's very little to be done in my department. It means starting over. I can't see starting at the bottom. I've worked there for four years. I'd like to get out. I never cared for that type of work anyway. There was good money in lathe work. Now I see it's coming to an end. I still don't know anything definite about what I want to do. *I'm wondering what the future is.* I'm still in the same position I was before.

[*He rationalizes his escapism.*]

D. With the girl?
P. No, before I met the girl. This uncertainty of what's ahead, what there is for me, what I want to do. That uncertainty of not knowing what I want.
D. At that time you were not quite sure whether you would dare to approach a girl—you remember?
P. Yes.
D. So that has changed.
P. Yes. That's changed. Like everything else.
D. How far did it change?
P. Well, I've gone as far as possible—sexually. That wasn't what I was looking for. I found I could take it or leave it.
D. And what did you do—take it or leave it?
P. Like everything else—that still don't seem to fill that feeling I have of something I want to do. That's the way we left it the last time.
D. What do you mean?
P. When we were talking last time, we thought that was what was lacking—my sexual life. Now that I've had it, that still don't seem to fill that *empty space* that I have. I found it was something enjoyable, but it wasn't the thing I thought was lacking. I could do without it. It wasn't the thing I was looking for. (Pause)

[*His "empty space" remains unfilled: the mouth, the stomach. He wants to be nurtured.*]

D. What were you looking for?

P. Well, as far as I said before, I don't feel different than I did before. Going out, I'm always under that nervous strain.

D. Going out?

[*"Going out" means "eating out."*]

P. I've done it dozens and dozens of times since I saw you. Yet I never feel relaxed.

D. Going out with whom?

P. *With the boys, with other people*—doing anything. I guess it's a nervous feeling, nervous tension, tightening up feeling all the time. *Other people* do something for the first or second or third time, and don't get nervous. Yet with me—I just don't seem to be able to get rid of that feeling. I was out Saturday, *my birthday.*

[Here he states plainly that he can't be at ease "going out" with the "boys" or with "other people" (girls). He mixes them up, wanting to be passive and active with either of them.]

D. With whom?

P. I made a date with her. I picked her up in town. We went out; like other people seem to do. Go to supper, *eating out,* going to a show. Other people seem to feel that's an enjoyable evening. Yet to me—having that feeling all the time around me—I like to do it, but I can't say I enjoy it.

[*He ruminates the conflict in the same terms as in the third interview: "eating out" means swallowing the forbidden food. That leads to "nervous tension, being tied in knots," and nausea.*]

D. Last Saturday?

P. I was with her. But being with anyone—I can go to a restaurant by myself or go to a movie or go to a party, with couples or alone—it don't seem to make any difference. I still have that feeling.

D. Feeling of what?

P. Tightness, nervous, like talking to you now. I perspire tremendously. Why, I don't know.

D. What comes to your mind?

P. Why do I feel that way? I can't explain it. Yet I've done things dozens of times, done it over and over again. Yet I always feel that way. Just *sitting* in the movies, quiet. I just break out in a sweat for no reason at all. I can't see any reason for it. I can feel it running down inside of me. I can't account why I should feel that way. There don't seem to be any reason for it. Yet I always feel it. I don't know whether it's pressure or what it is. Maybe I get in a warm place.

[*Sitting down is giving in to passivity.*]

D. *Pressure?*

[*His feminine ego makes full use of the iron curtain of prefabricated, screening terms. These include the pretense of ignorance as a defense against the already established preponderance of the ego's more mature, masculine part.*]

P. My blood pressure. That's why. That's the reason why I was sent to you in the beginning.

D. The doctor . . .?

P. With me—they give me the name of *essential hypertension.* It's necessary. That's all I can get out of it. Yet the cure or causes they don't know. If that's the cause of my feeling *warm,* I don't know. Maybe *sitting in warm places.* When I feel warm, I *flush* up very easily. That's why when I get in a close place, I feel warmer than the ordinary person, because my pressure is up. When I'm not doing anything *active,* just *sitting down*—other people find it *relaxing.* Yet to me it's an ordeal—everything I do. There's nothing there that relaxes me. I can't seem to find it. Like the dancing. I can't say I enjoy it. I *dance* around a little while and I'm all out of breath, break out in sweats, overexertion. I get so tired moving around. My *heart* begins to pump a little harder, the pressure brings it up even higher. Yet I do like to dance. But after one or two dances I'm just all *sweated up* and *tired.* It's that way with everything. I get no enjoyment because I don't feel comfortable.

[*He rehashes the words "essential hypertension, feeling hot, flushed, heart pounding, sweating, sensitive, high-strung."*]

D. What do you mean?

[*The interviewer maintains a benevolent impartiality. It is obvious that the event of his birthday makes the patient feel sad, and he clings to the interviewer for support.*]

P. Well, doing anything, going out, doing anything active. Feel very tired, warm, flushed up. Maybe I'm *sensitive,* high-strung. It affects me quicker probably.

D. What do you mean that you're sensitive and high-strung?

P. Something *sentimental,* or a scene on the *screen,* something *sad.* It seems to affect me more so than anybody else. Maybe others feel it and don't show it. I think I do anyway.

D. Are you thinking of a certain picture?

P. No. Nothing in particular. Sexually it seems to be that way, too. I seem to be high-strung before I even start. Before I start it's all over. I get no enjoyment. The girl doesn't either. I'm off before I even get close to her sometimes. I work myself up so that usually before we even get together, it's over, as far as I'm concerned. Once it's over I just lose interest.

D. Interest?

P. Interest in going at it again. I'm not content. She's not content. I just seem to make a mess of it like everything else I try.

[*His objections to the heterosexual masculinity become manifest in the symptom of premature ejaculation.*]

D. Why a mess?

P. Well, it don't seem to be done right, not getting the full benefit of it. There seems to be more to it than just that. You try it and it's over with before you even start.

D. Because you get hot?

P. And I go off sometimes before we even get together. *I'm not satisfied;* she's not satisfied. There should be more to it than one quick flash and it's over with. I read up on it. I loaned a book. There was one part that said there were people who were that *sensitive,* high-strung, just from contact—just touching somebody. I don't know if it's anything to overcome that or if it's possible even. Maybe a little saltpeter or something. I've never taken the stuff. I understand it can prevent you from getting all excited. Maybe it would hold me off long enough for me to get some enjoyment.

[*His disappointment stems from the exaggerated anticipation of a sexual experience in which all derivatives of this activity—passive and active—should become satisfied simultaneously. This hope is foredoomed.*]

D. What do you mean, all excited?

P. I always seemed to be that sensitive. I get worked up very fast. (Pause) I don't know what else there is. (Pause) Maybe there's something you could ask to get me started on something else. I don't know why I feel that nervous tension all the time. I can't think of anything just now. If I knew, that's it. If I knew the reason why I felt that way, then I'd know what should be done. I don't seem to know what it is I'm trying to fight. They know the blood pressure is high, but what's the cause, they don't know.

[*His blood pressure is high because he is continually fighting off the feminine claims, and vice versa.*]

D. What do you mean—trying to fight?

P. Well, if you know what's causing it—I know blood pressure is sometimes caused by kidneys. Well, if they know your kidneys are bad, they treat you for that. They don't seem to know what the cause is. They don't seem to know what to try, what the remedy might be for it, whether it's medicine or rest or just what it is. I tell people I've high blood pressure, and they ask me if I'm on a diet, no red meat. All the doctors I've seen have never put me on a diet. A lot of people say it's not good for people with high blood pressure. I'm so thin. They're surprised when I tell them I've high blood pressure. Most people with that are fat, old. It's just something that the doctors—as far as I know—they can't seem to find the cause, why. They have found since the Draft that quite a few boys, young like myself, have high blood pressure. What's causing it, they don't know.

[*The passive oral wishes claim their rights, but are prohibited.*]

P. *I'm not fighting it.* There's nothing to grab hold of, don't seem to know what the remedy is. That's why they tell me. They've given me pills that brought the pressure down for a while, but as soon as I stop, it seems to go up again. It's just a temporary period when I'm taking the pills. Lately I haven't been taking any. I don't know what makes me feel this way. Maybe it's one of the symptoms of the "headachy feeling"; unable to concentrate. That seems to be another thing that's caused by blood pressure according to ads in the papers. I just happened to see that those are the symptoms of high blood pressure. It seems to fall in line with the way I feel. Can't concentrate, seem to be *in a fog.* Unable to concentrate is as good a way to put it—unable to think. Don't know what it is I want. (Pause)

[*The patient rambles on disgruntledly. His resistance cannot be attacked frontally, unless he has aligned all his defenses. Only then may the confrontation be tried again and his mature ego fortified.*]

D. On what do you want to concentrate?

P. On what's ahead. There just don't seem to be anything there.

D. You mean you always had this trouble? That when you started to concentrate on something, to know what's ahead of you—then your mind got blank? Is that it?

P. Yes.

D. You never got really interested?

P. No. I never did find anything that would interest me enough so that I would want to follow it through. I used to do my work, but just enough to get by. There wasn't anything that I did extra good in. I did my work just to do and have it over with. I have a kid brother. My youngest brother. . . .

D. Your brother?

P. He's as tall as I am. He's twenty, he loves baseball. He could live there and sleep there. He gets so much enjoyment going to the games and being with the people. He finds enjoyment doing that. *I know there's nothing that interests me that much.* In fact, I've never seen a professional baseball game. I never took to it that much. I've seen baseball games. It didn't seem to be the thing that I'd go out of my way to see. There's a ball field down near my house. *I'd go if I had the time.* But to go into B—— to see the game. . . . it wouldn't interest me that much. It's the same way with everything else that I've ever thought I'd ever like to try. It just wouldn't seem to be worth enough, or it wouldn't interest me enough for me to go after or fascinate me enough that I want to see it through. Like boxing. . . .

D. Boxing?

P. *I like to see boxing matches,* but I wouldn't go out of my way. If I have gone, it's just that I felt like going that particular night. *I would go,* but to go out of my way every Monday—it wouldn't interest me that much. Like my brother: he'd give anything to go to the baseball game. I know of nothing that would interest me that much. I have yet to find something that I would want to *go day after day to see.* It seems to me there must be something that would interest me enough so that I would like to follow it. It wouldn't have to be working—a hobby or something. Something I could sit down and do. Some people like to whittle, save stamps. I've tried a few of those things. They seem to do for a while and then I lose interest. It doesn't interest me enough to follow through.

[*He already admits that he likes to watch baseball or boxing, but he shies away from too much interest. He has to divide his "interest" equally between the active and passive parts: sitting down or sports, but not doing any of it day after day.*]

D. Always?
P. I have yet to find anything that *interests* me or something that I wanted enough. *I think I feel there must be something.* Everybody seems to have something that they like to do more than anything else. Like *sports* or maybe just *sitting home and reading,* going out to dinner or a baseball game. They seem to have something that they like better than anything else. Some people like the work they're doing. Probably you like this type of work. You find enjoyment out of it. Like me—either work or play, there still isn't anything that I like well. Nothing. But I say *I like to dance,* but I don't enjoy it, because I don't feel comfortable after a while, all heated up, all excited. Don't feel comfortable. So I go once in a while. I *like it enough,* but I really don't enjoy it the way I should. I think moving around, the exertion. It brings up the pressure and I feel very uncomfortable, so I just. . . .

[*How much is enough?*]

D. . . . stop.
P. Stop.
D. Was that always the case whenever you became interested?
P. No. There was always something. It wasn't enough. There wasn't anything that interested me enough. Well, I just gave dancing as an example of the pressure part of it. Other things where there wouldn't be any *activity* to it, reading or carving—it wouldn't interest me enough to do every day. There's nothing there that I would want to do day in and day out.
D. Why not reading?
P. Reading, photography, taking pictures, developing pictures—nothing strenuous; that type of work or hobby.
D. Why not doing both—dancing *and* reading? See you again.

Discussion

As can be seen, the therapeutic result had been considered by the patient as satisfactory for almost two years. During this time he had felt no need to ask for any medical advice. However, it had to be expected that a patient who was identified with both sexes would not remain satisfied with heterosexual experiences, since it cannot—or not completely—provide the gratifications of the opposite ones. His disappointment stems from the exaggerated anticipation of a sexual experience in which all derivatives of this activity—both passive and active—should become gratified simultaneously. That wish could not be fulfilled.

The beneficial therapeutic result proves that a therapeutic process does not end with the interview; its content, and with it the image of the interviewer, remain as a stimulus in the patient's mind. Therefore, the ego rearranges its defenses in the interval, and what had been stirred up will be gradually resettled. Likewise, the ego can reorient itself against the conflictuous forces.

In this case, the adult ego of the patient had been given an opportunity to face—under the protective screen of the transference relationship—the infantile hostility against the father figure. As the interview revealed, the patient was able to overcome his phobic fears and to act on a more mature sexual level. That was due to the psychodynamic process set in motion by the sector therapy, without any manipulation of the patient's reality life. His acting out on the basis of the increased ego strength created a new reality, which raised him to a higher level of maturity, and which made many of his defenses superfluous.

All this could be achieved through a therapy which clarified conflictual issues by working in one sector. In order to settle more of the remaining conflicts, the whole associative procedure would have to be followed up in further treatment. This might be done in the same sector, or, if that should not appear promising, another sector should be chosen for further treatment. With this goal in mind, this interview was carried through and then terminated to await the patient's reaction.

By and large, it was always kept in mind that a surgical approach may prove unavoidable.

The factors contributing to the development of the hypertension in this case, as seen from the point of view of psychovasomotor interaction, and as they appeared in the sector investigated during these interviews, are manifold. However, they may be summarized as follows:

1. The pent-up hostility against the father who thwarted his infantile desires, irritated the patient's vasomotor system (rage reaction).

2. Fear of betrayal of his hostile feelings led to palpitation, blushing, perspiration.

3. Being ashamed of his dark complexion (like father had), he tried to be different, i.e., red-faced, to pass as one of the "Irish Christians" with whom he associated. That became a parasympathetic stimulus for his facial capillaries.

4. The need to fight off his passive feminine impulses led to overactivity and hypermotility, which made him aware of his palpitation and perspiration.

5. The patient's attempt at giving in to his heterosexual wishes by dancing, made him feel flushed, hot, blushed and red-faced.

6. The feeling of being a failure in the male role, and the fear of being recognized and exposed, produced more blushing and palpitation.

Psychotherapy does not treat the vasomotor system; it deals with the subjective awareness of the functional vasomotor disturbance and the emotional factors connected with it. In this case, they had been the center of the sector therapeutic approach.

(*Note:* The patient's blood pressure following this interview was 168/110.)

Follow-Up

Two years later, the patient was contacted by telephone through the Social Service. He seemed willing to give information, but only in response to direct questions. According to him, he had not seen any doctor since the last interview. His work was still on the same job, five nights a week, and he slept during the day. However, he thought five nights were too much for him. Otherwise he said he felt pretty good and was going out a little. He was told that he could ask for an appointment whenever he wished. Since this last call, the patient was not heard of again.

Eight years later, an indirect inquiry about the fate of the patient brought to light that he had never returned to the physician who first referred him for psychotherapy. However, it was learned that he had since married and was living in his own home. A letter sent to him at his new address, asking for further information, remained unanswered.

Consequently, the Social Service tried to contact him personally, and succeeded in reaching him on the phone. The patient very readily gave the following information: He was feeling fair, and doing "light work," i.e., bookkeeping. His mother had not been too well and "in and out of the hospital." The father died nine years ago, two months after the patient had his last interview at the Psychiatric Department. His sister married three years later, while his younger brother still lives with the mother.

For more than two years following the discontinuation of his treatment, he did not see another doctor. However, his pressure symptoms reappeared, and he consulted a surgeon who performed a sympathectomy more than seven years ago. The patient considers his operation as a success. Once a year he has to go for a check-up of this operation. He claims that he is still suffering from its "aftereffects," which he feels in "nervous tension." Finally, a year ago, he married the girl with whom he had the courtship during his psychotherapeutic treatment. To the question whether he had any children, he replied, "Not yet."

The medical record of the patient shows that he had a bilateral lumbodorsal splanchnectomy. The average ambulatory lying blood pressure readings a year ago were 139/88, and the ceiling cold during the cold pressor 146/98. An X-ray of the chest showed that the heart is normal in size and contour. The kidney function was normal; likewise, the ophthalmoscopic examination showed no abnormality.

The record (six years after the operation, and ten years after his psychotherapy) further contains the information that the patient has been having "quite a few headaches" during the past year, which seem to be due to "tenseness."

CHAPTER VIII

Critique and Conclusions

In surveying the problems which have arisen for consideration in the therapeutic interview situations in this volume, it is apparent that the clinical material has highlighted a number of theoretical observations. By and large, the dynamic and associative theories of psychiatric interviewing are only the ultimate consequence of a movement of long development which received its decisive motives equally from epistemological and clinical considerations. The advantage of the dynamic and associative approach over other techniques is based not only on the empirical material but has also a general systematic value. This value is due principally to the solution of problems encountered in the selection and evaluation of the clinical and historical material as well as the evaluation of therapeutic changes. Particularly does this approach help to find a better answer to the problem of the relativity of the pathological and the normal, the concept of mental illness per se, the meaning of "cure" and the objective criteria by which such evaluations are made. However, the associative approach to interviewing, being based mainly upon the techniques of psychoanalysis, has made it difficult for many to comprehend the difference between psychoanalysis and psychoanalytically oriented psychotherapy. Numerous symposia have been held on this subject and distinctions made concerning what is done or can be done in one or the other.

It has been opined that psychotherapy is primarily either supportive or exploratory, and that it cannot produce any persistent intrapsychic or structural modifications, but can only operate by way of persistent transference effects or by rechannelization or realignment of the various techniques of defense of the ego. Such statements are true only in the broadest sense. In connection with uncovering measures, sector therapy, in leading the patient as quickly as possible into the past, exposes the ego to the original conflicts which the child's ego could not handle and aids in their resolution in terms of the present. Supportive measures can as a rule only be applied to part aspects of the ego and, as has been shown, can be made part of the interview situation and effectively utilized only when the advantages and disadvantages of such support are clearly kept in perspective, and an understanding of the conflict between these part aspects of the ego has been ascertained.

While various psychotherapies may employ any of the technical tools used in psychoanalysis, it is only the latter that allows the optimum control of the therapeutic procedure and is the most economic and effective in terms of time. In the long run, short-term therapy is often a lengthy process.

It is a common conception that in psychotherapy the therapist is more active and less neutral. This too is a relative matter. Perfect neutrality can seldom be maintained in any interpersonal relationship, and each therapist or analyst has his own value system.

The depth of the regression is another difference that frequently is discussed in comparing psychotherapy and analysis. This, of course, depends upon the type of therapy. As a rule, in sector therapy, the transference neurosis cannot become as regressive as in analysis because of the more frequent confrontations with the present reality situation. Therefore, the therapeutic effect appears to be due to a combination of insight and transference on a vacillating level of regression and ego control. From a somewhat different point of view, as the patient in sector therapy is guided back into the past, he regresses for short periods in the interview situation. However, the therapist does not try to influence the patient's regression in a specific direction.

The goal of sector therapy is the relinquishment of the patient's defenses only in the chosen sector. The consistency of silence may be used here as in analysis, and likewise the associative material, to give the patient an opportunity to experience the irrationality of his infantile transferences.

It is obvious that an agreement on definitions and terminology is a prerequisite for the comparison and evaluation of any therapy. The associative anamnesis and sector psychotherapy have been developed with such problems and criteria in mind. Some acquaintanceship with the fundamental terminology and principles of psychoanalysis has to be taken for granted. Practically all of those entering the field of psychiatry today have a greater or lesser reading acquaintanceship with some psychoanalytic principles and terminology. The type of resistances to this subject that are encountered in teaching residents today are of a different order than those of only a decade ago.

Psychodynamic teaching has often been accused of being too dependent upon the unique individuality of the psychoanalytic system of reference and of failing to reconcile its theories with the newer facts of neurophysiology, medicine and "statistical" psychiatry in general. However, in these interviews, it has been made obvious that the nature of the unconscious makes it important that a certain control of one's unconscious is a prerequisite in dealing with its manifestations from both instinctual and ego-defensive aspects. It is hoped that these recorded interviews will aid in the recognition of this.

When the problem of the *selection, evaluation,* and *therapeutic usage* of the clinical material is considered, it has been shown that some of the unconscious meanings of a patient's symptoms and the interpersonal, interbodily, and intra-ego relationship difficulties for which the symptom appears to stand are best revealed to both patient and doctor by this associative type of interviewing technique, coupled with the principle of *guided* and *guarded interference.* Actually the combination and permutation of these five variables produce an infinite variety of problems. The associative anamnesis and sector psychotherapy attempt to minimize these problems.

When the problem of interference by the therapist is taken into consideration, the advice most frequently given concerning this is that it should be minimal and nondirective. It has been shown that free associations are far from being a completely undirected process, and the word, minimal, is subject to many interpretations according to the exigencies of the interview situation. The patient-doctor relationship is always a mutual and reciprocal one even though the interviewer's role is, as a rule, one of benevolent impartiality. An important factor in any interference by the therapist is that he must always be aware of how much and in what way he directs the associative material. Such procedures as nondirective guidance or counseling are misnomers and contradictions in principle. Thus, we would agree with the statement that "a careful examination of some of the comments given by counselors in nondirective counseling shows them to be rather potent comments carrying the situation radically beyond the point at which the patient has spontaneously arrived." Reformulating what a patient has said in the direction of the affective rather than the intellectual content may be an excellent principle in this type of counseling with certain compulsive obsessional and intellectualistic individuals, but it might serve the purpose of an escape from insight with others such as histrionic and affectively labile individuals. Direct questioning not belonging to the associative material rarely has a place in the interview situation. It has been shown in the illustrative case material that direct questioning may be mixed with the associative material and may be necessary when establishing the important matter of the family frame and the significance of dates and ages. Also, without some types of confrontations to subserve the purpose of interpretations, any "counseling" or "clarification" would remain an ineffective therapeutic procedure. The differences between *clarification* of material and *interpretation* have been competently discussed.

The recorded interviews in this book have been used to demonstrate that in sector psychotherapy the interviewer does not need to limit his role to that of a passive listener, but is able to select key words of the patient for repetition, stimulation, and confrontation in a manner which selectively intensifies some of an almost infinite variety of associative material, and channelizes it in a manner which tends directly and indirectly to do several things:

(1) *Reveal* to both the doctor and the patient the meaning of a symptom or problem in terms of historical relationships in the inner world of the ego and the body image and the outer world of people and objects.
(2) *Effect* a better synthesis of these inner and outer "worlds" and thus obviate the need for more primitive ego defenses.
(3) *Aid* in the development of more practical long-term solutions of a patient's difficulties.
(4) *Utilize* interview time effectively and economically.
(5) *Separate* analytically oriented, goal-limited therapy from "wild" psychoanalysis or "wild" psychotherapy.

In attempting to unify one's concepts of psychotherapy, it must be borne in mind that true unity is never found in arranging and rearranging clinical details as such, or even in the so-called objective criteria which are ultimately based on some theoretical presuppositions. The closest approach to a unity will always be found in one's own intellectual constructs chosen in accordance with one's own experiences with the peculiarities of the field of psychotherapy, and accepted or rejected according to multiple observations as to their effects. The recorded interview has the pre-eminent value of allowing for a detailed exposition of the constructs and reasoning processes that lie behind the vicissitudes of the interview situation. True unity and objectivity, which epistemological curiosity drives us to seek in our constructs, lies always in the reciprocal connections of observed "facts" and in the logical conditions at the time they are appraised. This in respect to psychotherapy is what was meant by the stressing of *relationships,* whether interpersonal or intra-ego, whether in the past or the present, rather than people, objects, organs, social milieu or events per se.

Associative anamnesis as utilized in sector psychotherapy has placed on record its ability to demonstrate to the therapist and the patient the repetitive patterns of relationship that are the significant part of the psychotherapeutic reality, with all the ideational mnemonic, and affective overtones that are so much a part of these automatisms. Such automatic relationship patterns are the chief concern of both therapist and patient, knowingly or unknowingly, and whether they appear in the form of acting out or are symbolized by various mental and/or bodily signs and symptoms.

A survey of the literature on the problems of psychotherapy, shows that the theories behind any attempts in this direction are in principle of unlimited variability. Associative anamnesis and sector psychotherapy owe their advantage to the possibility of demonstrating their basis in terms of both theory and practice, in greater detail and with a minimal amount of technical terminology, which unfortunately at the present time has been shown to be almost unlimited in its interpretability, especially with beginners. Making the unconscious conscious still remains the *sine qua non* of all psychoanalytically derived therapy. With associative anamnesis, the substitution of confrontation for interpretation, and the use of the patient's own terminology, tend to insure that this is done only at the level of understanding and assimilation permissible on the part of both the therapist and patient. Technical difficulties concerning the overcoming of resistances and various transference-countertransference reactions are minimized. Thus the therapist is best enabled to remain, in the words of Freud, "impenetrable to the patient and like a mirror reflecting nothing but what is shown him"; and what has been shown can be used to best advantage.

In reference to clinical experience in the field of psychotherapy, regard for both mental and bodily phenomena in the interview situation, and their unified exposition has always remained the fundamental basis of the theory behind sector therapy. If the therapist is not to become a mere technician, he must constantly endeavor to provide himself and others with an exact exposition of the totality of these phenomena. Only a theory that unifies the greatest number of observed phenomenological details and minimizes the contradictions inherent in unconnected observations, will satisfy our rational selves. Thus, various aspects of the therapeutic interview should all be considered. These should include the origin and development of the symptoms and the regressive process, as manifested by changes in libidinal and aggressive interpersonal and intra-ego relationships and the body image; and therapeutic situational elements such as ego splitting, identification with the therapist, suggestion, abreaction, role taking, medicinal aid, secondary gains, etc. In any case, the most satisfactory theory of interviewing should be able to *demonstrate* the role of any of these factors and determine its hierarchical importance. Such a theory will be satisfactory directly in proportion to how it explicitly evaluates and accounts for any and all of these part aspects.

It has been extremely gratifying to observe that residents trained in the use of associative anamnesis and sector psychotherapy, and to whom these techniques were demonstrated, tended to develop a conviction of the existence of the unconscious and its relationship to a symptom that was not at all superficial or intellectualistic. Combined with case supervision, their training has resulted frequently in a high degree of therapeutic effectiveness. As a corollary of the use of this method, the *resident* has tended to develop an increased awareness not only of his patients' problems, but also of his own. Just as confrontation of a patient with his own words frequently forces him to face and master unpleasant personal realities, so does the confrontation of a resident with his own recorded interviews force him to admit and master shortcomings in his personality in regard to his technique. Thus the resident becomes aware of the scope and the ubiquity of introjective-projective processes that are so universal as to allow him to treat most of the verbal material in the interview as a modification of the secondary elaboration process met with in the communication of fantasies and dreams. In this manner he has not only been aided to understand his own conflicts, but has received a tool enabling him to cope with the anxieties attendant upon the practice of any type of effective insight therapy.

Psychotherapy based on psychoanalytic premises has assumed the reduction of what has been taken as fixed and absolute criteria based on the manifest speech and actions of a patient to a system of mere relationships between a complex and hierarchical group of ego functions and levels of consciousness. What has perplexed the descriptive school of psychiatry has always been the limitless relativity and multidetermined nature of all the phenomena described, and the ensuing fact that such phenomena would not remain fixed by individual data. It is true that as a rule one is able to grasp only a few minor or major details isolated in time and distorted in the unconscious. Also it is difficult to see how one can ever pass from the perception of details concerning an individual to an objective view of the individual throughout his entire life; however, renunciation of all objectivity regarding psychotherapy is not necessary.

The truly objective element in modern psychotherapy is concerned with laws of relationship, for instance, as revealed in the recorded associative interview situation. Here it can be demonstrated that words like "normal" and "cure" can mean very little save in relationship to a given standard of abnormality and sickness. For those who do not fully comprehend this, it may seem that phenomenological relativism is being used as an escape from an accurate definition of diagnostic criteria and an objective appraisal of the "results" of therapy. This problem has existed among psychiatrists of all schools when any attempts were made to evaluate a type of therapy in a more succinct manner. The problem of evaluation has frequently been confused with the problem of comparison, and some have seen any attempt at an objective evaluation as an attack on the basic premises of all dynamically oriented insight therapy and on the qualifications of those who practice it.

Those who stress the therapy procedures as a scientific discipline have tended to feel that the large number of complex variables, semantic difficulties, and the absence of reliable data make it necessary that an objective evaluation be preceded by at least a clarification of terminology. Others who have stressed the application of these techniques as an art have felt that some of the various procedures implicit in the evaluation process itself, as for instance recording, would cripple a vital element in technique. This is a problem from the point of view of the physical sciences reminiscent of that encountered in the measurement of subatomic particles where the disturbances of motion caused by their observation becomes an integral part of the motion itself. These interviews should help to disprove this point of view. There have been some who felt that for best results a therapist should be timeless in his approach, oblivious to results, and serenely detached from evaluation problems lest his attitude be construed as an aggressive and self-defeating attempt to pressure a patient into conformity. Such attitudes can be defended only as partial truths.

In the past few decades, a greater realization of the sterility and limitations of descriptive and diagnostic psychiatry has driven psychiatrists in great numbers to the psychoanalysts with the plea that they make their therapeutic know-how available for the many, especially in the field of so-called short-term therapy. The difficulties and limitations attendant upon such a mass conversion are now being revealed more clearly. Descriptive and nonanalytic concepts frequently are confused and not broadened merely by the addition of psychoanalytic terminology. Particularly has this been so in the field of psychotherapy. Here there have been distortions of even elementary psychoanalytic principles in accordance with the personalities of those who practice psychotherapy. The "intellectual persuasionists" in particular have tended to use current ego-analytic terminology in an effort to by-pass the anxieties and resistances connected with infantile sexuality. The abreactionists have in a counterphobic manner championed the release of instinctual tensions through all sorts of procedures which lessen the ego control and, unfortunately, its synthesizing and integrating abilities as well.

The interviews in this volume have demonstrated that one interview is capable of producing all the material, both ideational and affective, that can be utilized in the time allotted. An avoidance of sterile intellectualism or a mutual acting out between the therapist and patient make it necessary that the trainee psychotherapist and those who participate in teaching him must continually evaluate their metapsychology, terminology, and procedure, and what it accomplishes. For this purpose, recorded interviews have been valuable. Especially from the point of view of case control work, recorded interviews have demonstrated considerable usefulness. Too often resident control seminars tend to become forums where clever constructions are spun out over a few fragments of the rich clinical material, and disagreements may occur over what is meat and what is bone.

It seems not justified to claim that "prescientific knowledge of human nature is a well-developed faculty which every healthy person possesses without any systematic learning," and that "everybody who tries to encourage a despondent friend or reassure a panicky child practices psychotherapy." Those procedures cannot go under the label of a science. These interviews should go far to demonstrate that a psychoanalytically based psychotherapy is a distinctly different procedure from common-sense psychotherapy, inasmuch as an expanded and conscious awareness enables far greater control of the therapeutic situation to be effected. Such an awareness adds immeasurably to the worth of any evaluation of a therapy.

The problem of evaluation lies mainly in the abstracting and standardization of the observed results. What is of interest in the problem of evaluation is not a "cure," a word too broad to be of use, but a "change" and how it has come about. From this point of view, what has to be measured is the relative increase in perspective and integrated insight. Here a utilitarian point of view is permissible; i.e., how does a patient get along with himself and with others. A sector therapy interview showing change during therapy has been included in this volume (Chapter VI, Part 3).

Some of the therapeutic interviews have been chosen for the purpose of illustrating how in Freud's words "the pure gold of analysis has been alloyed with the direct copper of suggestion." The use of the type of ego split employed in sector therapy illustrates this; however, even the suggestions are taken, as a rule, from the patient's own wishes and in the patient's own wording, and reinforced rather than introduced. Such a differentiation has an economic advantage; i.e., the suggestion is practically certain to carry weight.

The initial stress that associative anamnesis places on the words of the patient for the purpose of teaching has led some of its critics to put undue overemphasis on the verbalization aspects. This method actually lays as much stress on what the patient does and how he feels, as on what he says. However, the meaning of nonverbal cues is difficult to understand and communicate in other than verbal terms, especially in the early phases of therapy and also from the standpoint of teaching the inexperienced therapist. What associative anamnesis and sector therapy stress above all is a rational and conscious understanding and awareness of everything the therapist says and does. In sector therapy no attempt is made to indulge either the infantile ego, the instincts, or the introjected parental aspects of the ego, except when absolutely necessary to preserve a therapeutic relationship; and, above all, only when the therapist is aware of the relation between the various ego elements. The concern is not with the projections and introjections of the patient per se, which are present in everyone, just as in everyone there is a constant shifting between narcissistic and anaclitic relationships. The concern is rather with the anxiety connected with these necessities, and the maintenance of the goal to reduce these anxieties through the strengthening of the ego's over-all perceptual and synthesizing powers. Accordingly, sector therapy is much more than a verbalization technique. From the point of view of the libido theory, the therapist preserves a positive transference and becomes a surrogate ego figure. The relation of anxiety to the synthetic abilities of the ego is a reciprocal one. Increase in perspective diminishes the former and increases the latter. Thus, the patient is helped to work through his problems, sharpen his perceptions, and attain new object satisfactions.

Associative anamnesis as utilized in sector psychotherapy is a special category of the associative type of interview. It should be understood that this type of interviewing does not depend upon intuition. The intuitive approach and its drawbacks have been discussed previously. Some have confused the associative-anamnesis technique with the question-answer type. Questions like "What does this remind you of in your past?" or "What are your associations to this?" have no place in associative anamnesis, as they are too unsubtle for the great majority of psychiatric patients, and are unproductive of usable material for confrontation; yet they are frequently considered as associative interviewing. It is gratifying, however, to note that some authors have clearly revealed their understanding of this technique, especially in reference to the importance of correlating the time and onset of symptoms and the emotional elements that appear during the interview situation.

How one utilizes a technique will always be dependent upon personal factors in both the patient and therapist. In the long run it is the goal of associative anamnesis and sector psychotherapy to permit the maximum adaptation of communication processes to the enhancement of therapeutic efforts.

The case material in these volumes has been chosen to demonstrate that sector therapy can be utilized in cases that call for insight therapy and for whom psychoanalysis is not available. With psychotics and borderline patients, the readily accessible, deep, unconscious material can be developed along the sector of its relation to everyday reality occurrences in both the present and past. In this way, the preoccupation with bizarre body-image material and fantasies in their ego-defensive aspects can be avoided. With obsessive-compulsive patients, words, having high affective values, can be stressed and connected; however, there is great difficulty in the avoidance of word games and the sexualization of words. Sector therapy is especially useful in cases of psychosomatic disorders, as its proper use keeps the field centered around the basic symptom and prevents it from being enlarged to a degree that is not economic from the point of view of time. Sector therapy is the ideal choice for anxious patients, since the role of the doctor allows the patient to curtail and limit the amount of anxiety-producing material. It is the choice of therapy with patients who are being considered for analysis, as the transition to analysis can be made with a minimum of difficulty. "Psychopaths" and the type of patients who act out are handled as well as possible with this method simply by the avoidance of difficult transference material and the stress that is laid upon perspective. As is the case with all therapies which attempt insight, the success will eventually depend upon the ability of the therapist to understand the patient's symptom and its meanings in terms of the patient's life. When the therapist has done this, a communication of this understanding to the patient will follow inevitably.

In conclusion, sector therapy is primarily an exploratory psychotherapeutic technique adapted to the controlled use of supportive measures. It has the following characteristics:

1. The therapist shows a benevolent impartiality.
2. A regressive transference neurosis of a very transient character may occur.
3. Free associations are encouraged, but reality and fantasy, past and present, are continually linked up.

4. Symbolic expressions are underscored and included in the vocabulary of the interviewer.
5. A split of the ego into a mature and immature, or child and adult part, is induced.
6. Confrontation is utilized instead of interpretation.
7. Transference problems are minimized by deflection, confrontation and integration with the past, before becoming too strong.
8. Symbolized transference reactions are continually linked up with overt reality reactions.
9. Guided acting out is not excluded.
10. Transference interpretation plays almost no role.
11. The transference is utilized to further the exploration of unconscious material, but the resolution of the transference is not intended.
12. Support of a failing ego is only occasionally provided when its import is understood.
13. The resistances of the patient are by-passed when feasible, if their removal arouses too much anxiety.
14. The removal of the symptoms of the illness is achieved as a by-product, and solutions are found to derivative conflicts.
15. Recognition of the internal conflicts is achieved through confrontation of the adult ego with the acting of the immature ego.
16. Sector therapy does not aim at a quick solution of a problem.
17. Sector therapy is a mixture of directive and nondirective therapy. It does not introduce the suggestion factor any more than psychoanalysis.
18. Theoretically, sector therapy provides an easier functioning of the ego *in the chosen sector* by making it more free from conflict.

Only prolonged observation can settle the question whether or not sector therapy can produce a significant change in the chosen sector. In the majority of cases, the psychotherapist employing this method plans to stop at an intermediate part of the personality, and does not try to carry the therapeutic goal beyond a certain sector.

Freeing the ego from conflict in one sector must ultimately strengthen the ego as a whole. This will be reflected more perhaps by a better interpersonal adjustment and social adaptation than by a demonstrable modification or alteration in the ego structure. Such a result is the most desirable goal in any psychological therapy.

BIBLIOGRAPHY

ALEXANDER, F. Current Views on Psychotherapy. *Psychiatry,* XVI, 1953.
—— Psychoanalysis and Psychotherapy. *J. Am. Psa. Assn.,* II, 1954.
—— et al. *Psychoanalytic Therapy: Principles and Application.* Ronald Press, New York, 1946.
BERMAN, L. Some Problems in the Evaluation of Psychoanalysis as a Therapeutic Procedure. Paper read at the Symposium on the Evaluation of Psychoanalysis, at the Boston Psychoanalytic Institute, Feb. 2, 1953.
BIBRING, E. Psychoanalysis and the Dynamic Psychotherapies. *J. Am. Psa. Assn.,* II, 1954.
DEUTSCH, F. *Applied Psychoanalysis—Selected Objectives in Psychotherapy.* Grune & Stratton, New York, 1950.
DUNBAR, F. *Psychosomatic Diagnosis.* Paul B. Hoeber, New York, 1943.
EISSLER, K. R. The Chicago Institute of Psychoanalysis and the Sixth Period of the Development of Psychoanalytic Technique. *J. Gen. Psychol.,* XLII, 1950.
—— The Effect of the Structure of the Ego on Psychoanalytic Technique. *J. Am. Psa. Assn.,* I, 1953.
FINESINGER, J. E. Psychiatric Interviewing. *Am. J. Psychiat.,* CV, 1948.
FREUD, S. (1922) Psycho-Analysis. *Collected Papers,* V. Hogarth Press, London, 1950.
FREUD, S. (1937) Analysis Terminable and Interminable. *Collected Papers,* V. Hogarth Press, London, 1950.
FREUD, S. (1939) *An Outline of Psychoanalysis.* W. W. Norton, New York, 1949.
FREUD, S. (1919) Turnings in the Ways of Psycho-Analytic Therapy. *Collected Papers,* II. Hogarth Press, London, 1924.
FREUD, S. (1912) Recommendations for Physicians on the Psycho-Analytic Method of Treatment. *Collected Papers,* II. Hogarth Press, London, 1924.
GILL, M. M. Psychoanalysis and Exploratory Psychotherapy. *J. Am. Psa. Assn.,* II, 1954.
—— REDLICH, F. C., and NEWMAN, R. *The Initial Interview in Psychiatric Practice.* Int. Univ. Press, New York, 1954.
GLOVER, E. The Therapeutic Effect of Inexact Interpretation: A Contribution to the Theory of Suggestion. *Int. J. Psa.,* XII, 1931.
KAUFMAN, M. R. Problems of Therapy. In *The Psychosomatic Concept in Psychoanalysis,* ed. Felix Deutsch. Int. Univ. Press, New York, 1953.
KNIGHT, R. An Evaluation of the Psychotherapeutic Techniques. *Bull. Menninger Clin.,* XVI, 1952.
MARGOLIN, S. Report of Panel on Psychotherapy. *J. Am. Psa. Assn.,* I, 1953.
MASLOW, A. H., and MITTELMANN, B. *Principles of Abnormal Psychology.* Harper & Bros., New York, 1951.
MURPHY, W. F. and KLIGERMAN, S. The Associative Anamnesis in Teaching Insight Therapy. *Dis. Nerv. Syst.,* XI, 1950.
—— and WEINREB, J. Problems in Teaching Short-Term Psychotherapy. *Dis. Nerv. Syst.,* IX, 1948.
RANGELL, L. Similarities and Differences between Psychoanalysis and Dynamic Psychotherapy. *J. Am. Psa. Assn.,* II, 1954.

ROGERS, C. R. *Counseling and Psychotherapy, Newer Concepts in Practice.* Houghton Mifflin, Boston, 1942.

—— Significant Aspects of Client-Centered Therapy. *Am. Psychologist,* I, 1946.

—— and DYMOND, R. F. *Psychotherapy and Personality Change.* Univ. of Chicago Press, Chicago, 1954.

STONE, L. Psychoanalysis and Brief Psychotherapy. *Psa. Quart.,* XX, 1951.

SULLIVAN, H. S. *The Psychiatric Interview.* Norton, New York, 1954.

WEISS, E. and ENGLISH, O. S. *Psychosomatic Medicine.* W. B. Saunders Co., New York, 1943.

WHITEHORN, J. C. Experiences in the Treatment of Schizophrenic Patients. Address, read before the N. E. Soc. of Psych., Boston State Hosp., Nov. 16, 1950. Reproduced at Norwich State Hosp., Norwich, Conn.

NAME INDEX

I refers to Volume I

II refers to Volume II

SUBJECT INDEX

I refers to Volume I

II refers to Volume II